ATLAS OF BUTTERFLIES
IN BRITAIN AND IRELAND

JOHN HEATH, ERNEST POLLARD

AND JEREMY THOMAS
of the
Natural Environment Research Council
Institute of Terrestrial Ecology

*Illustrated by Sarah Anne Hughes
and Peter Creed*

VIKING

Published in association with the
Natural Environment Research Council and the
Nature Conservancy Council

VIKING
Penguin Books Ltd, Harmondsworth, Middlesex, England
Viking Penguin Inc., 40 West 23rd Street, New York, New York 10010, U.S.A.
Penguin Books Australia Ltd, Ringwood, Victoria, Australia
Penguin Books Canada Ltd, 2801 John Street, Markham, Ontario, Canada L3R 1B4
Penguin Books (N.Z.) Ltd, 182–190 Wairau Road, Auckland 10, New Zealand

First published 1984
Reprinted 1985

British Library Cataloguing in Publication Data

Pollard, Ernest
Atlas of butterflies in Britain and Ireland
1. Butterflies—Great Britain—Geographical distribution—Maps
2. Insects—Great Britain—Geographical distribution—Maps
I. Title   II. Thomas, Jeremy   III. Heath, John, 1922–
912′.1595789′0941   G1812.21.D4

ISBN 0–670–80006–6

Set in Monophoto Photina
Printed in Great Britain by
Richard Clay (The Chaucer Press) Ltd,
Bungay, Suffolk

CONTENTS

INTRODUCTION

During the last thirty to forty years the countryside of Britain and Ireland, and particularly that of lowland Britain, has been radically altered by the activities of man. The countryside has always been subject to change as social and economic factors have altered the nature and intensity of farming, and agricultural techniques have themselves improved, but the agricultural revolution of post-war Britain has resulted in change of an order greater than anything since the first clearance of our native woodlands. Hedges have been removed; permanent pasture and heathland have been ploughed, reseeded or treated with herbicides and fertilizers; conifer plantations have replaced many ancient deciduous woodlands; wetlands have been drained. In the uplands, improvement of marginal land by drainage and the application of fertilizers, and the widespread planting of conifers in the formerly treeless landscapes, have had a major impact. In addition to these changes in farming and forestry, there have been the direct and indirect effects of urbanization: direct, through the extension of building land into agricultural areas, and indirect, through such factors as the increased use of rural land for recreation and the growing demand for minerals (including sand and gravel) and water.

The same period has seen, in response to these changes, the creation of conserved areas of countryside such as National Parks, Areas of Outstanding Natural Beauty, and, specifically for the conservation of wildlife, national and local nature reserves. There are many other public and private categories of land set aside to safeguard valued areas, and recently increased control over other sites, which remain otherwise unprotected, through the creation of Sites of Special Scientific Interest. In effect, the capability that man now has to destroy our rich and varied landscape, created by many centuries of cultivation and management, has been recognized, and measures have been taken to retain and protect some of the outstanding areas and their associated wildlife. However, the area of protected sites is very small in relation to the total countryside, and protection itself is rarely sufficient to ensure the conservation of the wildlife of a site. Conservationists are well aware that nature reserves are usually rich in wildlife *because* of the management

they have received in the past; if they are to retain their richness, some form of management must continue. In order to assess the effect of changes in the wider landscape on wildlife and the effectiveness of conservation inside and outside nature reserves, we need information on the distribution and status of our plant and animal species. This book is an attempt to provide such information for just one group of insects, the butterflies, and, to the limited extent possible, to assess the impact of land use change on this group.

Butterflies are, in most of their characteristics, typical insects, and the impact of environmental changes on the butterflies is probably similar to the effect on many other insect groups. Butterflies are, however, atypical in one respect: because of their beauty and because, unlike most moths, they fly by day, they have attracted the attention of naturalists more than have any other insects. They have been studied and collected since the days of the Victorian naturalists and earlier (the first account of the British butterflies was written by Christopher Merrett in 1666). Among the results of this interest are a written record of the past distribution and status of butterflies and the very comprehensive modern distribution maps, which together provide a basis for the assessment of change, particularly over the last 150 years.

The first attempt to present data on the distribution of the British Lepidoptera in an organized form was made by H. J. Fust in 1868 when he published tables of the distribution as then known, using the botanist H. C. Watson's geographical provinces and sub-provinces as the recording units. From this time on, a great deal of information was made available as published records in the entomological journals, and eventually, in 1945, Ford's *Butterflies* was published, with, now familiar, dot distribution maps of butterflies. These maps provided a great stimulus to further improvement of our knowledge of the distribution of the Lepidoptera of the British Isles. One enthusiast, R. C. Crewdson of the Lancashire and Cheshire Entomological Society, set out to collect together all the published records and plot them on maps. Although he showed many maps, all hand-made, at the annual conversaziones of the 'L. & C.' in the 1960s, unfortunately, none was ever published.

The next step forward came in 1954, in another discipline, when the Botanical Society of the British Isles launched their Distribution Maps Scheme. This culminated in the monumental *Atlas of the British Flora* (Perring and Walters, 1962). The botanical atlas pioneered the use of the ten-kilometre square of the National Grid as the unit for mapping plant and animal distributions, which, together with standard recording cards, enabled the use of modern data processing methods. It also stimulated similar work by other biological societies, and the value of the information acquired to the expanding field of nature conservation was recognized. In 1962, the Nature Conservancy set up the Biological Records Centre, based at Monks Wood Experimental Station in Cambridgeshire, to develop the growing interest in biological recording by amateur naturalists. Since then, many atlases and distribution maps have been produced for a wide variety of plant and animal groups. Usually, the leading national society or an individual expert has initiated and organized each scheme, while the Records Centre has taken care of the data handling and production of maps.

The addition of an entomologist to the staff of the Biological Records Centre in 1967 saw the start of a comprehensive recording scheme which included all the British and Irish Macrolepidoptera, that is, the butterflies and larger moths (Heath, 1967). This scheme used the methods and recording cards developed for the botanical atlas. The principal difference from other schemes was that this scheme was run in its entirety by the Records Centre staff, with J. Heath as organizer. The response from lepidopterists was so enthusiastic that it was possible to produce the first provisional maps of butterflies in 1970 (Heath, 1970). Interest continued to grow and the volume of data received increased steadily, until, at the end of the scheme in 1982, some 2,000 contributors had sent in records from 98 per cent of the 3,600 ten-kilometre squares in the British Isles.

The fifteen years covered by the scheme saw great advances in data handling, from electro-mechanical machinery to advanced electronic computers, and also changes in the requirements of the users of the distribution data. New recording cards were needed and a recorders' instruction book was published (Heath and Scott, 1974, 1977). These changes have made possible a major improvement in the availability of data to research workers and conservationists, although the process of changing systems has slowed the production of the finished atlas.

The processing of the records by the Biological Records Centre includes checks of grid reference against the locality name and vice-county given by the recorders. Discrepancies are corrected or, if this is not possible, the record rejected. However, there is no doubt at all that the maps contain some errors, mainly due to mistakes in the identification of the butterflies. Not all butterflies are easy to identify, and recorders vary in their expertise. We have scrutinized doubtful records and accepted or rejected them according to factors such as the experience of the recorder, the advice of local experts, the difficulty in identification of the species in question, the existence of supporting evidence such as a photograph or written description, and so on. A 'final provisional' set of maps was circulated to recorders for their comments in 1982.

The maps should not be regarded as complete. The absence of a record in a square does not necessarily mean the absence of the butterfly, only that we have not received a record. Coverage of the country by recorders has not been uniform and is lowest in parts of the country where the human (and therefore recorder) population is low. Some maps of animal and plant distributions are, in the early stages of recording schemes, maps of recorder effort. This is certainly not the case with butterflies; the range is clearly shown for virtually all species, even though, within the range, there may be minor omissions. The records do not distinguish between breeding colonies and isolated individuals that may have wandered from their habitats. Where this problem is thought to be of significance we have commented in the accompanying text.

In addition to the field records sent in by recorders, we have attempted an historical reconstruction of the earlier distribution of butterflies, extending back into the nineteenth century and, in a few cases, even further. The survey of the early literature records of the distribution of butterflies has not been comprehensive; this would have been a vast undertaking. The main sources used have been the lists prepared for many of the English counties for the Victoria Histories, local lists, and the standard texts on butterflies, particularly Tutt (1905–14). An extensive list of these sources is given by Heath (1976). The review of the Scottish records by Thomson (1980) has been invaluable, but relatively few old records are available for Wales and Ireland. These old records are much more complete for the rare and local species, which naturally attracted greater interest than the common species. In general, the old literature and

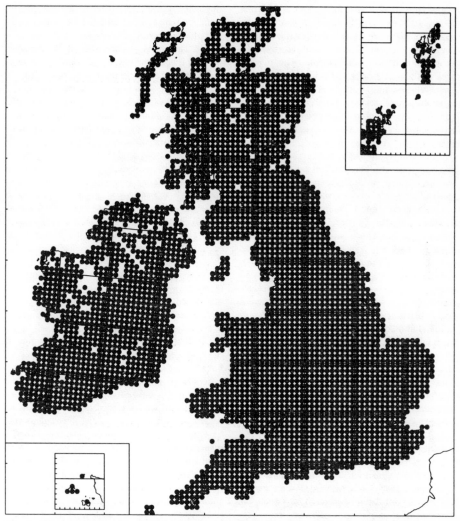

Map showing the coverage achieved. At least one record has been received from each square with a solid dot.

museum records cannot be located as precisely as the recent ones, and there is a relatively large proportion of 'doubtful' records which are now impossible to check. However, we believe that, although they should be treated with a little more caution than the modern records, they provide an essentially accurate picture of the former range of butterflies.

There are sixty-two distribution maps in the atlas. We have included maps for three regular and sometimes common migrants which breed here but overwinter rarely or not at all. These are the clouded yellow, the red admiral and the painted lady. A number of other much rarer migrants have not been included. The best known of these are probably the monarch (or milkweed), which occasionally arrives in the west from North America, and the Camberwell beauty, which appears to come here from northern Europe although its continental distribution is wide; it is generally seen in the east of the country (e.g. Chalmers-Hunt, 1977). Good accounts of these and other rare migrants, the bath white, pale clouded yellow, short-tailed blue, long-tailed blue, and Queen of Spain fritillary, are given by Frohawk (1934). (Berger's clouded yellow was not recognized as a separate species at the time Frohawk was writing.)

The date classes used for the maps are: pre-1940, 1940–69, 1970–82. The first class is largely of literature records as described, while the second is mainly from the field records of the early contributors to the scheme, who referred back to their notebooks and collections. The last class consists almost entirely of field records sent in as they' were obtained. The early period is a very long one, stretching back into the nineteenth century and, in a few cases, even earlier, and, for some species, includes periods of major expansion, contraction or both. The records from the first date class are therefore best regarded as the maximum range reached during the period. The speed of decline of some species in recent years has been such that even the much shorter second and third date classes conceal significant changes. Where such changes are known to have occurred, they are discussed in the text. It is a characteristic of the type of map used that contraction of range is shown clearly but expansion of range is not, because later records supersede earlier ones. Again, expansion of range, where it has occurred, is discussed in the text.

The islands of Orkney and Shetland and the Channel Islands are shown as inset maps. The Channel Islands are perhaps closer in some elements of their flora and fauna to mainland Europe than to the rest of Britain, but their butterflies do not include any species which are absent from the rest of Britain, apart from one recently introduced species of skipper, which we have omitted.

In addition to the distribution records of the Biological Records Centre, we have also included data from the Butterfly Monitoring Scheme. This scheme was begun in 1976 to monitor changes in the abundance of butterflies at some eighty sites throughout Britain, although only one Irish site is included at present. Counts are made at a frequency of one a week along a set route, averaging about five kilometres, through each site from April to September inclusive. An index of abundance is calculated for each species. This index does not provide a measure of absolute numbers but can be used to show change in abundance from year to year (Pollard, 1977). The main use of the data from the scheme, in this book, is in the maps showing the flight periods of butterflies in different parts of the country, but we have also included data on changes in abundance for a few species. These mainly illustrate the magnitude of short-term fluctuations in numbers, often caused by the weather, which can occur over a few generations. The period of monitoring is as yet too short to provide much of a guide to long-term changes. It is important, also, to distinguish between short-term fluctuations in numbers which occur within surviving colonies and the prosperity of a species in Britain as a whole. These may be very different. For example, on well-maintained sites, the adonis blue spectacularly increased in numbers from 1977 to 1982, and we illustrate one example (page 75). However, during the same period, the *total* number of colonies of this butterfly in Britain declined because other sites were destroyed, while few, if any, new ones were colonized.

The texts are intended as a commentary on the maps, and provide also a brief account of current knowledge of the natural history and ecology of each species. Original accounts of the British butterflies, such as those of Newman (1870), Tutt (1905–14), Frohawk (1934) and Ford (1945), are very few; many books have since been published which do no more than repeat the information given by the early writers. Where errors were made, these too have been repeated. New errors regarding the food plants have been introduced because the old Latin names of plants have been misinterpreted. The cumulative result is that the 'accepted' list of larval foods is so confused that it is fully accurate for only five of the twelve species of butterfly that we happen to have studied in depth. Indeed, in three cases, the generally quoted food plant was never used. No doubt we will be guilty of perpetuating errors ourselves, but we have tried as far as possible to restrict our accounts to original observations and have provided references to support these. Literature references are given in the conventional way, e.g. (Baker, 1978) with the full details in the References (page 147). Many field observations have been made by colleagues who have allowed us to quote them; these we have referred to using the name of the observer but no date, e.g. [K. Porter].

In the texts, we have tried to define the requirements of each butterfly as precisely as possible, given current knowledge. We have put particular emphasis on describing not just the species of plant used by the larva, but the conditions under which the plant must be growing. For example, some species require plants growing in sparse or closely cropped turf, others can feed only on the flowers or fruits of mature plants, yet others need shade, and so on. The ecology of about a quarter of our butterfly species has now been studied in some depth. In almost all of these cases the detailed features of the resources required by the larvae have been shown to be of critical importance to the distribution, status and long-term survival of the butterflies. In contrast, although the overall abundance of flowers, for adult food, may sometimes be important, there is no evidence that particular flower species have any special importance. Butterflies generally seem able to use a wide range of the available species.

We have generally omitted from the texts detailed descriptions of the butterflies themselves, and also aspects of their natural history which have been fully described in other books. We do include, however, some new information about the approximate number of individuals in populations we have studied. We have also tried to distinguish between species that live in more or less self-contained colonies and those which are more mobile and fly through the countryside, laying eggs when they find suitable food plants.

The taxonomic order and nomenclature of butterflies follows Bradley and Fletcher (1979), and the nomenclature of plants Dony *et al.* (1974), which provides recommended English names. Use of Latin names is restricted to instances where these may be more familiar than the English names, as with the grasses, and where closely related species are mentioned.

The Biological Records Centre is part of the Institute of Terrestrial Ecology, and part of its work is financed by the Nature Conservancy Council. The authors would like to thank both of these organizations for their support. Both the mapping scheme and the Butterfly Monitoring Scheme, which is also partly supported by the Nature Conservancy Council, are dependent on the effort, largely voluntary and unpaid, of many hundreds of recorders from all over Britain. Without them this atlas could not have been produced.

The production of the maps, and the computer data files on which they are based, have been largely the responsibility of P. T. Harding, head of the Biological Records Centre, and Mrs D. M. Greene. We are very greatly indebted to them for their painstaking work with a vast number of records.

Other past and present members of B.R.C. have contributed greatly to the atlas in a variety of ways. The lepidoptera recording scheme owes its beginning to the initiative of the former head of B.R.C., F. H. Perring. We would also like to thank Mrs D. W. Awdry, Miss E. F. Blenkiron, Mrs C. D. Binge, Mrs R. Cooke, Mrs J. Croft, Miss F. Griffith, Miss R. J. Harper, Mrs J. L. Ling, Mrs J. Scott, Mrs E. Tasker and Mrs S. M. Weller.

We have been greatly assisted with the Irish records by Miss E. ni Lamhna, of the Irish Biological Records Centre, and J. P. Hillis, and with the Scottish records by G. Thomson. M. J. Skelton made a major contribution to the early years of the scheme and, more recently, J. G. Moller has given valuable help with the computer-handling of the records.

The butterfly monitoring scheme is administered by Mrs M. L. Hall. We are grateful for her help and for that of Mrs T. J. Bibby and Mrs J. M. Welch, who have also been closely involved with the monitoring scheme.

Many people have contributed to the accounts which accompany the maps, and these people are acknowledged in the text. We would also like to thank the following for more general help with the manuscript: J. P. Dempster, J. N. R. Jeffers, M. G. Morris, D. A. Ratcliffe, A. E. Stubbs, M. S. Warren, and K. J. Willmott.

Finally, we would like to thank Miss J. M. Abblitt, Mrs G. M. Pywell and Miss R. A. Weller, who typed the manuscript.

THE SPECIES

CHEQUERED SKIPPER

Carterocephalus palaemon

This very local butterfly has a curious distribution consisting of two widely separated centres: one in the west of Scotland and the other in the east midlands of England, extending well into Lincolnshire. There are also a few nineteenth-century records from south-west England which should, perhaps, be treated with caution. However, in view of the rapidity with which this butterfly has disappeared from central England in this century, they can by no means be dismissed.

The chequered skipper was first recorded from Clapham Park Wood, Bedfordshire, in 1798 (South, 1906). In the next 100 years it was discovered in scattered woods throughout the midlands. By the twentieth century it had disappeared from its very few sites in the south and west midlands, but was plentiful on several sites in the east, especially in north Northamptonshire and Leicestershire. It also occurred in the ancient Lincolnshire lime woods to the north of that county and in a few sites to the south of these.

During this century the chequered skipper has experienced an almost continuous decline in England, although it did briefly re-expand and colonize a few new sites in the 1950s and 1960s, for example Monks Wood (where it had previously occurred in the nineteenth century) and Woodwalton Fen in Cambridgeshire.

Although the chequered skipper remained plentiful in a few of its English localities until the end of the 1960s, a sharp decline had already started. The severity of this decline only became apparent when no English record was received by the Biological Records Centre in 1972 or 1973. Intensive surveys were organized (Farrell,

1975). Nearly all former sites and other potential areas were searched, but no chequered skipper was found. However, one very small colony was independently reported in Rutland, and was confirmed by several entomologists in 1975. It has not been seen there since, despite many searches in every year.

We organized another survey in 1980 in which forty of its most recent English sites were visited, but again no chequered skippers were found. There is a lingering hope that this butterfly still survives in England, for it is easily overlooked, but all recorded colonies are almost certainly extinct.

The history of the chequered skipper in Scotland is much more cheerful. The butterfly was unknown from that country until Mackworth-Praed (1942) discovered a colony near Fort William, Inverness, in 1942, although it has since been shown that a museum specimen exists that had been found a few years earlier. The Inverness locality became a place of pilgrimage to entomologists, but for thirty years no one suspected its occurrence elsewhere; then, in the early 1970s, colonies were reported in Argyll, just when it was dawning that the butterfly might be extinct in England. This exciting discovery prompted further surveys, particularly by the Scottish Wildlife Trust, and almost immediately colonies were found over a wide area; our present map of twenty-four recent ten-kilometre squares is considered by Thomson (1980) to be incomplete. There is no suggestion that this butterfly has recently spread in Scotland, merely that its inconspicuous colonies have been overlooked; it had even been missed on two nature reserves. Most of these colonies are small, but one is continuous along eight kilometres of roadside verge (Thomson, 1980).

Very little is known of the ecology of the chequered skipper, or of the reasons for its decline in England. Its main larval food plant on at least one English site (Castor Hanglands) was false brome grass (*Brachypodium sylvaticum*), although eggs were also laid on tor-grass (*B. pinnatum*) (Collier, 1966). In Scotland false brome was seen to be ignored by females on two sites studied by K. J. Willmott and P. Grey, and all egg-laying they observed was on purple moor-grass (*Molinea caerulea*). R. Collier has, however, found eggs on false brome in Scotland. Purple moor-grass is readily eaten in captivity, although large tough plants have been found to be rather unpalatable [M. Brooks]. The eggs are laid singly under blades of grass from mid May to mid June, when the adults fly. The young larva makes a tube by spinning together the edges of its leaf (Tutt, 1905; Collier, 1966). It feeds on the rest of the leaf above and below this, often until only the midrib and tube are left, when it leaves to spin another tube. The larva is fully fed by October, when it hibernates in a silk hibernaculum spun among grass. In April, it spins a tent of grass in which it pupates.

Most English colonies of the chequered skipper occurred in sunny open woodland (especially in broad rides) or in grassland associated with woods. Much rough land adjoining woods has been destroyed in the present century, and most woods have become progressively shadier due to the replacement or abandonment of coppices. However, this hardly explains the sudden disappearance of this butterfly from so many, apparently very different, sites. There has been much speculation about the cause or causes, but no satisfactory explanation has been advanced.

In Scotland the adults are usually seen in damp rank pasture which is dominated by large exposed clumps of purple moor-grass. These clumps are, however, not used for breeding. Females fly instead to small scrubby areas, usually on the edge of copses, or to scattered mixtures of oak, birch and hazel; there they lay their eggs on small plants of moor-grass shaded by bog myrtle or other shrubs.

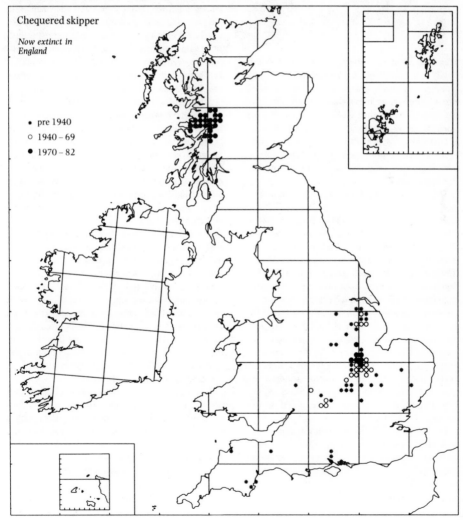

Chequered skipper

Now extinct in England

• pre 1940
○ 1940 – 69
● 1970 – 82

SMALL SKIPPER

Thymelicus sylvestris

This is a common butterfly in much of Britain, but it has a well defined, presumably climatic, limit, and does not occur in the extreme north-east of England or in Scotland. There are a few old Scottish records which Thomson (1980) considers to be of doubtful validity. Like all of the grass-feeding skippers, it is absent from Ireland. In contrast, its main food plant, Yorkshire-fog (*Holcus lanatus*), is a common grass throughout the British Isles.

Most textbooks list a variety of 'soft' grasses as food plants of this butterfly, with Timothy (*Phleum pratense*), creeping soft-grass (*Holcus mollis*) (Frohawk, 1934), Yorkshire-fog and false brome (*Brachypodium sylvaticum*) (Tutt, 1905) most often mentioned. Other species are eaten in captivity. However, K. J. Willmott and K. Porter have independently recorded, from many observations of egg-laying in the wild, that Yorkshire-fog is by far the most important food plant. Porter found that in Oxfordshire 40 per cent of Yorkshire-fog plants had eggs on them, while creeping soft-grass, present in the same sward, was not used at all. At a site in Surrey, K. J. Willmott found that every Yorkshire-fog plant out of several hundred held eggs, although he has also found a few eggs on Timothy and has once seen an egg laid on false brome.

The behaviour of the egg-laying female is very distinctive. Only mature grasses are chosen and, after first inspecting the dead or fading flower-heads with a buzzing flight, the female runs her abdomen up and down a flowering stem, inserting her ovipositor into the leaf sheath. Eggs are laid in batches of three to ten within each sheath; although Porter has found up to thirty-three eggs in a single stem, these are presumably from several females.

Frohawk describes how the newly hatched larvae construct silk chambers for hibernation and do not feed until the following spring. They then feed within tubes formed by binding grass blades together; later they eat other leaves as well, leaving highly characteristic wedge-shaped notches similar to those that the Lulworth skipper makes on tor-grass (*Brachypodium pinnatum*). The pupa is formed within a net-like silk cocoon at the base of the food plant, which incorporates, and is covered by, grass leaves.

The small skipper occurs commonly on rough grassland where the sward is allowed to grow tall, but is rare or absent in well-cropped pasture. It may be found in quite small areas or in strips of land, for example on road verges and field boundaries among cultivated fields. Marking experiments indicate that numbers may be much larger than is suggested by casual observation, as at any one time most of the adults will be resting among vegetation.

The range of this butterfly has remained largely stable over the period for which records are available, apart from an apparent decline in north Wales. On a more local scale, numbers must have been considerably reduced by the intensification of agriculture, although it remains a common species throughout most of its range. The small skipper was one of the few butterflies that did not decline after the 1976 drought, perhaps because the larvae hibernate before feeding; much of the harm done to other species was the result of desiccation of larval food plants.

There has been a general assumption, which we shared, that the flight periods of butterflies are later in the season in the north of their ranges than in the south. Our data for this species, and for many others, suggests that this is by no means always true. The flight periods throughout the country are often closely synchronized.

Flight period of the small skipper at five sites in England in 1979 and at one site in three different years.

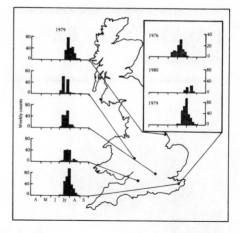

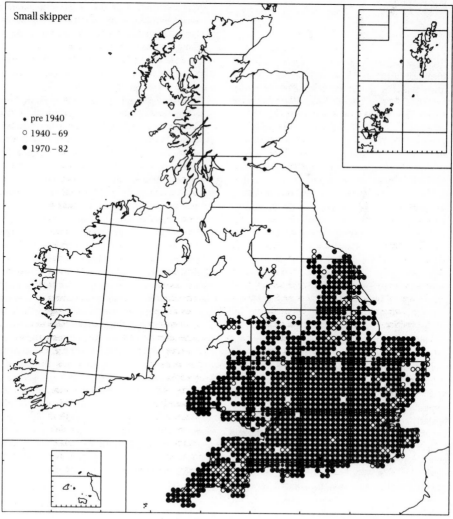

Small skipper

* pre 1940
○ 1940 – 69
● 1970 – 82

ESSEX SKIPPER

Thymelicus lineola

The Essex skipper is a relatively recent addition to the list of British butterflies, although it may have been common in the south-east for a very long time. It was distinguished from the small skipper only in 1889 in England (Hawes, 1890), although it was known on the continent before then. The differences between adults of the two species are slight, and they are the only species not separated in the Butterfly Monitoring Scheme. The most reliable distinguishing feature is that the Essex skipper is black beneath the tips of the antennae rather than orange, as in the case of the small skipper (Heath, 1969). The larvae are more easily separated: the head capsule of the Essex skipper is a distinctive brown and white colour. After its presence in Britain was known, collections were re-examined and Essex skippers were found, in the words of a contemporary entomological journal, 'in several cabinets doing duty for . . .' the small skipper.

Essex and small skippers often fly together in unimproved grassland, hedgerows, verges and similar situations. Insufficient is known of the ecology of the two species for any confident statement to be made about the situations in which one or the other would be expected to predominate. Certainly the Essex skipper is particularly common on some calcareous grasslands, but it is also reported to be the characteristic skipper of some wetlands and coastal marshes, and is very abundant on light acidic soil in east Kent. The Essex skipper is generally recorded as emerging slightly later than the small skipper, but

there is considerable overlap of flight periods. The comparative ecology of these species is clearly in need of study.

The flat eggs are laid in the sheaths of grasses. Only the tightest sheaths are chosen, and dead stems are often used. K. J. Willmott has watched egg-laying twenty to thirty times in the wild, always on cock's-foot (*Dactylis glomerata*) or creeping soft-grass (*Holcus mollis*). Yorkshire-fog (*Holcus lanatus*), which has looser sheaths and is favoured by the small skipper, was apparently never used. The eggs do not hatch until the following spring, when the larvae separate and live solitarily. They spin leaf blades into tubes, from which they emerge by day to feed, beginning with the leaf tips. Over 100 wild larvae have been found by Willmott, usually on cock's-foot, but often on creeping soft-grass and very rarely on false brome (*Brachypodium sylvaticum*) and torgrass (*B. pinnatum*). Frohawk (1934) records Timothy (*Phleum pratense*) as a food plant. The larva pupates in a cocoon formed within spun grass leaves.

In North America the Essex skipper, known as the European skipper, has been introduced and is a pest of Timothy grass in hay and seed crops. It has now become quite widespread there. It was first recorded at London, Ontario, in 1910. Burns (1966) describes the typical pattern of spread. Newly established populations persist at low levels for several years and then appear to expand rapidly to reach very high densities, before declining to a lower level. It is possible that these new populations, often derived from one or a few individual founders, may show local genetic differences. Transportation to new areas may well be in hay. McNeil and Duchesne (1977) sampled hay bales from areas of high populations and found approximately 5,000 viable eggs per bale!

The distribution map is probably incomplete as, even today, the species is almost certainly underrecorded because of its similarity to the small skipper. Many people assume, because of statements made in textbooks, that it is restricted to wetlands in the extreme south-east and do not look for it elsewhere.

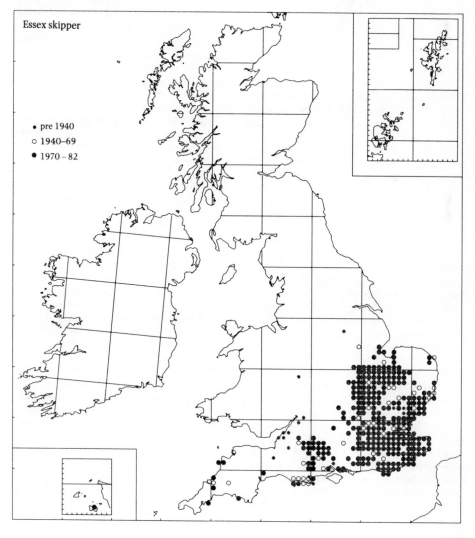

Essex skipper

- • pre 1940
- ○ 1940–69
- ● 1970 – 82

LULWORTH SKIPPER

Thymelicus acteon

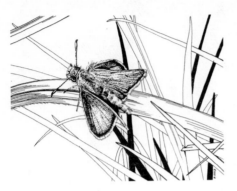

The Lulworth skipper is one of our most locally distributed butterflies, yet is often abundant within its restricted range. Colonies occur only near the south coasts of Dorset, Devon and Cornwall, and these areas are the extreme northern limit of its European range. Its British stronghold is the downland and cliffs of the Isle of Purbeck, extending as far west as Weymouth. A few colonies have also been reported from the Dorset coast west of Portland, and at least two of these survive. The latest record of the few Devonshire colonies is from the late 1950s, but there is little reason to believe that these are extinct, except in Torbay. Lempke (1980) recently discovered a population in Cornwall, very close to Tutt's (1905) nineteenth-century record near Polperro. There have been other occasional sightings of Lulworth skippers farther inland in Dorset, and two from the Isle of Wight. These are not permanent colonies, and probably originated from strays or, more likely, escapes or introductions. The adult found on Hod Hill, north-east Dorset, was almost certainly released there.

We made a survey of the status of this butterfly in Dorset in 1978 (Thomas, 1983b). It was found in all likely habitats throughout its main area. Eighty-three separate colonies were identified, of which as many as forty-six had not been recorded previously. Several areas supported very large populations: indeed, it was the commonest butterfly on some sites and rough estimates indicate that nearly a million adults emerged on the army ranges east of Lulworth in that year. Similar high numbers were recorded in Purbeck in 1975 to 1981.

All colonies of the Lulworth skipper in Dorset are on chalk or limestone grassland. Those in Devon are reputed to have been on old red sandstone, but this is unlikely, for the larval food plant, tor-grass (*Brachypodium pinnatum*) – not false brome (*B. sylvaticum*) as is stated in most textbooks – is common only on calcareous soils. In Dorset a small colony on the acid heathland of Hartland Moor National Nature Reserve and another on a clay soil were both actually breeding on chalk rubble that had been imported as ballast for railways in the nineteenth century.

Nearly all colonies in Dorset in 1978 were found on south-facing slopes, especially in areas that were sheltered from the wind. All were breeding in abandoned or patchily grazed grassland in which tor-grass grew to an average height in each site of at least ten centimetres. Most large colonies bred in much taller grassland. Female Lulworth skippers generally chose the tallest clumps of tor-grass for egg-laying and ignored plants under ten centimetres tall. The eggs are laid inside the sheaths of mature, often dead, flower stalks. The larva rests in a tube constructed of a folded tor-grass leaf, closed with silk, and ascends at night to feed on the tenderer blades, making characteristic wedge-shaped notches. The adult stage extends over about eight weeks in July and August. Marking experiments suggest that there is little interchange of individuals between nearby colonies. The adults feed and fly only in still warm weather, and then only infrequently; for this reason populations may be much larger than indicated by casual inspection. Even so, it is hard to overlook this butterfly because it is so numerous on most of its sites.

Because they are either very steep or actually unstable, the historical breeding grounds of this skipper have been virtually unscathed by development or agricultural improvement. Moreover, much of Britain's unimproved grassland has been only sporadically grazed in recent years, especially since the dearth of rabbits after myxomatosis. In these conditions tor-grass spreads rapidly and also grows into the tall clumps favoured by the Lulworth skipper. While these conditions are unsuitable for several species of butterfly, they are ideal for this skipper; in one site where grazing was relaxed a monitored population increased more than twenty-fold, whereas numbers were almost unaltered where the habitat was unchanged (Thomas, 1983b).

There is strong circumstantial evidence that similar increases have occurred on many sites, and that the Lulworth skipper is now more numerous and has more colonies than at any time since its discovery near Lulworth Cove in 1832 (Dale, 1886). It has not, however, spread to other calcareous ranges which are now equally dominated by tor-grass, perhaps because the climate is unsuitable in these areas or because the butterflies' powers of dispersal are too poor.

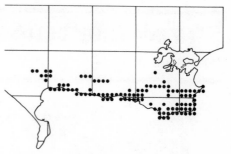

The distribution of the Lulworth skipper in south-east Dorset in 1978, plotted by one-kilometre squares.

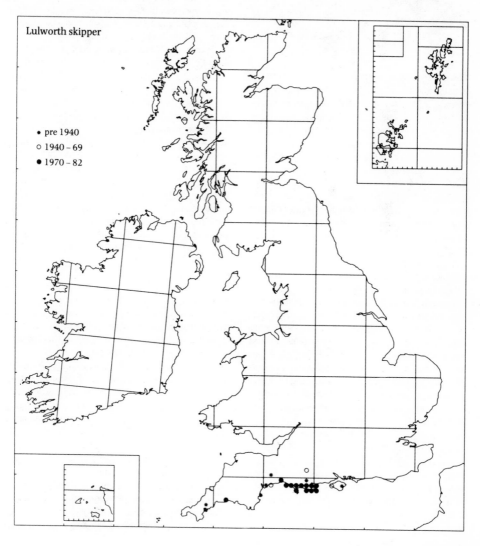

Lulworth skipper

• pre 1940
○ 1940 – 69
● 1970 – 82

SILVER-SPOTTED SKIPPER

Hesperia comma

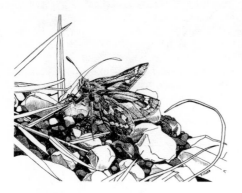

The silver-spotted skipper is restricted to calcareous grassland, where its larvae feed on sheep's-fescue (*Festuca ovina*). It is a common insect in central and southern Europe, and was once widely distributed on most of the chalk and limestone outcrops in the southern half of Britain. It has not been reliably recorded from the flatter areas of Salisbury Plain or, more curiously, from many of the downs of central Dorset, Purbeck and the Isle of Wight. This skipper has never been considered a common species in Britain; colonies were always extremely localized, and it probably needs a warm dry microclimate in order to survive here.

This species has experienced a severe decline during the past thirty to forty years. The situation had become so serious that, in 1982, the Joint Committee for the Conservation of British Insects chose it for its annual butterfly survey. All 'post-1960' localities and many former sites and other areas that appeared suitable were examined, and it is believed that virtually all the existing colonies were found. It was sometimes hard to determine the exact boundaries between adjoining sites, but a subjective division gave fifty-three colonies of this butterfly breeding in thirty-three more or less discrete localities. Ten of these were large, with more than 1,500 adults each, but over half the colonies were very small.

In earlier centuries the silver-spotted skipper bred in Yorkshire, but its most northerly known sites today are in the Chilterns, where there are at least seven colonies, including the largest. It also survives in east Kent (five colonies), Sussex (two), Surrey (twenty-eight), Hampshire (seven)

and Dorset and Wiltshire (one colony each). In Surrey there is a string of small interconnected colonies which breed along the south-facing scarp of the North Downs. A similar continuity of local distribution apparently once occurred in many other parts of its range, but today this skipper is usually reduced to discrete isolated sites.

Adult silver-spotted skippers are active only in very warm sunny weather, and it is easy for the casual observer to miss a colony; some entomologists prefer to search for the relatively large, pudding-basin shaped eggs, which overwinter on the food plant. Females select small plants that abut on to bare ground (especially chalk scree), and ignore fescue growing in a dense sward. A colony can be supported by less than half a hectare of sparse *Festuca* grassland, although the big populations occupy sites that are five to twenty-five hectares in size. Other large sites have a patchy and predominantly dense sward, but support small numbers of butterflies which breed on odd suitable plants growing along paths, in rabbit scrapes, etc.

Nearly all the current breeding areas of this rare butterfly are steep south-facing slopes. Some have such crumbly skeletal soils that the grass grows sparsely enough for egg-laying, even if the site is ungrazed; abandoned chalk pits also come into this category. However, most sites need a varying degree of grazing to reduce the vegetation, and most have an extremely short turf. Any domestic stock can produce suitable conditions, but over half the occupied sites found in 1982 were being grazed by rabbits alone.

Several factors have contributed to the decline of this butterfly [D. J. Simcox, C. D. Thomas]. Sheep's-fescue has been eliminated from about one fifth of former sites by the agricultural improvement of pasture, and by ploughing from a further 6 per cent. Afforestation and urbanization account for another 15 per cent of extinctions. However, a decline in grazing both by livestock and, since the 1950s, by rabbits has undoubtedly been the main cause of losses. There are several accounts of this butterfly's disappearance as soon as its site became overgrown (e.g. Frazer, 1977), and there was a spate of extinctions in the years following myxomatosis. In 1982, nearly two-thirds of the sites that had lost this butterfly still contained sheep's-fescue in abundance, but about half of these were ungrazed and too overgrown to be suitable. The other half appeared ideal (though many had clearly been overgrown in the recent past), due to local resurgences of rabbits since the late 1970s. Moreover, since 1982 it has become profitable for farmers to stock these un-improved pastures in a few regions. In districts where a colony had survived there have already been small scale recolonizations of recently grazed sites; examples are known from the North Downs scarp and from nature reserves in Hampshire and Sussex.

A few more of the sites that appear to be suit-able may be recolonized eventually, but most are too isolated from existing colonies for this to be a likely natural event. In the longer term there is no assurance that it will remain profitable to stock these unproductive pastures, or that the resurgence of rabbits will prove permanent. It is likely that the silver-spotted skipper will remain a great rarity in Britain, but its future should be safe so long as our conservation organizations ensure that suitable habitat is maintained on those sites that they control; fortunately, over half the known colonies, including the three largest, breed either on a nature reserve or on land owned by the National Trust.

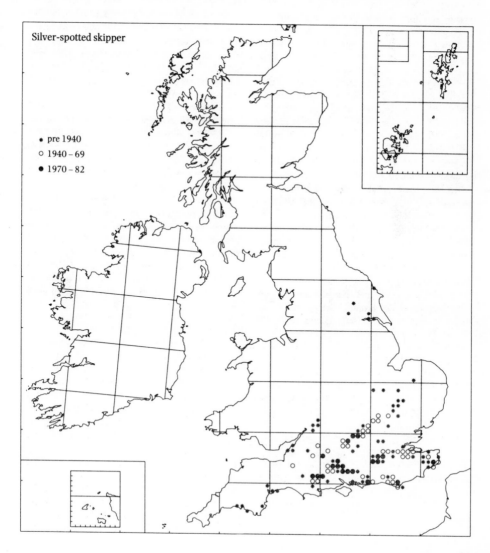

Silver-spotted skipper

• pre 1940
○ 1940 – 69
● 1970 – 82

LARGE SKIPPER

Ochlodes venata

The large skipper can be distinguished from the other common grass-feeding skippers, the small and the Essex, by its larger size and by the mottling of the wings. Like these skippers, the large skipper can occur in small areas of land, where it forms apparently self-contained colonies. These colonies may be larger than one thinks, because the adults spend much of their time settled on vegetation. The range of sites in which it may be found is large, including grassland, hedgerows, and woodland edges and rides, but all have tall grasses in common. It is more often found in sheltered situations than its close relatives.

The long flight period starts in late May in early seasons, and may extend into August, although June and July are its main months. This emergence is normally earlier than that of the small skipper, although there is considerable overlapping. It is interesting that in our figure the earliest emergence in 1980 was in the north-west. The food plants are grasses; the range of species used is uncertain. K. J. Willmott has occasionally seen eggs laid on false brome (*Brachypodium sylvaticum*), but nearly all egg-laying and wild larvae found were on cock's-foot (*Dactylis glomerata*), which is the main food plant recorded by other entomologists. M. S. Warren twice saw eggs laid on the wood small reed (*Calamagrostis epigejos*) in Northamptonshire. The eggs are laid singly, under a leaf blade, and the larva binds the leaf together in the form of a tube, from which it emerges to feed. After hibernation, in the larval stage, growth is completed in the spring; pupation is in a cocoon, which is within a 'tent' formed of grass blades. Like other skippers, the large skipper larva has an anal comb with which it ejects faecal pellets from its tube. Frohawk (1934) records distances of up to a metre!

There has been a slight contraction of the range of this butterfly in the extreme north-east, which occurred in the nineteenth century. South of this it is generally a common species, although, like most other grassland butterflies, the number of its sites has declined dramatically locally, due to the intensification of agriculture. Its absence from Ireland is in striking contrast to the situation in the west of Wales, where it is widespread.

Flight period of the large skipper at five sites in Britain in 1980 and at one site in three different years.

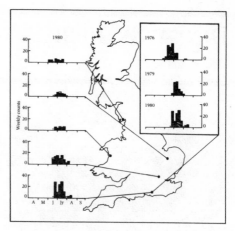

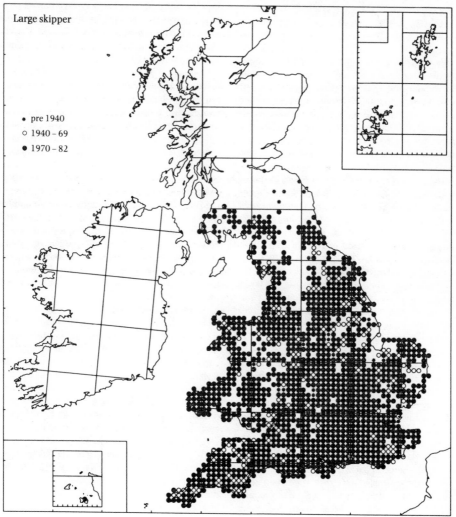

Large skipper

- ● pre 1940
- ○ 1940 – 69
- ● 1970 – 82

DINGY SKIPPER

Erynnis tages

This butterfly has a wider range than the other British skippers; it is the only skipper that is found in Ireland and occurs further north than the chequered skipper in Scotland. As one of our less conspicuous butterflies, it may have been under-recorded. Nevertheless, we believe that the pattern of its distribution is accurately represented here, although it might yet be discovered in new parts of Ireland (ni Lamhna, 1980).

Dingy skippers fly in discrete colonies in spring, with an occasional partial second brood in the summer. Each colony, typically, contains rather few adults; one exceptionally large dingy skipper colony, breeding on three hectares of coastal undercliff, was estimated to contain 300 adults on its peak day in 1978 [C. D. Thomas]. A slump occurred in all monitored populations after the 1976 drought, very probably because the larval food plant, common bird's-foot-trefoil (*Lotus corniculatus*), was 'scorched' and inedible on most sites that summer (e.g. Thomas and Merrett, 1980). Some small colonies became extinct in that year.

Adult dingy skippers make rapid buzzing flights and spend long periods basking in sunspots, usually on bare ground. At night and in cool weather they roost on dead flower heads (especially knapweeds) and grass, with their wings draped around the plant. This gives an extraordinarily moth-like impression. When egg-laying, the females fly close to the ground searching for the food plants, apparently preferring those that are partly concealed by other vegetation (Frohawk, 1934) although exposed ones are also used. Common bird's-foot-trefoil is the food plant

on nearly all sites, but greater bird's-foot-trefoil (*L. uliginosus*) is used on some heavy soils, and horseshoe vetch is also used on chalk or limestone. The eggs are laid singly, but several are often found on the same plant. Each is placed at the base of a leaflet, on the upper surface. Like the orange tip's egg, it soon turns bright orange and is very conspicuous.

The larva spins a few leaflets together and lives between them, feeding first on the cuticle and later on entire leaves. Fresh tents of leaflets are made from time to time, until, in August, the larva is full-fed and spins a rough cocoon around the *Lotus* leaves. It hibernates and, next spring, pupates in this cocoon.

Common bird's-foot-trefoil is abundant throughout the British Isles. As a fairly low-growing herb, it is commonest in short or sparse swards, and it flourishes under disturbed conditions, for it is a rapid colonizer of bare ground. Before the last war it was widely sown in fields to 'sweeten' the pasture, but it has been eliminated from most intensively cultivated land since then by herbicides, fertilizers and the seeding of other fodder plants.

Dingy skippers occur in many of the situations in which its food plant grows in abundance. Colonies are often found in wet areas, but are commoner and are usually larger on well-drained soils or artifices, such as downs, dunes, heaths and embankments. Small colonies may also occur along woodland rides and in associated rough land.

Although widespread, this butterfly is much more localized than the common blue butterfly, which also feeds on *Lotus*. In Ireland the dingy skipper is restricted to limestone areas and is, curiously, absent from most of the coastline; in Britain it is quite frequently found in coastal areas. Unlike the common blue, it is absent from practically all the smaller British islands. Its distribution in Scotland is unusual, with two distinct centres in the north-east and south-west. Its precarious status has been maintained over the last 100 years in the former region, but there has been some loss in industrialized areas in the latter (Thomson, 1980). Isolated colonies still survive through most of northern and central England and Wales, and the butterfly becomes increasingly more frequent towards the south of England. Being a rather drab and inconspicuous butterfly, changes in status have not been widely noted, except for the local extinctions that have occurred in many woods (e.g. Smith and Brown, 1979; Pratt, 1981). It seems likely, however, that many colonies also declined along with bird's-foot-trefoil in overgrown uncultivated swards following the death of rabbits through myxomatosis, and it is certain that a great many more colonies have been destroyed through intensive farming.

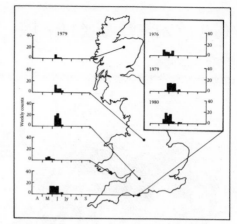

Flight period of the dingy skipper at five sites in Britain in 1979 and at one site in three different years.

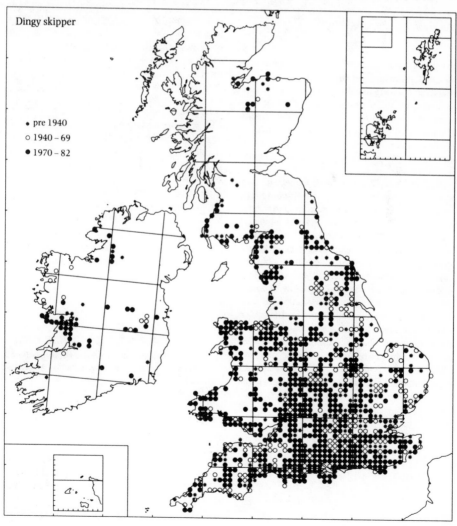

Dingy skipper

• pre 1940
○ 1940 – 69
● 1970 – 82

GRIZZLED SKIPPER

Pyrgus malvae

This small spring butterfly is locally distributed in sheltered meadows, on downland and in open woodland rides. It usually forms discrete sedentary colonies, of which most are probably very small; one apparently abundant Dorset colony was estimated to consist of about 150 adults in 1978. In years when numbers are high it can spread widely through an area, as it did in Monks Wood in 1980.

The flight is rapid with blurred wings, and only on settling can it be identified with certainty. The black and white 'chessboard' pattern of the wings is then very distinctive. The male is lighter in colour than the female and has a conspicuous fold close to the anterior edge (costa) of the forewing. There are several food plants, including species of *Potentilla* (tormentil and cinquefoil), wild strawberry and common agrimony. Frohawk (1934) also includes blackberry and raspberry. The eggs are generally laid singly on the underside of a small leaf. In their early stages the larvae live within silken shelters spun on the uppersides, but later spin entire leaves together and feed within this tent. Pupation is said to be at the base of the food plant or nearby (Frohawk, 1934), and

overwintering is in this stage. There is usually only one generation a year, but in exceptionally warm seasons there can be a small second generation.

The range of the grizzled skipper has not changed greatly, although there has been some contraction in the extreme north. It has probably been under-recorded compared with most butterflies, because it is rather inconspicuous. It is commonest in central southern Britain, but even there it is only locally distributed. It has undoubtedly become much rarer within its present range because of the loss of suitable grassland sites through agricultural improvement; this change shows in the small number of recent records. In the east of England, for example, it has become an uncommon species and may well decline further in the next decade.

Its precise requirements are not known, but, as with so many butterflies, the lush rank growth of improved grassland is inimical to the food plants of this species. In some areas it has survived well in the broader rides of conifer plantations. The results of the Butterfly Monitoring Scheme show a steady decline since 1976, although it did not decline immediately after the drought of that year, as did so many species.

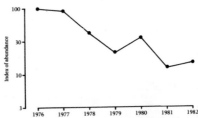

Changes in abundance of the grizzled skipper, 1976–82, as shown by data from the Butterfly Monitoring Scheme.

Flight period of the grizzled skipper at five sites in England in 1980, and at one site in three different years.

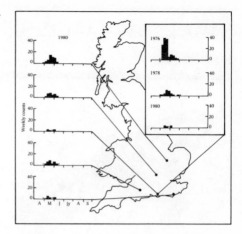

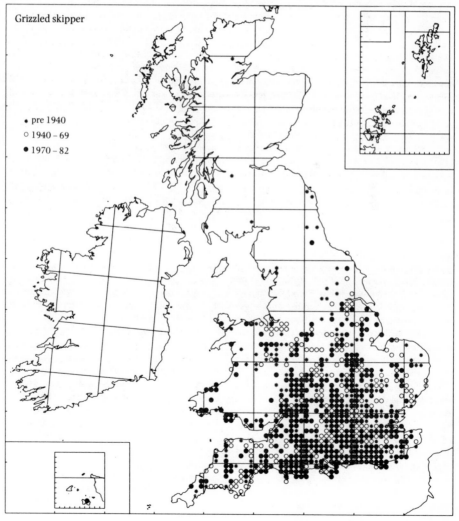

Grizzled skipper

- pre 1940
○ 1940 – 69
● 1970 – 82

SWALLOWTAIL

Papilio machaon

The British subspecies of the swallowtail, *britannicus*, differs slightly in colour from that in neighbouring continental countries, *bigeneratus*, and differs considerably in voltinism, habitat preference and food plants. The British swallowtail is a relatively sedentary, usually univoltine, fenland species restricted to one food plant, milk parsley; the continental form is bivoltine, has a number of umbelliferous food plants (including milk parsley), and is wide-ranging, reaching Britain and breeding here occasionally.

The swallowtail flies from late May to mid July. Eggs are usually laid on large flowering plants which project above the surrounding vegetation. The young caterpillars resemble bird droppings, but after the second moult they become light green with strongly coloured black and orange 'rings'. The caterpillar has an osmaterium, an extensible organ, situated behind the head, which emits a pungent smell when everted and serves to repel predators. Pupation is among vegetation close to the ground. In warm years there may be a small second generation, but usually the pupae of the spring generation go through the winter, often submerged for long periods.

The status and ecology of the swallowtail have been described by Dempster *et al.* (1976) and Dempster and Hall (1980), and this account is based on these studies. The key to understanding its ecology lies largely in a knowledge of the food plant, milk parsley. This plant flourishes in wet open fenland and, where conditions are good, individual plants are large enough to attract egg-laying butterflies. The Norfolk Broads provide some such areas, but when the spring water levels are low the plants become less vigorous and so less suitable for the swallowtail. The development of shrub and tree vegetation (carr) further worsens the situation. Traditional sedge and reed cutting techniques help to maintain suitable conditions, but such management may not be adequate if the water table falls. At Wicken Fen in Cambridgeshire, the swallowtail became extinct in the early 1950s due, it is thought, to the drying of the fen and the consequent decline in the quantity and quality of milk parsley. Several attempts have been made to reintroduce the species to Wicken, the last in 1975 (Dempster and Hall, 1980), but these eventually failed and it was concluded that re-establishment will not be possible until the fen can be made wetter.

Dempster *et al.* (1976) made a study of museum specimens of swallowtails from Norfolk and from Wicken Fen from 1880 to 1940. The Wicken butterflies were different from those of Norfolk in the period from 1890 to 1920 in several respects, particularly thorax width and wing size, with the Wicken individuals significantly smaller. It is possible that the isolated nature of the Wicken site led to selection for less mobile, small-winged, individuals which would be less likely to leave the area. Since 1920, the Norfolk butterflies have declined in the size of these variables, suggesting the possibility that these butterflies are now less mobile as a result of reduction in area and fragmentation of suitable habitat. As with most historical studies, the available facts are tantalizingly incomplete and the causes of the observed differences must inevitably be speculative.

The old records of the British and continental subspecies from other parts of the country are difficult or impossible to separate, and for this reason we have mapped only recent records known to be of the British subspecies. There is evidence that the continental race was resident in southern Britain early in the nineteenth century. Since that time numerous migrants have been recorded, but it has not established itself here except sporadically, as in the mid 1940s in south-east England (Williams, 1958). The British subspecies was certainly more widespread in eastern England than it is now (Bretherton, 1951a).

The future of the British swallowtail is dependent on the correct management of the Broadland sites. The area of open water and marsh has declined considerably over the last century. Dempster *et al.* (1976) believe that the swallowtail is in danger of further decline unless the water level can be raised and the growth of carr suppressed. They conclude that the best long-term solution would be to reduce the height of the land's surface by peat cutting, the way in which the Broads were originally formed. However, there has certainly been some success with the current management, by cutting vegetation to maintain open conditions, on some Broadland nature reserves.

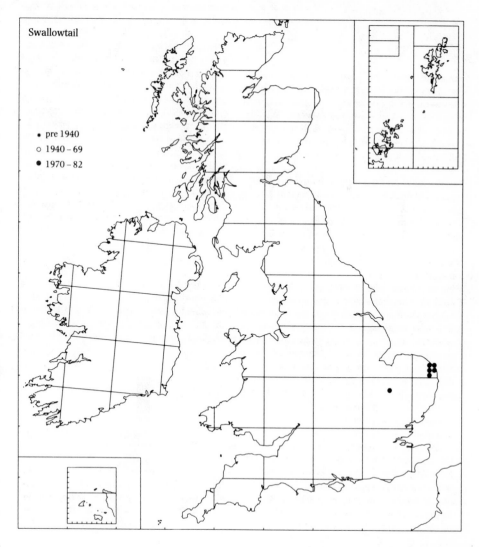

Swallowtail

• pre 1940
○ 1940 – 69
● 1970 – 82

WOOD WHITE

Leptidea sinapis

In Great Britain the wood white is, as its name suggests, predominantly a woodland butterfly. In Ireland it usually occupies more open situations, as it does on the continent, where Wiklund (1977a and b) has studied the adult behaviour in Sweden. Warren (1981) has recently studied the distribution and ecology of the wood white in Britain.

The flight period is long, from the end of May until July or even August. As with many butterflies, males are seen more frequently than females, because the males spend more time in flight, searching for mates. There is usually only one generation, but there may be a small second emergence in more southerly localities. In Northamptonshire, second generations occurred in the warm summers of 1976 and 1982. Several authors state that tuberous pea (*Lathyrus tuberosus*) is the main food plant, but this is an error. The main food plants are meadow vetchling (*L. pratensis*), bitter vetch (*L. montanus*), bird's-foot-trefoils and tufted vetch, all leguminous plants. The eggs are laid singly and the larvae do not move far from the egg site until approaching pupation. Overwintering is as a pupa, which is secured by its girdle to a plant stem.

The Irish subspecies of the wood white (*juvernica*) has a distinctive olive-green tinge to the underwings. It is widespread and fairly common (ni Lamhna, 1980), and has recently been spreading to new areas. In contrast, the wood white has always been extremely local in England and it has become considerably more restricted in the last 100 years. It became extinct in most of the northern and eastern sites in the nineteenth century, and in the same period was also lost from the New Forest and the Isle of Wight. The present English distribution is centred in three main areas: Herefordshire and Worcestershire; Northamptonshire and Oxfordshire; and the Surrey–Sussex border. There are also scattered colonies throughout south-west England. In recent years, that is since 1970, there has been some expansion of range, and there are now believed to be about ninety colonies in England and Wales. Several of the new populations are known to originate from deliberate introductions, which suggests that its distribution is to some extent restricted by poor powers of dispersal. The flight of the wood white is slow and laboured in comparison with most other butterflies.

Provisional results from a population study (Warren, 1981), which is still in progress, suggest that the weather during the flight period affects fecundity and the survival of very young larvae, and so is responsible for annual fluctuations. Fine weather results in large numbers of eggs, good larval survival, and an increase in the number of adults in the following season. There is no evidence, however, that bad weather caused the contraction of range in the nineteenth century.

It seems likely that the decline in coppice management of woods affected the wood white adversely, as it is essentially a species of rides and open areas within woods. Similarly, the recent spread was probably aided by the availability of substantial areas of young conifer plantations on ancient woodland sites with rich herbaceous floras. Over 40 per cent of current wood white colonies in England are in Forestry Commission plantations,

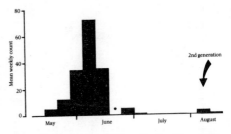

Flight periods of the wood white at Yardley Chase, Northamptonshire, in 1982, showing the small second generation. A dot indicates no count in that week.

but it is unlikely that many of these will survive as the trees mature and shade out the food plants. A number of new colonies has also been found along disused railways. In addition to being breeding sites, these may provide pathways for dispersal.

It seems likely that the conservation of the wood white will depend on appropriate woodland management. Warren (1981) has provided recommendations for the necessary width of rides in commercial plantations and also suggests suitable ride management. The present period of expansion may end soon unless these measures are taken.

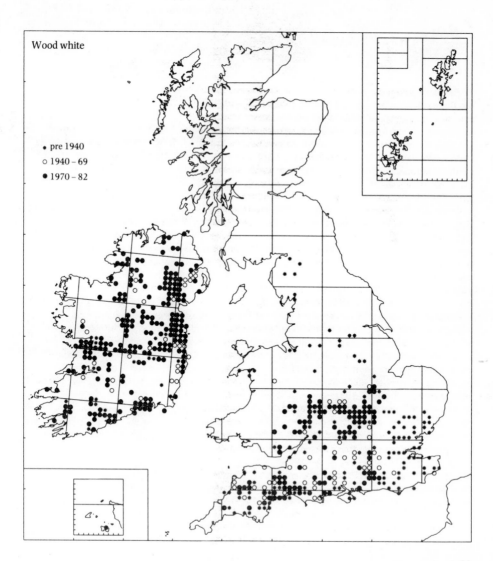

Wood white

• pre 1940
○ 1940 – 69
● 1970 – 82

CLOUDED YELLOW

Colias croceus

The clouded yellow is much the commonest of our three migrant *Colias* species. Migration in this and most migratory butterflies does not involve movement to and from overwintering areas by the same individuals, as is the case with many birds; individuals of the clouded yellow may move south in autumn, but northward flights in the following spring are by a later generation of butterflies.

Winter generations of the clouded yellow are mainly restricted to the Mediterranean region, and later it expands to breed widely in northern Europe. Its abundance in the British Isles seems to depend largely on the numbers that immigrate and breed in May and June, producing a new generation of butterflies in August and September. These may in turn migrate further north, but later in the season there is good evidence for a return, southerly, movement (Williams, 1958). The occurrence of this species is much more erratic than that of the other major migrants the red admiral and the painted lady; the 'clouded yellow years' are noted and long remembered by lepidopterists. Williams (1958) quotes 1877 and 1947 as the outstanding years of abundance. In the 1940s there were several years of large numbers, and Ford (1945) wrote that in 1941 'I was in Cornwall in August of that year and in some places on the Lizard peninsula the fields were yellow with these butterflies as if scattered with flowers, and a distant "white" was almost as

likely to be a specimen of the pale female form *helice* as a member of the Pierinae.' The pale females make up about 5–10 per cent of the population.

There is little chance of overwinter survival of clouded yellows in this country, as there is no hibernation stage; it requires a constant succession of food plants and to find these it must frequently move to a new locality. The food plants are leguminous plants such as vetches (Higgins and Riley, 1970), clovers and lucerne. Frohawk (1934) records a female laying 500 eggs over a period of eight days in captivity.

Our map of this and the two other major migrants should be interpreted rather differently from the other distribution maps. These migrants can be seen in any part of the country and do not have a defined 'range'. The map provides an indication of the areas where the probability of seeing them is greatest. Thus, the chance of seeing the clouded yellow is highest in the south of England and southern Ireland, nearest to the source of immigration, and elsewhere around the coast. It is likely that concentrations of migrants reach land in coastal areas and then disperse as they move inland, or, alternatively, that in some circumstances coasts provide natural 'channels' along which migrants move.

After 1947, there was not another 'clouded yellow year' for a quarter of a century, and it was feared that these might be a thing of the past, because large enough numbers might no longer build up under the intensive agriculture that is now practised over much of Europe. Happily, these fears were unfounded. In the spring of 1983 occasional adults were reported throughout southern Britain, and these bred well in the warm summer of that year, to produce a very large second generation. Although not quite matching Ford's description of 1941, clouded yellows did at least outnumber the brimstone in most areas of the southern counties in 1983, and were exceptionally abundant on some southern downs.

Records of clouded yellows at sites in the Butterfly Monitoring Scheme in 1983.

Clouded yellow

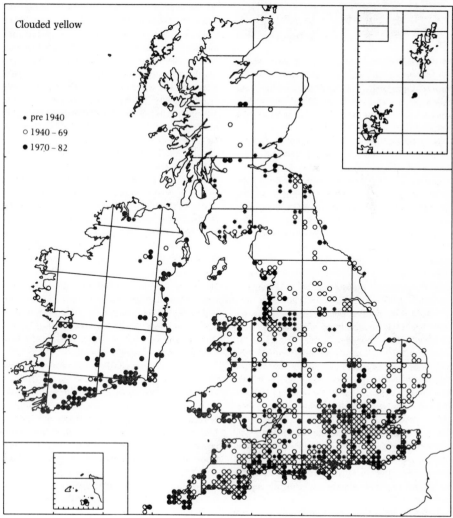

• pre 1940
○ 1940 – 69
● 1970 – 82

BRIMSTONE

Gonepteryx rhamni

The word 'butterfly' may first have been used to describe the butter-yellow male brimstone. The female is greenish-white and is sometimes mistaken in flight for the large white, which is of similar size. At rest, the leaf-shaped outline of the brimstone is unmistakable.

Brimstone adults are very long lived, probably on occasions surviving for a full year, although half of this is spent in hibernation. The hibernation sites are thought to be usually among evergreen foliage (e.g. ivy or holly (Frohawk, 1934)), where their shape and colour make them very difficult to see. On mild winter days the brimstone may fly briefly and then return to hibernation. The males emerge first in the spring and the females are probably mated soon after they emerge. Eggs are laid on the two buckthorns, alder buckthorn (*Frangula alnus*) and purging buckthorn (*Rhamnus catharticus*). The adults have a remarkable ability to locate their food plants, and even very isolated buckthorns are likely to be found with a few eggs in May or early June, especially if the shrubs are in sheltered and sunny situations. The eggs are laid mainly towards the tips of shoots, on the undersides of the leaves. The earliest eggs are laid on unopened buds or even on the wood of the twigs close to buds [M. G. Morris]. They have been found between 0.6 and 4 metres and are almost certainly laid higher (Bibby, 1983). The caterpillars are cryptic, glaucous green, and rest along the mid-ribs of the leaves. They usually move away from the buckthorn to pupate among low-growing vegetation.

Whereas in the spring brimstones are very active and spend much time in flight, in the late summer and autumn they are more likely to be seen at flowers such as thistles and teasel, feeding up before hibernation. There is some evidence from the Butterfly Monitoring Scheme of migratory behaviour (Pollard and Hall, 1980). In those woodland sites where the food plants are absent or only sparsely distributed, brimstones are recorded over a relatively short period after hibernation. They appear to have left the woods by the end of May. However, at wetland sites, where buckthorns are often abundant, the brimstones continue to be recorded throughout June and may overlap with adults of the new generation in July. The woods appear to be used primarily, although certainly not exclusively, for hibernation, while the wetlands are mainly breeding sites. There may be similar spring movements to areas of chalk scrub with abundant purging buckthorn. This behaviour may perhaps be best regarded as incipient migratory behaviour, but it is easy to see how this short-range movement could have evolved into major migration between breeding and overwintering areas in a species such as the monarch.

It is a characteristic of nearly all butterflies that the male flies earlier than the female, although, of course, they overlap considerably. The general assumption is that there is a selective advantage for males to emerge early, so that they have a good chance of finding unmated females. The brimstone is truly 'the exception that proves the rule'. Male and female brimstones emerge together in the summer, when they do not pair, but simply feed up before hibernation. In the spring, however, the males emerge earlier from hibernation to await the females.

The distribution of the brimstone closely resembles the combined distributions of the two buckthorns. Both buckthorns and brimstones are very rare in Scotland. In Ireland alder buckthorn is rare and the brimstone is largely confined to limestone soils where the purging buckthorn occurs. Individuals are quite often seen well away from their normal haunts, even in built-up areas, and this no doubt is a consequence of their wandering behaviour. There appear to have been no major changes in range over the period of the records.

Flight periods of the brimstone at five sites in England in 1980, and in three years at one site. Wicken Fen (a) is wetland with abundant food plants and Potton Wood (b) a conifer wood with few food plants.

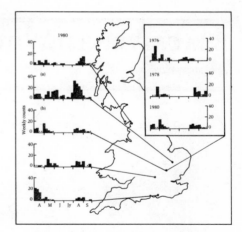

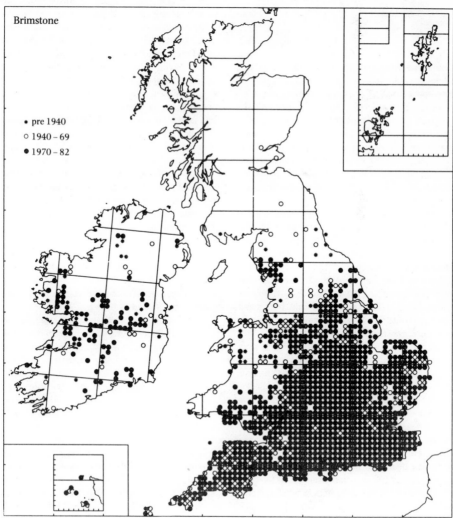

Brimstone

• pre 1940
○ 1940 – 69
◕ 1970 – 82

BLACK-VEINED WHITE

Aporia crataegi

The black-veined white was sufficiently well known in 1666 to be included among the twenty-one species which comprised Christopher Merrett's first national list of butterflies, and colonies still bred in most counties south of Yorkshire in the early nineteenth century. There was then a severe decline, punctuated by periods of local abundance, until by 1900 it was reduced to a few populations in Kent, and, possibly, in Worcestershire and Sussex. It became extinct in Britain in the mid-1920s.

More recently, there have been similar losses on the continent. Colonies once bred in at least twenty-four counties, although, except in a few areas such as Kent and the New Forest, most entomologists considered it to be a rare or local species in their neighbourhood. Numbers fluctuated greatly on all recorded sites, and because of this some collectors believed that the species was a migrant. There is little evidence to support this view; most populations seem to have bred regularly, if erratically, on the same discrete sites, or at least in particular districts, for many years.

The demise of the black-veined white has been well chronicled by Allan (1948), Bretherton (1951b) and Chalmers-Hunt (1960–81). It was lost quite early in the nineteenth century from counties that had few populations; for example, in Dorset there has been no record since 1815 (Dale, 1886), although it had previously been abundant near Weymouth, and eight out of ten known Sussex colonies had disappeared by 1840 (Pratt, 1981). It survived longer in its strongholds, even occurring 'in thousands' in several parts of the New Forest in 1860–70, although it

was already local elsewhere in Hampshire (Goater, 1974). The New Forest populations collapsed after 1870 and the last known Hampshire black-veined white was 'taken' in about 1883. Elsewhere, it had been recorded regularly in the Forest of Dean up to 1879 and was seen in the Cotswolds and Monmouthshire, respectively, in 1879 and 1887 (Bretherton, 1951b).

The greatest populations of this butterfly bred in Kent. They occurred locally throughout the county during the first half of the nineteenth century but were restricted to the north-east corner after 1885 (Chalmers-Hunt, 1960–81). As elsewhere, they fluctuated enormously in numbers; at Wye it was 'the commonest butterfly . . . but had disappeared from the district by 1859' (Goss, 1887), and Chalmers-Hunt describes 'phenomenal numbers' from many other sites in the mid 1850s, only to be followed by 'a remarkable decline'. Indeed, the butterfly was not recorded at all in Kent from 1875–82. Small populations had, in fact, just survived in the extreme north-east corner of Kent, and it was regularly seen in several colonies in the Great Stour valley, and as far south as Dover, during the next forty years. It even became locally abundant again in 1893, 1896, and 1902–6. However, the next decline was to be the last, and the butterfly was extremely rare after about 1914; the last confirmed record was at Herne Bay in 1922 (Chalmers-Hunt, 1960–81). Another colony apparently survived at Craycombe, Worcestershire, until 1923 (Green, 1982).

There have been at least three sightings of single adults since the 1920s, but no colony is known to have existed. All the sightings were near the south coast, leading Bretherton (1951b) to believe that they were probably strays from France. It is also possible that they came from captive stock. It is a common practice for the larvae, which are strikingly coloured, to be collected abroad, and many are known to have escaped or been released. There have also been several deliberate attempts to reintroduce the butterfly, starting in the late nineteenth century (which caused some entomologists to believe that its resurgence in Kent was due to this), and on at least three occasions from 1930 to 1964 in Kent, while 'hundreds' were released on Holmwood

Common in Surrey in the 1970s (Pratt, in press). Although temporary colonies may have re-established themselves in Kent in the 1930s, all introductions are believed to have failed, mostly in their first year.

There has been much speculation about the causes of decline of this attractive butterfly, including a thorough examination of most possible factors by Pratt (1983, in press). There has been little apparent change to its habitat. Colonies bred on hedgerows and wood edges, where the gregarious larvae fed mainly on hawthorn and blackthorn leaves. In the Kent orchards they also attacked cultivated damsons, plums and apples, where the larval webs and later the pupae were sometimes found in enormous numbers, although never reaching the pest densities that can occur on the continent.

It must be noted that little is known of the precise requirements of the black-veined white, and that changes in status in some other species have followed an inconspicuous alteration to their sites. Out of many other possible factors examined, Pratt found that there was a weak correlation between wet Septembers and low numbers in the following season. However, he points out that the species survived periods of even wetter Septembers in the eighteenth century, and poor weather is unlikely to have been the only factor involved. At present, the cause of the dramatic decline of this butterfly remains a mystery.

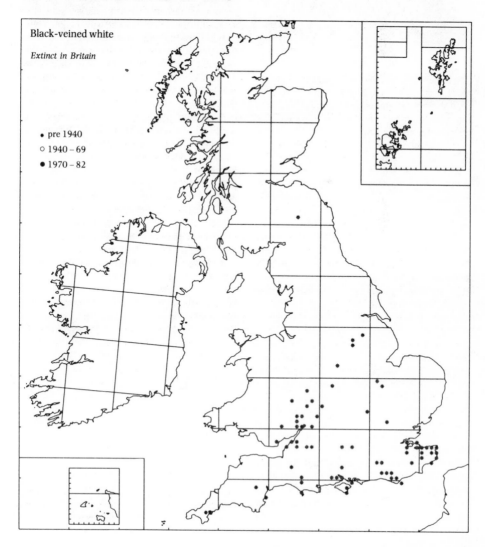

Black-veined white

Extinct in Britain

- pre 1940
○ 1940 – 69
● 1970 – 82

LARGE WHITE

Pieris brassicae

The large white has been recorded from virtually every part of the British Isles and is a familiar pest of cabbages and other brassicas. It is likely that nearly all the large whites we see fed as larvae on cultivated plants, even if the butterflies are found miles from farms or gardens, as they fly strongly and range widely. There are numerous recorded wild host plants, mainly Cruciferae but including a number of other families. The role of these plants in supporting wild populations, particularly in this country, is probably very small.

The eggs are laid in large batches. There is evidence that the presence of a batch on a plant will deter further females from laying (Rothschild and Schoonhoven, 1977). The larvae are gregarious and very conspicuous, perhaps advertising their noxious taste to birds, although some birds will take them (Baker, 1970). They leave the plant to pupate, often choosing a tree trunk or wall. A prepupal larva is quite often found surrounded by the small cocoons of the parasitic wasp *Apanteles glomeratus*, whose larvae have emerged from the caterpillar. There are normally two generations a year, although it is possible that in parts of Scotland there is one resident generation (Graham-Smith and Graham-Smith, 1929), with migrants flying from the south in some years. It hibernates in the pupal stage.

The large white is migratory, but the extent and frequency of migrations is not certain. As Williams (1958) comments: 'In spite of hundreds of records we are still without a good understanding of the pattern of movement of this common species.' The records from the Butterfly Monitoring Scheme suggest that in recent years migration has played only a small part in annual fluctuations. Increases and declines have been substantial but gradual, with no sign of the erratic changes which would be expected to characterize migratory movements. The only major change in numbers in the recording period of the monitoring scheme was the sharp decline after the 1976 drought. The seasonal appearance of the two generations of adults is very regular, year after year. This too is inconsistent with major migratory movements; that is, on a continental scale. It is possible that the 'migration years' are simply years of exceptional abundance over large areas. In such conditions, many individuals may disperse and fly from the continent to Britain and vice versa. A contrasting view is that there are more regular northerly spring movements and southerly late summer movements, achieved by orientation to the sun (Baker, 1969). Clearly, while such different views are possible, the scope for research remains enormous. The early appearance of the large white and the long flight period at some western sites is intriguing, but we do not know what the significance of this is.

The biology of the large white has been reviewed in detail in a comprehensive monograph by Feltwell (1982). Valuable information on genetic and environmental variation and on many other aspects of the biology of this species has also been obtained at Cambridge, where the large white has been kept in continuous culture for many years (e.g. Gardiner, 1963) on natural and artificial diets.

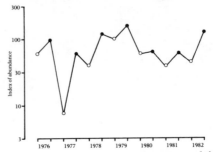

Changes in abundance of the two generations of the large white, 1976–82, as shown by data from the Butterfly Monitoring Scheme. There was a sharp fall in numbers following the drought of 1976.

Flight periods of the large white at five sites in Britain in
1980, and at one site in three different years.

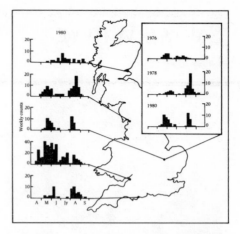

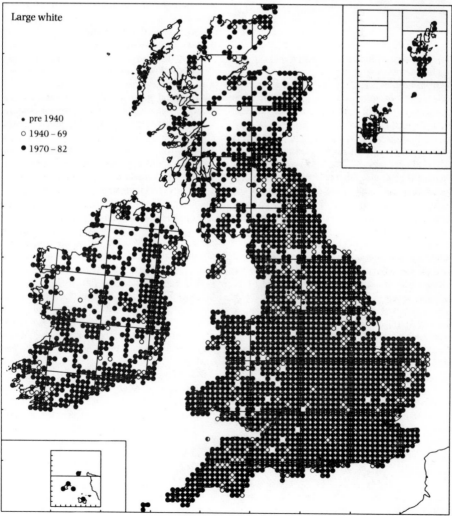

Large white

• pre 1940
○ 1940 – 69
● 1970 – 82

SMALL WHITE

Pieris rapae

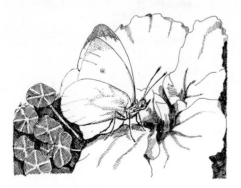

Like the large white, the small white is essentially a pest of cultivated brassicas and is most abundant in areas where these are grown on a large scale. It is not quite as widespread as the large white, as it is absent or rare in the Outer Hebrides and in Shetland, but it is nevertheless a very common species. Its wild cruciferous food plants include garlic mustard, hedge mustard (Richards, 1940), hoary cress (West, 1982) and wild mignonette (Brooks and Knight, 1982). Richards also notes that the small white lays readily on sea kale, but the larvae rarely, if ever, survive. Both large and small whites will also feed on garden nasturtiums (*Tropaeolum*).

The eggs are laid singly, usually on the under surface of the leaves. The larvae are solitary and cryptic, in contrast to the gregarious large white larvae, and are usually found in the heart or younger leaves of brassicas. They may pupate on the plant, but the second generation larvae usually leave to find more secure overwintering sites such as buildings, tree trunks, or perhaps hedgerows. The pupal colour is somewhat variable and is affected by the background colour of the pupation site.

There have been a number of population studies of the small white in this country and in countries such as Canada and Australia, where it has been introduced and become a serious pest. Dempster (1968), in Britain, found that there is heavy predation of young larvae by ground beetles and harvest spiders. Application of a persistent pesticide, DDT, resulted in an increase in the number of larvae later in the season because the number of predators was reduced. In another experiment, it was found that the presence of weeds increased the number of predators and reduced larval numbers, although the weeds also reduced crop yield (Dempster, 1969). It tends to lay its eggs at the edges of fields in the shelter of hedgerows. For this reason, it is probably a more serious pest in sheltered gardens than in large arable fields.

Baker (1970) showed that, in gardens, bird predators of this species and of the large white were more important than in arable fields. Eggs of the small white were taken by house sparrows and garden warblers, larvae by house sparrows and tits, and pupae mainly by tits. Song thrushes take the caterpillars on the ground when they move to find pupation sites. The green larvae of the small white are conspicuous on the ground, whereas the black and green large white larvae, so conspicuous on brassicas, are harder to see and taken less by birds when on the ground.

The small white is very mobile, and migratory flights have many times been reported (Williams, 1958). Baker (1969) suggests that this and other species regularly move north in the spring and early summer and south in the late summer and autumn, and that orientation is achieved by flying at a constant angle to the sun. These views are not fully accepted (e.g. Johnson, 1969). There is certainly some evidence of directional movements in this species, but their regular nature has yet to be confirmed. In Japan, Ohsaki (1980) found that immature females disperse, but on reaching maturity they remain in areas where food plants occur.

The numbers in the second generation are consistently much larger than in the first and it is possible that the second generation is reinforced by migrants. We believe there are two or sometimes three generations a year, but Richards (1940) considered three or four to be the usual number.

Flight periods of the small white at five sites in Britain in 1979, and at one site in three different years.

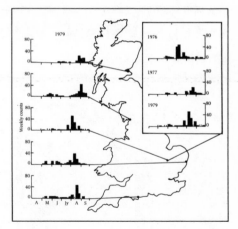

Small white

- • pre 1940
- ○ 1940 – 69
- ● 1970 – 82

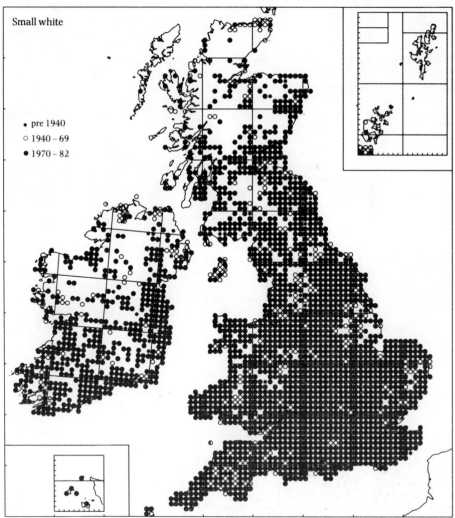

GREEN-VEINED WHITE

Pieris napi

This species differs in several aspects of its ecology from the closely related large and small whites. The green-veined white is mainly restricted to wild food plants, as opposed to crops which are the main food plants of the large and small whites. In the south it appears to be a mobile species with open populations over large areas. In the north there may be some more discrete colonies. The large and small whites are, of course, highly mobile. No doubt because it is less mobile and so gene flow is more restricted, the green-veined white is more variable than these other species. Several subspecies have been described, but their true status is unclear and there is also considerable variability within populations (Thomson, 1970; Dennis, 1977).

There are usually two generations a year, the first in April–June and the second in July and August. Occasionally, there is a small third generation. Some of the first brood larvae produce pupae which go right through to the next spring, so the second generation is partial. In some parts of the country, at high altitude, there may be only one generation (Lees, 1970).

The general biology and ecology of the green-veined white have been briefly described by Lees and Archer (1974). The eggs are usually laid on the under-surface of leaves. Its main food plants are cuckooflower, garlic mustard, hedge mustard and watercress. In the south the range of habitat is wide and includes woodland rides, hedgerows and grass verges. It is uncommon on open down-land and in other dry areas. In the north it is more closely restricted as a breeding species to river and stream sides and damp meadows. However, it is widespread on moorland as an adult, often where the larval food plants are sparse or absent. It shares food plants and often habitat with the orange tip, but, while the orange tip feeds almost entirely on developing seeds and pods, the green-veined white caterpillar is restricted to the leaves. It pupates away from the food plant, usually on nearby vegetation.

This is one of our most widespread and common butterflies. It is absent only from parts of the uplands. The results from the monitoring scheme show a marked decline in numbers after the 1976 drought, but as several of the food plants are associated with damp situations, this is not surprising. After 1976 numbers quickly built up again, and in eastern England it was exceptionally abundant in 1979.

Flight periods of the green-veined white at five sites in Britain in 1979, and at one site in three different years. Upper Teesdale is an upland site where there may have been only one generation in that year.

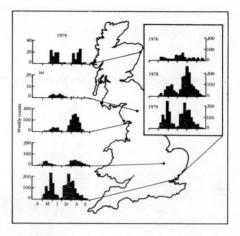

Green-veined white

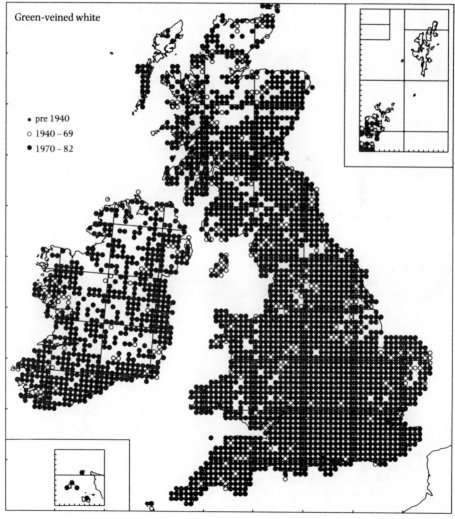

- • pre 1940
- ○ 1940 – 69
- ● 1970 – 82

ORANGE TIP

Anthocaris cardamines

The male orange tip is a welcome and familiar spring butterfly. The female is much less well known, as it lacks the orange tips to the forewings and, at a cursory glance, might be confused with the small or green-veined whites. The orange tip is common in open woodland and along hedges and lanes over much of the British Isles. Its food plants include a range of crucifers (Courtney, 1982, states that thirty-three species of Cruciferae and two of the related Resedaceae have been recorded), but the most frequent are probably cuckooflower and garlic mustard. It has recently been recorded on the introduced garden crucifer *Arabis albida* (Owen, 1976). Courtney (1980) has studied this species in northern England, where populations are localized along river banks, and the butterfly is less wide-ranging than appears to be the case further south. In Cheshire, Dennis (1982a) found that the average linear distance moved by marked males was 400 metres, but he considered that actual distances must often be much greater than this.

The eggs are laid in the young flower heads of the food plant. They are extremely conspicuous, as they turn a bright orange colour one or two days after being laid. The larvae are cannibalistic and there is evidence to show that the presence of an egg on a flower head deters butterflies from laying further eggs, as their chance of survival would be small (Wiklund and Ahrberg, 1978). Nevertheless, plants in favourable positions can receive several eggs. Development is usually completed on a single plant, the food changing from flowers to seed capsules and then, perhaps very occasionally, to leaves. The fully grown larva is beautifully camouflaged to mimic the seed capsule (siliqua), along which it lies. The pupa also closely resembles a siliqua and it is something of a surprise that it usually leaves the food plant to pupate, probably choosing another plant stem. Overwintering is in the pupal stage and the species has just one generation a year, although, very occasionally, second generation individuals may emerge in late summer.

The distribution of this butterfly in the first half of the nineteenth century was virtually continuous from England into the Highlands of Scotland, although populations were more discrete and sparser further north. In the latter part of the nineteenth century the orange tip was lost from the most northerly parts of England and from southern Scotland (Smith, 1949). Since about 1950 there has been a steady recolonization, and it appears, in some of these areas, to have exceeded its previous range (Harper, 1968; Long, 1979–81; Thomson, 1980). On a local scale there has undoubtedly been a considerable decline in regions of intensive agriculture, both where there has been widespread hedgerow removal, drastically reducing garlic mustard, or improvement of damp meadows, where cuckooflower was formerly abundant. Dennis (1982b) has demonstrated that the orange tip exploits most of the available habitats in an area of mixed farming in Cheshire, partly by females moving out into the farmland from the main riverside centres of population. A life-table study of the orange tip in the north-east of England (Courtney, 1980) indicated that weather during the oviposition period affects abundance in the following season, as described for the wood white. Weather may also have played a part in the changes of range, but it is likely that other, unknown, factors are also involved.

Courtney showed that survival of larvae differs on different food plants. This might be expected to result, through natural selection, in the adoption of only the most suitable plant species, but Courtney suggests that this does not happen because of the overriding importance of egg production. It is more important to lay as many eggs as possible than to spend time in the careful selection of the best food plants.

Flight period of the orange tip at five sites in Britain in 1979, and at one site in three different years.

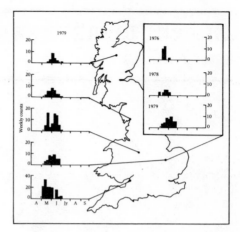

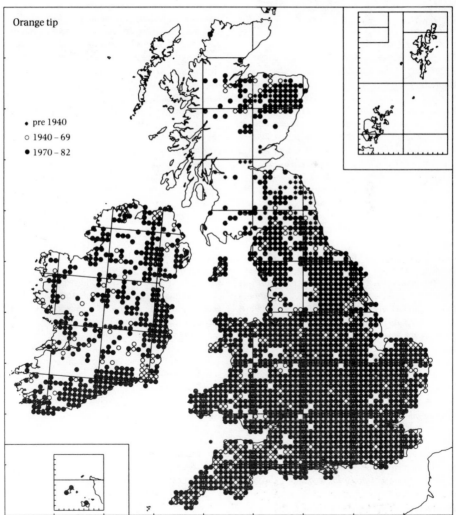

Orange tip

- pre 1940
- 1940 – 69
- 1970 – 82

GREEN HAIRSTREAK

Callophrys rubi

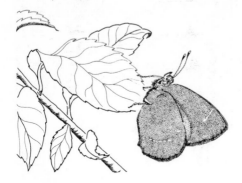

The green hairstreak is the commonest and most widespread of the five British hairstreaks, and is the only species that is not associated with trees at some stage in its life cycle. Colonies are only locally distributed in most counties, even though they can exist on a wide range of soils and in several habitat types. The only common feature of these habitats is that shrubs are nearly always present. Typical sites for this butterfly are un-improved calcareous grassland; acid heaths, moors, and bogs; and permanently rough scrubby grassland such as occurs on many sea cliffs and on railway embankments. The green hairstreak also breeds in small numbers along some wood edges and rides.

The larval food plants are equally varied, de-pending partly on the habitat type. The com-monest plants used are common rock-rose on calcareous grassland; bilberry on most moors (almost exclusively in Scotland (Thomson, 1980) and perhaps in Ireland); and any species of gorse on southern acidic and neutral soils. Each of these species can, by itself, support colonies of this butterfly. Many other food plants have also been described, particularly the developing flowers of buckthorns and dogwood, and many legumes, such as the common bird's-foot-trefoil and dyer's greenweed.

Our marking experiments indicate that the green hairstreak forms discrete, self-contained colonies which typically contain only ten to twenty males (females probably occur in equally small numbers, but are hard to estimate because of their behaviour). However, extremely large populations develop in occasional years on cer-tain sites, notably along the warm gorse-filled coastal valleys of Devon and Cornwall, and on some bilberry moors in Scotland.

Many green hairstreak sites are fairly small and most are on hillsides. The behaviour of the adults is very distinctive. Males are highly territorial, and spend most of the day perching on particular shrubs which are used year after year. These tend to be prominent plants in the lower parts of the site, often in a hedge. Each bush usually holds a single male, which sorties in a characteristic jerky flight to investigate any passing butterfly. When this happens, the original male often loses his perch to another, and, on a typical site, the males regularly swap places between the few perching shrubs that are present. The females are much less conspicuous and often fly over adjoining open land, searching for egg sites.

The eggs are laid singly on fresh leaf tips or in flower buds, depending on the food plant. Tutt (1905) records that the ovipositor is flattened, presumably to aid penetration into flower buds. The green striped larvae feed by day and are beautifully camouflaged on most plants. They descend to pupate on the ground in mid to late summer. The pupa (which is famed for its capa-city to squeak when disturbed) is attractive to ants and is probably always buried by them, like several of the blues; one was found deep inside a *Myrmica sabuleti* nest [J. A. Thomas]. The butter-fly overwinters as a pupa and there is a long emergence period in spring and early summer.

Numerous former green hairstreak sites have been destroyed during the present century through the agricultural improvement or recla-mation of old grassland, heaths, moors and bogs, and through intensive forestry. However, a few colonies still survive in woodland or areas of rough scrubby ground in even the most inten-sively managed agricultural regions. In War-wickshire, five of the twelve remaining known colonies occur on railway embankments or cut-tings (Smith and Brown, 1979). The butterfly remains locally common in other regions which still contain a greater abundance of its habitat, for example in south-west England, Wales, west Scotland, and in Ireland, where it is thought to have been under-recorded and may be much more widespread than our map suggests (ni Lamhna, 1980). It seems inevitable that green hairstreak colonies will continue to be lost through the destruction of their habitats, but the butterfly is in little danger of extinction over most of its present range.

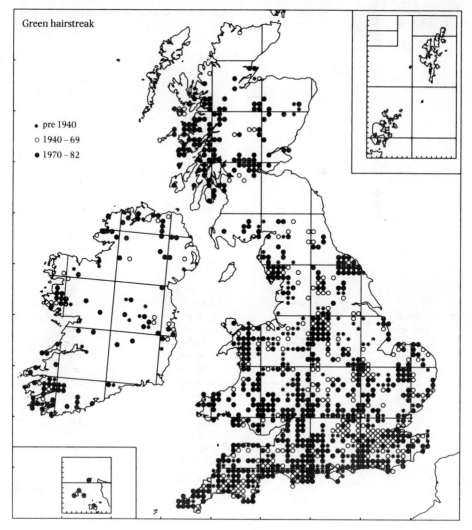

Flight period of the green hairstreak at five sites in Britain in 1979, and at one site in three different years. Ballard Down (a), on chalk, and Studland (b), an acid heath, are two sites close together which illustrate the very diverse habitats of this butterfly.

Green hairstreak

* pre 1940
o 1940 – 69
● 1970 – 82

BROWN HAIRSTREAK

Thecla betulae

Although the brown hairstreak has a wide southerly distribution, it is, none the less, a scarce butterfly and is mainly confined to localities which have heavy soils and high densities of woodland and hedgerows. The adults emerge in late summer (it flies in August and September and is the latest of our single-brooded butterflies) and congregate for mating on particular tree-tops, usually in woods (Thomas, 1974). The females later disperse along wood edges and especially hedges, laying their eggs in ones or twos low down on any unshaded, but generally sheltered, *Prunus* that is encountered; this is nearly always blackthorn in Britain and Ireland. Although the females spread their eggs at low densities over tens or even hundreds of hectares, colonies breed constantly in the same areas, and the brown hairstreak cannot be considered to be a migratory butterfly. The white eggs remain on their bushes for eight months before hatching in early May, and are particularly conspicuous between November and April when the twigs are bare. Indeed, most records of the brown hairstreak are made in this stage, although larvae may also be 'beaten' from their resting pads on the undersides of leaves in mid June. Adults are seen rarely in the wild, for they spend most of their lives resting on tree-tops, where they obtain their main food, aphid honeydew. Nearly all sightings are of egg-laying females.

The brown hairstreak was often overlooked in the past, but was intensively surveyed in the 1970s by Thomas (1974) and T. Tolman, and the map of recent records is considered to be reasonably complete. The impression given by this map is of a commoner species than is the case, for a single colony often extends at low densities over two or even four ten-kilometre squares, and it is unlikely that there are more than 150 colonies of the brown hairstreak left in Britain. These tend to be small compared with those of many other butterflies; for example, numbers in a strong colony which was studied in Surrey in 1969–76 fluctuated between forty and 300 adults which laid 665 to 4,160 eggs (Thomas, 1974). By contrast, the purple hairstreak sometimes laid about a million eggs in the same area.

The present British range of the brown hairstreak extends as far north as the Lincolnshire lime woods, and in the nineteenth century it was regularly recorded in the Lake District. Colonies were also once found through most of the woody districts of the east midlands, East Anglia, and Kent, but have declined dramatically in the last thirty years, and the species may now be extinct in all these regions. The brown hairstreak has also declined in the rest of the midlands, where it is now locally common only on the clays around Oxford. Farther south it is fairly common in parts of Somerset, but its present strongholds are undoubtedly south Wales, the wealden clays of west Sussex and Surrey, and the wooded valleys of north Devon, where eggs can be found on almost any sheltered hedgerow. Its existence as an Irish species, which was once in doubt, is now clearly established, although its exact status is still unclear.

Although there is no reason to believe that the brown hairstreak has declined in the west weald, north Devon, or south Wales, its overall status in Britain is much lower than it was thirty years ago. This may be due to the drastic loss of hedgerows in some areas, but this does not explain all losses, for example from Kent and south Devon. It may also be that the management of remaining hedges is nowadays too intensive in some regions, for modern cutters removed from 80–100 per cent of eggs on a sample of hedges in the weald, and the butterfly probably only survives in this area because trimming occurs spasmodically and many hedges are cut only once every few years. Periodic hedge cutting is, of course, necessary to maintain the low growth required by this species.

The mechanization of hedge management and the continued loss of hedgerows probably means that the brown hairstreak will continue to decline in Britain, but it is not a species that is imminently threatened with extinction.

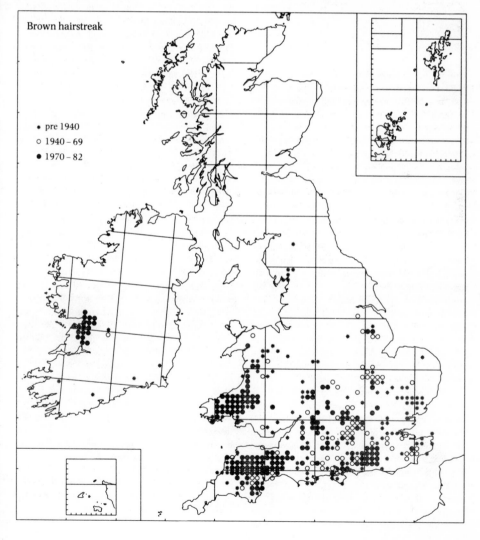

Brown hairstreak

- pre 1940
- 1940 – 69
- 1970 – 82

PURPLE HAIRSTREAK

Quercusia quercus

This beautiful butterfly is widely distributed in deciduous woodland, especially in southern Britain, but, like the other woodland hairstreaks, it is easily overlooked except in years of great abundance. It flies from mid July to late August, and overwinters as an egg. These are laid, usually singly, on the twigs and especially on the buds of most species of oak, including the native sessile and pedunculate oaks and the introduced turkey oak; there appears to be no preference for any one species (Frohawk, 1934; Thomas, 1975; Tutt, 1905–14). Eggs are conspicuous on the bare winter twigs. They hatch at leaf-break in late April. The young larvae enter expanding buds, and later spin webs at the base of leaf stalks among the old scale leaves which they closely resemble. The scales, which would normally fall, are trapped by the webs, hiding the larvae. They emerge to browse on the oak leaves by night. Pupation occurs on the ground under leaf litter or moss, or sometimes on large branches. There is some evidence that the highest death rates in the life cycle occur in the pupal period (Thomas, 1975).

A few records suggest that a purple hairstreak colony may occasionally be supported by a single isolated oak, and they have been reported on scattered, but frequent, hedgerow oaks in Norfolk [D. A. Ratcliffe], but nearly all populations are confined to woods. Adults are sometimes seen in enormous numbers on particular tree-tops, but whether this is due to an aggregation mechanism, or to a local abundance of honeydew, by far the most important adult food, is unknown (probably the latter, because in other years the adults seem to be evenly distributed over large areas). Like other woodland hairstreaks they fly only rarely, but sometimes clouds of hundreds may be dislodged by jarring overhead branches.

Eggs may be found dispersed over the canopies and exposed edges of oaks throughout a wood. All aspects are used. M. G. Morris found fairly uniform densities at various heights on a large tree at the junction of four rides in Monks Wood, and Thomas (1975) found eggs evenly distributed on all oaks along fifteen kilometres of indented wood edge in the Sussex weald. Numbers fluctuated enormously on that site; the same lower boughs of fourteen trees contained only twenty-six eggs in winter 1973/4, but this had increased to 1,495 three years later after the hot summer of 1976. By extrapolation, the total egg population in that wood almost certainly exceeded a million individuals that year. Extremely high numbers were recorded in many other regions in 1976 (e.g. Holloway, 1980), and similar population explosions have been a feature of purple hairstreak colonies in the past (e.g. Tutt, 1908).

Our map shows that the purple hairstreak is well distributed through southern Britain but becomes increasingly rare in the north. It is one of the scarcest Irish butterflies, being largely confined to hillside oakwoods between Wicklow and Derry (ni Lamhna, 1980). Thomson (1980) considers that it is still locally common in Scotland, and probably more widely distributed than our records suggest: he has recently found it in all localities that he visited where it was recorded in the nineteenth century. It is possible, therefore, that colonies are also more widely distributed in northern England than is indicated here. It is less likely to have been overlooked at former sites in the industrial midlands, where there is also an absence of recent records. In the south it is a highly characteristic species of large broadleaved woods, and is especially common in heavily wooded regions such as the west weald. Although the butterfly is still periodically abundant on many of its remaining sites, the total number of colonies must have declined very considerably during the present century, due to the clearance of some oak woods and the conversion of many more to conifer plantations.

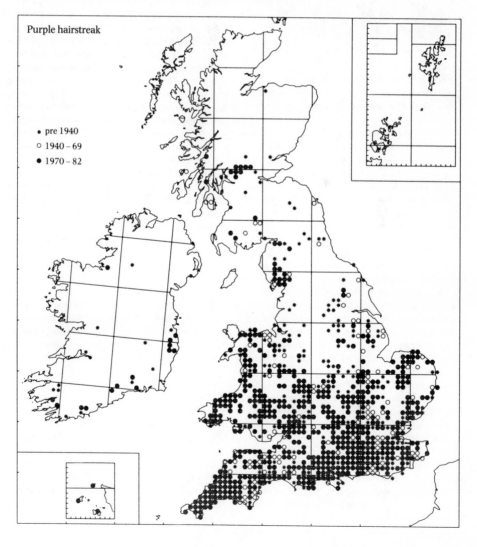

Purple hairstreak

• pre 1940
○ 1940 – 69
● 1970 – 82

WHITE-LETTER HAIRSTREAK

Strymonidia w-album

The white-letter hairstreak is certainly a very local butterfly, but it is also one of the most easily overlooked. The extent of its former distribution, shown by this map, may be a surprise to many entomologists. However, many post-1969 records refer to extinct colonies, which have been lost in the past decade when their larval food plant, elm, died from Dutch elm disease.

The favourite food of this butterfly is usually stated to be wych elm (*Ulmus glabra*) – e.g. 'by far its favourite' (Tutt, 1905–14) – but there is no doubt that many colonies breed entirely on English elm (*U. procera*) or on one of the other species or hybrids. Indeed, it is likely that a minority of all colonies have occurred on wych elm. But, whatever the species, a population is usually confined to a discrete small group of trees, or often a single tree. These may be situated within woods, on their edges, or often as isolated plants in hedgerows or even gardens. Most colonies breed on large trees, but these are not essential; some large populations have been recorded from quite small, three to five metres tall, isolated hedgerow wych elms. However, colonies are not known to be supported by immature saplings, presumably because of the feeding habits of the very young larvae.

Adult white-letter hairstreaks emerge in mid July. They are occasionally found some distance from their food plant (e.g. Archer-Lock, 1980), but it seems that such behaviour is exceptional, except perhaps when the elms are dying of Dutch elm disease, and that colonies usually remain strictly on or near their breeding tree(s) and are usually very inconspicuous. Sometimes an indi-vidual may descend to feed from privet, bramble, or other flowers, but it seems certain that the main adult food is honeydew, and that most of the adult life is spent sitting on a tree-top. Thomas (1974) saw twenty to thirty flights in half an hour from beneath a clump of elms, but on climbing a nearby tree saw seventy individuals perching and feeding on the half-canopy of a neighbouring oak which was in view. Very occasionally, an adult flew off on a short gyrating flight, usually returning to the same branch.

The eggs are laid in July on elm twigs, usually at a node or at the base of a bud. The embryo soon develops into a fully-formed larva, but this does not hatch until the following spring. Most eggs are laid on the south side of mature flowering trees; nearby saplings are usually ignored. The young larva feeds on flowers in early March, but later bores into leaf buds, and eventually feeds on the fully-formed leaves. It is well camouflaged, but can often be spotted as a dark silhouette by looking up from underneath. The hairy pupa rests on the hairy twigs, and is also cryptically coloured.

Until recently, colonies were well distributed throughout England and most of Wales, and were perhaps commonest in the Midlands. They have always been rare in south-west England. As with so many butterflies, numbers had apparently declined in Kent, but were being maintained elsewhere, although all populations seem to fluctuate greatly in the short term. During the 1970s, a high proportion of elms (including many wych elms) were killed by Dutch elm disease, especially in the midlands. Anecdotal accounts indicate that most colonies known to recorders disappeared with their elms, although the severity of these losses cannot yet be quantified. Following a recent appeal for more information, Peachey (1983) tentatively concluded that most remaining colonies of white-letter hairstreaks could become extinct in a matter of years, except in the north; colonies on wych elm seem so far to have survived better than those on other elm species. There is limited evidence that a few colonies have survived the death of their large trees by breeding in diminished numbers on regenerating suckers. Unfortunately, these suckers remain infected through the roots, and generally die when they reach two to four metres in height. As the only detailed accounts of breeding on suckers refer to large flowering examples, the fate of most remaining colonies appears, at the time of writing, to be in the balance.

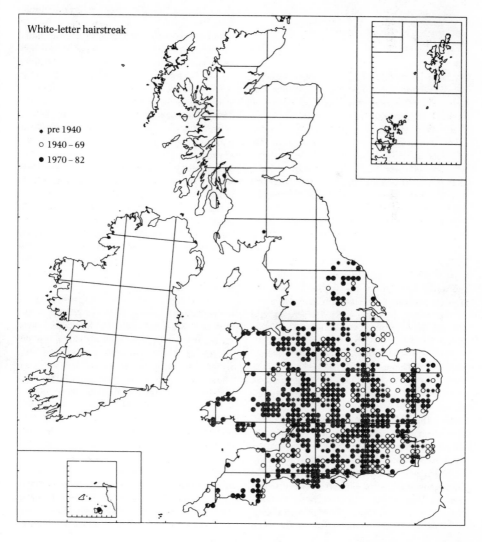

White-letter hairstreak

· pre 1940
○ 1940 – 69
● 1970 – 82

BLACK HAIRSTREAK

Strymonidia pruni

The black hairstreak is one of the least conspicuous of Britain's butterflies, but it is among the most comprehensively mapped as a result of intensive surveys that were made in 1969–75. It is a rare woodland species which has been recorded from just seventy-eight localities in Britain since its discovery in Monks Wood in 1828. Sixty-one of these localities are from the east midlands forest belt and the other seventeen are mainly old records which are scattered throughout the country. With one possible exception in Suffolk (which we have mapped), none of the latter is thought to be a native colony, most being attributable to introductions, escapes, mixed labels in collections and, especially, misidentifications of the white-letter hairstreak. Indeed, only one record from outside the east midlands is of a breeding population; this was introduced in 1952 to the weald (Collier, 1959), where it still survives. By contrast, breeding has been confirmed in fifty-seven of its east midland sites, although some of these also originate from old introductions (Thomas, 1973, 1974).

The British range of the black hairstreak is probably accurately represented by the map, although there may yet be more colonies to be found within this area. It is confined to the low-lying basin between Oxford and Peterborough, formed of Oxford clay and, to the north-west, of oolite overlaid by boulder clay. This is a heavily wooded region which still contains many large relics of the once continuous forests of Bernwood, Grendon Underwood, Waddon Chase, Whittleford, Salcey, Yardley Chase, the Huntingdonshire fen edges, Rockingham, and Nassboro. The black hairstreak has been recorded from all these forests in this century, and may even be considered as a characteristic member of their fauna, having been found in about half the woods which exceed twenty hectares in size.

Most populations of the black hairstreak are confined to small discrete areas of their woods where they persist for many generations, although there are occasional shifts in distribution. While there are usually more adults present than is at first apparent (many perch on tree-tops), most colonies are small and consist, at most, of a few hundred adults. These emerge in late June and early July and lay their eggs on *Prunus*, usually blackthorn, but also wild plum, if present. A few colonies have been entirely supported by wild plum in the past. Contrary to popular belief, the eggs are laid as readily on young blackthorn as on old plants, and some of the largest populations are known to have bred entirely on stands of young blackthorn. This is, however, the exception, probably because the butterfly is generally so slow to colonize new habitat that the blackthorn bushes are usually tall and mature when, eventually, colonization does occur. The black hairstreak overwinters as an egg, which is extremely inconspicuous. The species is more easily found by beating for larvae in late May (this is not recommended because of damage to bushes) or by searching in June for pupae, which closely resemble bird droppings.

The basic needs of a black hairstreak colony are for high densities of *Prunus* to grow in sunny sheltered situations, whether in glades, rides, scrub, wood edges, or even neighbouring tall hedgerows. These conditions are not, in themselves, unusual in British woods, and the black hairstreak can certainly exist outside the east midlands: for example, the introduced population in the weald has survived for thirty-one years and was the largest of all known colonies in the late 1970s, until most of the site was cleared in 1981 (Thomas, 1980a). It is likely that the present restricted distribution of the black hairstreak is a consequence both of its sedentary behaviour and of past regional differences in woodland management. Adults rarely leave their small breeding areas and are unusually slow to colonize new habitat, even within the same wood. At the same time their discrete sites are prone to destruction under all but the most gradual of forestry regimes. It is probably no coincidence that, for many centuries, the traditional management of the east midlands forests consisted of long coppice cycles, in which small areas of each wood were cleared annually, allowing the development of mixed stands of scrub, each of which survived for at least twenty years. Elsewhere in Britain coppice cycles were, at times, much shorter, and larger areas were often cleared in a single operation.

In recent years the black hairstreak has declined because modern forestry only rarely produces a continuity of suitable habitat. By 1970 there were only about thirty colonies left, but none is known to have been lost since then, mainly because of conservation measures which have prevented the destruction of existing breeding sites. The future of most of these seems to be reasonably secure, especially on nature reserves where some areas are being deliberately managed to produce suitable conditions.

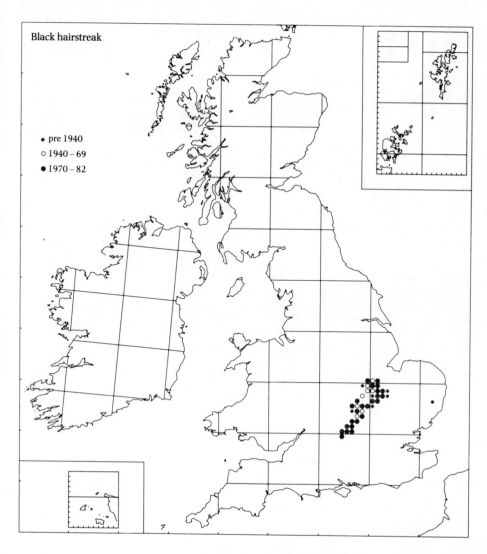

Black hairstreak

• pre 1940
○ 1940 – 69
● 1970 – 82

SMALL COPPER

Lycaena phlaeas

This colourful and active little butterfly is wide-spread in Britain. It is variable in its wing markings, even within populations, and there is considerable geographic variation. This reaches its extremes in central and northern Scotland and in Ireland. The northern Scottish form has fewer black markings and larger areas of copper on the uppersides, and up to half the individuals in some areas are of a beautiful form with a row of blue spots on the hindwings. In Ireland the small copper also has more copper coloration on the upper surfaces, while the undersides are greyer than in England.

The food plants are mainly narrow-leaved docks (sorrels) – common sorrel (*Rumex acetosa*) and sheep's sorrel (*R. acetosella*) – although broad-leaved docks are occasionally used. The distinctive white golf-ball shaped eggs are conspicuous in the petiole of the upperside, and sometimes underside, of the leaves. Most are laid singly, but, in times of abundance, several eggs may be found on each plant. Small unshaded plants are usually selected (Tutt, 1905). The larvae may easily be detected by their characteristic feeding grooves, leaving the upper epidermis intact, but transparent. There are two larval colour forms, a common green form and a scarce one striped with pink. Four larval instars are probably usual (Dempster, 1971), although five instars have been recorded. Overwintering is in the larval stage and pupation is among low vegetation. There are usually two broods, but occasionally three. Newly emerged adults may sometimes be seen as late as the end of October.

The small copper is found in open situations where its food plants occur on soils ranging from calcareous (mainly common sorrel) to acid (mainly sheep's sorrel). It is seldom seen in large numbers, and populations may occupy very small areas. Dempster (1971) describes a colony in a woodland ride which was restricted to a small patch open to the sun, although the food plants were abundant along the length of the ride. This was a 'good' site for the small copper, but the second, more abundant, generation comprised only about 400 individuals.

The range of the small copper has been stable in Britain over the last century, although there have undoubtedly been many local extinctions attributable to the agricultural improvement of farmland. Sorrels are relatively resistant to herbicides and will grow in improved pasture and even in arable fields. Despite this, small coppers were found in a recent survey to be about five times more abundant in unimproved, as compared with improved, pasture (Thomas, 1983), and it is a rare species in arable areas. Only one was seen during seven years' counts on a Cambridgeshire farm in the monitoring scheme. Sorrels thrive after ground has been disturbed or managed; a flush of both species occurs after hay meadows have been cut in July, and these conspicuous plants may then be peppered with eggs of the summer generation of small coppers [K. J. Willmott].

Dempster suggests that the small copper benefits from warm conditions during the flight period.

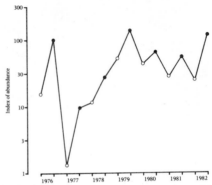

Changes in abundance of the two generations of the small copper, 1976–82, as shown by data from sites in eastern England in the Butterfly Monitoring Scheme.

Eggs are usually laid only in sunshine, and in cool cloudy weather fecundity may be low. It apparently declined sharply in numbers during a series of poor summers in the late 1960s. In spite of the possible association of abundance with sunny weather, the small copper crashed in numbers after the drought year of 1976 and increased again during the next three years, even though temperatures were below average. It may be that this increase was essentially a reoccupation of suitable habitat left vacant by the drought mortalities, and that this reoccupation would have occurred in any reasonable weather conditions.

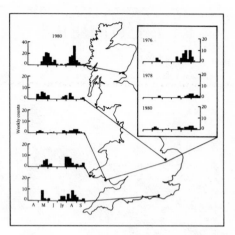

Flight periods of the small copper at five sites in Britain in 1980 and at one site in three different years.

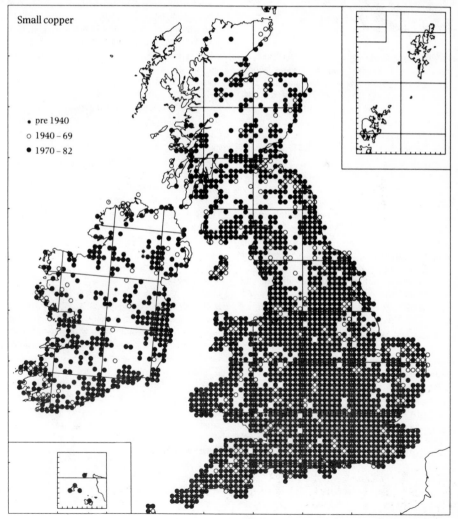

Small copper

- · pre 1940
- ○ 1940 – 69
- ● 1970 – 82

LARGE COPPER

Lycaena dispar

The British subspecies of the large copper, *L. dispar dispar*, is extinct, and the species is now represented here at one site, Woodwalton Fen, Cambridgeshire, by the closely related *L. dispar batavus*, a rare Dutch race. The British subspecies was always extremely local, centred mainly in the fen area around Whittlesea Mere in Cambridgeshire, which was drained in 1851. Extinction here slightly pre-dated the drainage of the mere. Recently a new description and a beautiful painting of the large copper, dated 1749, have been discovered. The locality was near Spalding in Lincolnshire and the record is the earliest known (Redshaw, 1982; Heath, 1983). The last British record was at Bottisham Fen in Cambridgeshire in 1851, although there are some later records considered doubtful by Tutt (1905–14).

It is possible that in the not too distant past (eighteenth century) the large copper was much more widely distributed. There are unconfirmed reports (discussed by Bretherton, 1951b) from Somerset and Suffolk, in addition to the mapped records from the Norfolk Broads which have been confirmed by specimens which have recently come to light (Irwin, in press).

The commonest of the three subspecies, *rutilus*, occurs locally in Europe, but is generally becoming scarcer. In the present century there have been several attempts to introduce the continental subspecies to the British Isles. The more successful were at Tipperary, Ireland (several introductions of *batavus* and *rutilus*, 1913–42); Wicken Fen, Cambridgeshire (where *batavus* survived for fifteen years after its introduction in 1927); and Woodwalton Fen (*batavus*, introduced

in 1927 and still present, although reintroduced from caged stock after extinction by summer floods in 1968). The food plant of *dispar* and *batavus* is the water dock (*rutilus* uses a wider range of food plants). The flight period is July to August, when the eggs are laid singly on the docks. Plants located away from open water, at the margins of fringing vegetation, are usually selected. Newly hatched larvae are yellow with long hairs, but they quickly turn green. They hibernate in the second instar, when they acquire a reddish tinge. Hibernating larvae move on to dead foliage on the ground and may spend long periods under water. Feeding is resumed in the spring, when the larvae move again to pupate on nearby vegetation.

Life table and habitat studies (Duffey, 1968; Bink, 1972) provide considerable insight into the ecology of this species. Annual fluctuations in the study populations, at Woodwalton and in Holland, were considered to be attributable to egg and early larval mortality. However, the pattern of annual fluctuations differed at the two sites over the same period.

It is likely that gradual changes in habitat suitability are more important than these annual changes, in terms of the long-term survival of the species. Duffey's work suggests that the docks must be both abundant and readily accessible to the butterflies, not obscured by the surrounding vegetation. Optimal conditions may occur for a short period in the development of fen vegetation after peat cutting, but in due course the docks in such areas become shaded over. An alternative and cheaper form of management, cattle grazing, has been tried at Woodwalton with some success. By this means, docks are kept adequately exposed and areas of bare peat are created for the establishment of new plants from seed (Duffey, 1977).

The population at Woodwalton has been maintained partly by caging spring larvae to protect them from predators and parasites. Reserve stock is also maintained elsewhere. The importance of this was shown in 1968, when exceptional summer floods resulted in the extinction of the Woodwalton population, and reintroduction was necessary. Duffey considers that the area of suitable habitat that can be maintained for the large copper is probably too small to enable the species to survive unaided. However, it has survived without help since 1979.

The loss of the large copper from Britain in the nineteenth century was probably associated with a decline in the traditional management of fenland, as the loss pre-dated the drainage of some large areas. Collecting may have been an exacerbating factor; after the larvae were discovered to feed on water dock the numbers of the large copper appeared to fall rapidly. In the 1820s there was a profitable local trade in larvae and pupae conducted by the fenmen, who collected from areas perhaps known only to them and sold to visiting entomologists.

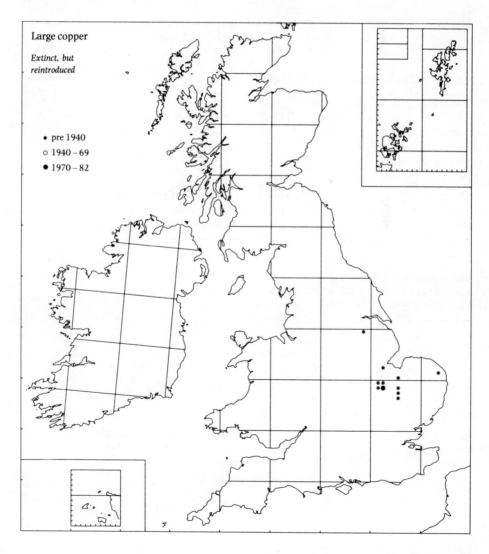

Large copper

Extinct, but reintroduced

● pre 1940
○ 1940 – 69
● 1970 – 82

SMALL BLUE

Cupido minimus

This attractive local species is the smallest British butterfly. Adults usually fly from late May to early July. There is also a small partial second generation in August on most southern sites, and occasionally elsewhere. The adults are relatively inconspicuous for a grassland butterfly; it is often easier to find a colony by searching the flower heads of kidney vetch for the small pale-blue eggs, or even for larvae. These leave the seed heads, full-fed, in late July to hibernate on the ground, apart from the few that form a second generation.

Small blue colonies breed year after year in the same discrete sites. Many of these are very small: during a recent survey in Dorset, several isolated adult populations were found in areas of 1,000–1,500 square metres, sometimes supported by fewer than 100 flowering vetches. Marking experiments indicate that the adults are sedentary and hardly ever leave their sites (Coulthard, 1982; Thomas, 1983c). In some areas, very isolated clumps of perhaps ten to thirty flowering kidney vetches regularly contain large numbers of eggs, and it is not certain whether these sites (often 100–200 square metres in size) also support separate permanent colonies, although there is circumstantial evidence that this is the case [A. C. Morton]. On small sites, every flower head usually contains several eggs. On others, where kidney vetch may be abundant over large areas, eggs usually occur at very low densities. Most of the populations measured by the Institute of Terrestrial Ecology on these two types of site contained fewer than 100 adults (Thomas, 1983c). A. C. Morton and Coulthard (1982) have

recorded even smaller colonies, of under fifty adults. In contrast, there are a few sites where the small blue regularly teems over areas of several hectares. These unusual populations must contain several thousand adults.

Although the range of the small blue extends to northern Scotland, it is much commoner in southern England, and most sites are in locally warm and sheltered situations, almost invariably with a southern aspect. It is especially characteristic of abandoned quarries, and railway and road cuttings in limestone and chalk areas; one very large colony has established itself on a new roadside bank in Sussex that was deliberately sown with kidney vetch, even though a tall continental variety was used. Many colonies also breed on south-facing downland slopes. Sites usually contain patches of tall sheltered grass or scrub where the adults roost communally by night and on which the males perch and form territories by day. Thomas (1983c) and A. C. Morton found distinct congregations of the males in such areas in southern England, but in Scotland, Coulthard (1982) found them to be distributed throughout the areas of kidney vetch. This difference may be related to the terrains of particular sites. In both regions, the distribution and density of the females corresponded to that of the food plant. The eggs are laid singly between the 'fingers' of the youngest vetch flower buds, typically on prominent plants growing in sunny situations in a fairly (but not very) tall sward. The larvae bore into the flowers, but are conspicuous in their later instars. They are only occasionally tended by ants in Britain, although this is a common event further south in Europe, where there are more species of ant that climb flower stalks.

The small blue was once well distributed through much of Britain and Ireland, but has always been extremely local. It has undoubtedly declined in the present century, and has virtually disappeared from most of northern and central England. It has also declined in Scotland; just thirteen colonies are known now from the northeast coast, mainly on ungrazed grassy banks beneath cliffs (Coulthard, 1982). There are also four further inland, and one on the Galloway coast, and it is likely that a few others have been overlooked (Thomson, 1980). It is largely a coastal species, too, in Ireland and south Wales, though this may partly reflect the distribution of its food plant. Curiously, very few colonies have been recorded in south-west England, where kidney vetch grows in great abundance along much of the coastline.

The stronghold of the small blue is the chalk and limestone of southern England. However, even here, there is evidence of a considerable decline; in the Cotswolds, where some colonies are extremely large, it had disappeared from twenty-one out of fifty-five known sites by 1971 (Muggleton, 1973) and in Dorset from twenty-three out of forty-eight former sites by 1978 [J. A. Thomas]. A total of sixty-eight colonies was found in Dorset that year (the forty-three 'new'

ones were in poorly recorded localities and were almost certainly long-established, but overlooked, populations). Probably a few more survive in this good county for the small blue, but most consist of extremely small populations. Many losses are attributable to the destruction of downland sites by ploughing or agricultural improvement, while others in the Cotswolds became overgrown following myxomatosis (Muggleton, 1973). However, in 1978 kidney vetch was abundant on many sites in Dorset where this butterfly once occurred. An isolated population at one of these sites had been exterminated a few years earlier when the area was heavily grazed and the flowers eaten, but this sedentary butterfly has not re-colonized the surviving plants since.

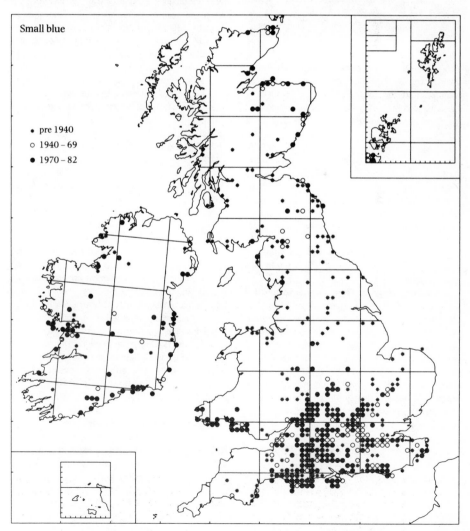

Small blue

- pre 1940
○ 1940 – 69
● 1970 – 82

SILVER-STUDDED BLUE

Plebejus argus

This butterfly was once locally distributed through much of Britain, but it has always been commoner in the south. Today the butterfly is still fairly common only on fragments of heath in south-east Dorset, south Hampshire and west Surrey.

Adults from different colonies generally vary in size, colour, and markings. Certain forms predominate in particular parts of the range, although there is also much local variation (de Worms, 1949; Dennis, 1977). The extremes are split into three subspecies: *masseyi* in the north; *caernensis* around Great Ormes Head, north-west Wales; and *argus* elsewhere. Occasionally, colonies of subspecies *argus* occur on southern chalk and limestone downland, which are termed race *cretaceus*.

The validity of raising these local forms of such a variable butterfly to subspecies level is perhaps questionable. In a fascinating exercise, Merchant (1956) released ninety *caernensis* adults into the Dulas valley, just sixteen kilometres from Great Ormes Head, in 1942. These soon founded several large colonies which still flourish. However, after thirty years they differed from *caernensis*; the adults had become nearly as large as subspecies *argus* on Anglesey (thirty kilometres away) and were similar in other respects (Dennis, 1972b, 1977).

The existence of different races and the inability to colonize new sites suggest that this is a very sedentary butterfly. However, once introduced to the Dulas, it then spread two kilometres north and west along the valley within twelve years (Hughes, 1956, 1960; Dennis, 1977). Many populations seem to survive at very low numbers; a relatively large colony in Dorset was found to contain only eighty adults on the peak day [J. A. Thomas]. Most breeding areas are also quite small; in one example studied by Sutton (1981), egg-laying was usually confined to 400 square metres, although adults spread over thirty-five to forty hectares in years of abundance.

The silver-studded blue has one generation a year which flies from mid July to mid August, except subspecies *caernensis* which emerges in early to mid June. Eggs are laid on the woody parts of a range of plants, including gorse and bell heather, and on dead grass and leaves on one Somerset heath (Sutton, 1981). They hatch the following spring. The larvae are difficult to rear in captivity, although they will eat gorse (mainly flowers, but also tender young spikes), common bird's-foot-trefoil, and several heather species. The wild *cretaceus* larvae feed on common bird's-foot-trefoil [K. J. Willmott] (Chalmers-Hunt, 1960–81), and *caernensis* also uses rock-roses. Wild larvae are incessantly tended by ants (Malicky, 1970) and pupae have been found inside ant nests [C. D. Thomas].

In the nineteenth century this butterfly undoubtedly bred in Scotland, for example in Berwickshire and Perthshire (Tutt, 1905–14), but few sites have been mapped because they are hard to locate precisely or are considered by Thomson (1980) to be possible errors. The only record for the present century, and the only known Scottish specimen, is from Loch Rannoch, 1936; it resembles *masseyi* (Thomson, 1980). The 'true' *masseyi* apparently became extinct in the mid 1930s, having once been locally abundant on mosses in north Lancashire and Westmorland (Birkett, 1957). The subspecies *caernensis* still survives on the limestone cliffs of Great Ormes Head, on nearby cliffs (Dennis, 1977), and in its changed form in the Dulas Valley. Most other Welsh colonies of *argus* are now extinct, although a few isolated colonies survive, for example on Holy Island. A famous colony exists on less than one hectare of heath sandwiched between two trunk roads in the midlands.

In England, the race *cretaceus* is probably now extinct in Kent, Surrey, Dorset and perhaps Hampshire, although populations survive on the limestone of Portland Bill. Occasional colonies of the race *argus* still exist on sand dunes along the East Anglian coast, but the butterfly has declined greatly in this region. Extensive losses have also occurred in south-west England, although a few colonies survive, such as those on slaty shale cliffs in south Devon and in sand dune slacks along the north Cornish coast.

The acid heaths of southern England have always been the stronghold of this butterfly, and it is still locally common, especially in south Dorset and the New Forest. In Dorset, colonies are restricted to wetter heaths, and may be found in almost every patch that survives. Sutton (1981) considers that occasional burning, or sporadic grazing, are essential to maintain this habitat. The species also occurs in west Surrey, but it has declined greatly in the central weald of Sussex.

The main causes of these considerable declines have been the reclamation of heathland, the drainage of mosses, and the agricultural improvement of calcareous sites. Some recent losses on chalk downland may have been caused by the grassland becoming overgrown due to the dearth of rabbits after myxomatosis. Further loss of habitat seems certain to destroy most existing colonies in the future, but, since populations can flourish on small areas of land, some can be maintained on nature reserves. It is fairly well represented on these and on a few other 'safe' sites, such as army ranges.

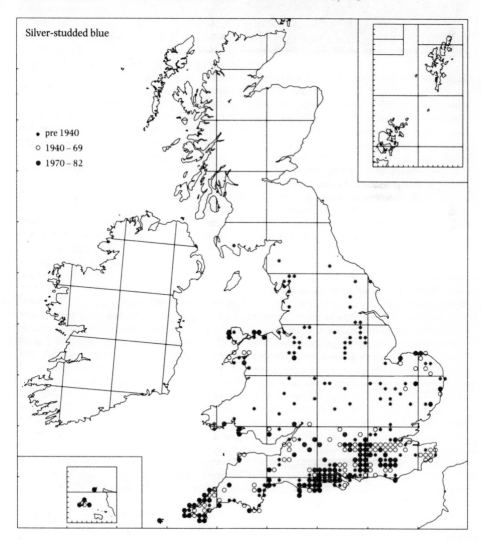

Silver-studded blue

- pre 1940
- ○ 1940 – 69
- ● 1970 – 82

BROWN ARGUS

Aricia agestis

Aricia butterflies are locally distributed throughout Britain, but are much commoner in the south. Until recently they were split into two main subspecies: *agestis* in the south and *artaxerxes* in the north. The Castle Eden Dene argus *salmacis* was sometimes considered a third subspecies, but was usually regarded as a race of *artaxerxes*. Today two distinct British species are recognized, thanks to the painstaking morphological, physiological, and genetic researches of Jarvis (1958, 1959, 1963, 1966) and Høegh-Guldberg (1966). These are *A. agestis* and *A. artaxerxes*, respectively the brown argus and the northern brown argus.

These two butterflies differ in various ways, principally in their number of generations each year (voltinism). Their larvae react differently to day-length, causing the northern brown argus to enter diapause earlier, and invariably to have one generation a year. The brown argus is bivoltine, or even trivoltine in captivity. Occasionally a few captive individuals may enter diapause after one generation, but these usually die and it is not known whether such diapause ever happens in the wild. The two species can be forced to interbreed in the laboratory, but this is unlikely to happen in the wild because of the different emergence times.

These species also differ in minor morphological features in all stages, and in their egg-laying behaviour. The adult brown argus has more pronounced orange lunules on the upper surface of the wings, and the ground colour is a warm redder brown. Although rather a dull butterfly, it is curiously attractive in flight, having a silver-grey appearance similar to that of the small blue.

Brown argus colonies occur locally as far north as Anglesey in the west and Lincolnshire in the east. They do not overlap with the northern species, although colonies of *A. artaxerxes* occur further south in central England, in the Peak District, where the brown argus does not occur. The brown argus is commonest on calcareous soils, especially on chalk and limestone downs. Other colonies breed on sand dunes and heaths, including quite acid formations, such as the lower greensand in the central weald of Sussex. A very few colonies breed on heavy clay soils; one example is known from a wood on the wealden clay of west Sussex, and others once occurred in the old county of Huntingdonshire. This butterfly is commonest in open grassland, but tends to be rather local, even on the chalk downs of southern counties. Although it is a sedentary species, populations evidently can be supported by fairly small areas of land, including grassy rides in woods.

Brown argus populations fluctuate greatly and rapidly in size. These short-term changes have not been synchronized on different sites which have been monitored, and no research has been done to explain the cause, although the lack of synchrony suggests that the weather is not an important factor. It is clear that many populations survive at very low numbers in most years. Frazer (1961) estimated a total emergence of 700 adults on a Kentish site where it was 'abundant', but J. A. Thomas estimated only thirty-seven adults to be present on the peak day of a small colony in Dorset, probably equivalent to a total emergence of about 100 adults.

The eggs are laid singly on the undersides of leaves of the larval food plant, common rock-rose on calcareous soils, and common stork's-bill on sandy soils. A few localities on chalk have neither plant present, and it is possible that dove's-foot crane's-bill (or another *Geranium*) is being used. This plant grows on these sites, captive females oviposit freely on it, and the larvae eat it as readily as rock-rose, given the choice (Jarvis, 1958).

The egg hatches after about one week, and the young larva feeds on the leaves of its food plant, making characteristic holes, but leaving the clear upper cuticle of the leaf intact. Older larvae eat whole leaves. Hibernation usually occurs in the third instar, but occasionally in the second or fourth. Wild larvae are nearly always attended by ants, both before and after hibernation. Harrison always found ants to be present (Tutt, 1905–14) but this is not invariably the case (Jarvis (1959) and ourselves). We found that at least two ant species, *Myrmica sabuleti* and *Lasius alienus*, may tend larvae on chalk downland in Dorset. Pupation occurs in the turf at the base of plants. The pupae are highly attractive to ants, and are almost certainly soon buried by them in earth cells, as is any sweet-tasting immobile object.

Common rock-rose is a low-growing plant of ancient calcareous pasture. It is destroyed by ploughing and agricultural improvement, and is eventually shaded out of tall abandoned pasture. Although the brown argus remains well distributed throughout the southern downland of England, very many colonies have been lost in recent years because of the intensification of agriculture. It has become a rarity in Warwickshire (two post-1960 colonies compared with nine in 1950–60; Smith and Brown, 1979), Northamptonshire, Cambridgeshire and Suffolk.

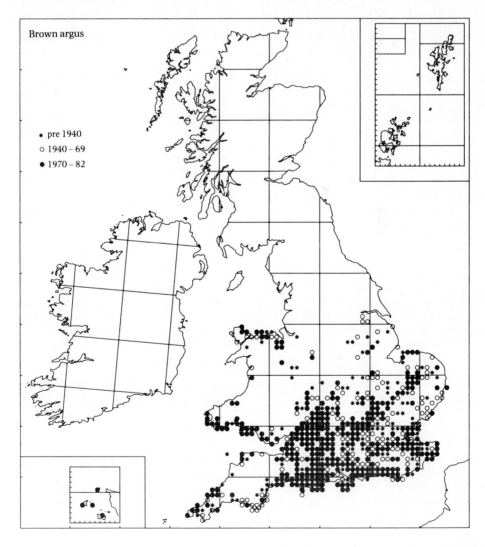

Brown argus

* pre 1940
o 1940 – 69
● 1970 – 82

NORTHERN BROWN ARGUS

Aricia artaxerxes

The northern brown argus was probably one of the earliest butterflies to recolonize Britain after the Devensian ice age gave way to a milder, though still cold, climate some 10,000–15,000 years ago (Dennis, 1977). Today it survives on scattered, generally isolated sites in Scotland and the north of England. Many of these ancient colonies have developed distinctive features, notably a conspicuous white spot on each of the upper forewings which contrasts strikingly with the deep brown ground-colour. These spots occur on nearly all Scottish specimens and were once the main characteristic that was used to distinguish them as a separate subspecies, *arta-xerxes*, or even species (opinions differed) from the plainer brown argus, subspecies *agestis*, found in England. Early entomologists made special journeys to secure Scottish adults, mainly from its classic site at Arthur's Seat, Edinburgh. Enormous numbers were collected, and there were bitter recriminations when it disappeared from there (in 1869) and from other areas (Thomson, 1980).

Other interesting colonies were found in the north of England. There, individuals varied greatly in appearance on any site, but generally resembled the brown argus (although a few white-spotted adults occurred), yet they had only one generation a year, as in Scotland. These were named the Castle Eden Dene argus (subspecies *salmacis*) after the most famous collecting site on the Durham coast. There was much speculation as to the origin of these colonies (Jefferson, 1958). Ford (1945) decided that they were hybrids formed where the northern subspecies, *artaxerxes*, and the southern one, *agestis*, met. However, once

these were found to be separate species (see brown argus, page 66), the Castle Eden Dene argus was shown to be merely a form of the northern brown argus. In fact, these colonies in the north of England are more like the northern brown argus on the continent, where the white-spotted form is unknown.

Throughout its range, this butterfly occurs in sedentary, self-contained colonies which are usually supported by small discrete areas of land. The two main colonies at Castle Eden Dene still breed on the same spots on either side of the Dene mouth that they used in 1827. No interchange of adults was detected during marking experiments made on both sides, and their combined populations totalled only 75–100 adults on the peak days of 1970–72 (Selman *et al.*, 1973), probably representing entire emergences of around 225–300 butterflies in each year. These colonies seem typical in size to many others of this species, although anecdotal reports suggest that some are even smaller.

The emergence date of the single adult generation varies within the range of the butterfly, from as early as mid June or even May in south-west Scotland to mid July–August on the east coast (Thomson, 1980). Despite the many observations made on all stages of the life cycle in captivity (e.g. Jarvis, 1966, 1969), there is still much to be discovered about its requirements in the wild. The main, and possibly only, food plant used is common rock-rose, although captive larvae will eat species of *Geranium*. The white eggs are laid singly on the uppersides of the rock-rose leaves, where they are very conspicuous (Brooks and Knight, 1982). The larvae feed on the leaves and are tended by ants.

There is a rough synchrony between the distributions of common rock-rose and the northern brown argus in Scotland, although the presence of the food plants has not been confirmed on all sites (Thomson, 1980). Colonies occur on base rich soils, especially limestones, at altitudes of up to 350 metres. Most sites in England and Scotland are warm, south-facing exposures or steep grassy slopes. Colonies are still locally distributed, though generally scarce in Scotland, and, while several have undoubtedly been lost from the south-west, Thomson (1978, 1980) has rediscovered other colonies and considers that the species is often overlooked. Overall, it does not seem to have declined seriously in Scotland. Colonies were always much more locally distributed in northern England, and have experienced considerably greater losses due to the destruction of the breeding areas, for example by coal-mining.

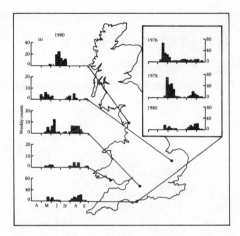

Flight period of the northern brown argus (a) at one site and of the brown argus at four sites in 1980, and of the brown argus in three different years.

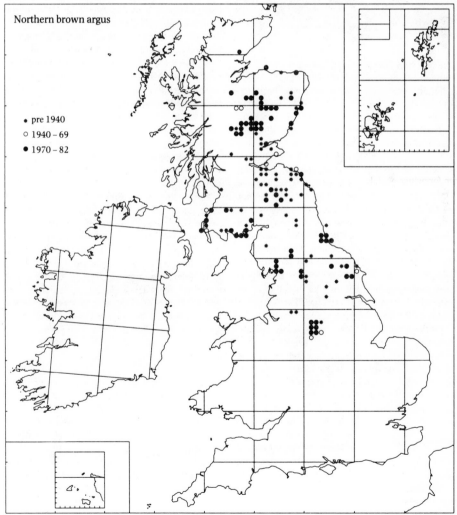

Northern brown argus

* pre 1940
○ 1940 – 69
● 1970 – 82

COMMON BLUE

Polyommatus icarus

The common blue is one of the most widely distributed of all British butterflies. The brightly coloured male is our commonest blue butterfly, but the female, which is normally brown in colour, is much less familiar to most people. Both sexes may vary greatly in colour and markings within any population, and tend towards distinct types in certain regions. The most striking of these, *mariscolore*, is sometimes regarded as a different subspecies (Howarth, 1973; Dennis, 1977), although Higgins and Riley (1970) do not accept this distinction. Although *mariscolore* was originally used to describe the common blue in Ireland, Thomson (1980) considers that the populations in north and west Scotland, including the Orkneys and Hebrides, also belong to this race. So vivid is its appearance that it is commonly misidentified as the large blue by entomologists who are only familiar with the smaller, drabber, race from the rest of Britain.

In the south there are two distinct broods, generally in May–June and late July–September. In northern England and Scotland there is usually only one generation. In Yorkshire there are cooler areas where univoltinism is usual (Pennines and wolds), whereas two generations are normal along the coast and in the Vale of York (Lees, 1969). The Irish race is apparently also univoltine. Frohawk (1934) states that the second generation everywhere is usually only a partial one, and that many larvae from the first generation enter hibernation.

Marking experiments indicate that the common blue forms discrete colonies which the adults rarely leave (Dowdeswell, 1981; Frazer,

1961, 1981). Males are especially sedentary, sometimes sticking to a particular small bank where they also roost communally on tall grasses (Frazer, 1981). Numbers fluctuated considerably, but often synchronously, in 1976–82 on sites contributing to the Butterfly Monitoring Scheme. A severe decline in 1977 was almost certainly caused by the 1976 drought, which killed most leaves of the larval food plant. Despite these fluctuations, common blues are rarely seen in thousands on a site as, for example, are the chalkhill and adonis blues.

Adults lay their eggs singly on the young leaflets and petioles of the larval food plant, common bird's-foot-trefoil, mainly on the undersides. Tutt (1905–14) states that on large plants only the terminal leaflets are chosen, and that eggs are laid especially where the herbage is cropped short. K. J. Willmott has noted a preference for laying on plants growing on ant hills and broken ground. Eggs have occasionally been recorded from other legumes, such as common restharrow, spiny restharrow, black medick, and white clover.

The larva feeds by day and hibernates in the third instar. In the final instar it possesses an active honey gland and is often attended by ants. Rayward (1907), however, noted that captive larvae were less attractive than those of some other blues. This was confirmed in the wild by J. A. Thomas; even so, nineteen out of twenty-five wild final instar larvae found on two sites were being milked, although none in an earlier instar was attended. The ants were the commonest species present: *Formica rufa*, *Lasius alienus*, and *Myrmica sabuleti*. The pupa is formed on the ground, and is attractive to ants in captivity.

Bird's-foot-trefoil is an extremely common low-growing perennial that can tolerate a good deal of disturbance. Colonies of the common blue may be found over most of the British Isles, especially on disturbed ground, sand dunes, rough pasture, and unimproved downland. It is essentially a butterfly of open grassland, but it is also found in wide grassy glades in sunny woods. Colonies occur as far north as the sand dunes of the south Shetlands. Thomson (1980) states that in Scotland it is absent only from mountains above 500 metres, and our maps suggest that the same may be true in Wales. Although its food plant was once sown, it is absent from modern improved pasture and from arable land. There can be little doubt that the number of colonies in Britain has declined enormously during this century, although this decline cannot be quantified. Bird's-foot-trefoil is also reduced or eliminated by dense tall pasture, and colonies of common blues are rare along unmanaged road verges, except on light soils or where there are banks. Similarly, it has probably declined on many abandoned rough grazings since the numbers of rabbits were reduced by myxomatosis in the 1950s.

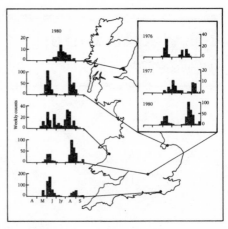

Flight periods of the common blue at five sites in Britain in 1980, and at one site in three different years.

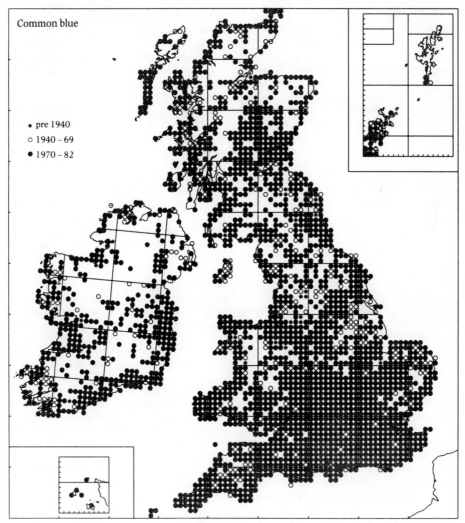

Common blue

- • pre 1940
- ○ 1940 – 69
- ● 1970 – 82

CHALKHILL BLUE

Lysandra coridon

This local butterfly is characteristic of old calcareous grassland in southern Britain. The larvae feed solely on horseshoe vetch, as do those of the much rarer adonis blue. Sometimes both butterflies breed on the same site, but there is no apparent competition for food. The chalkhill blue has only one generation a year and the larval stages hardly overlap; some plants regularly support a succession of adonis, then chalkhill, then adonis blue larvae again from March to October.

The adult stage, during July and August, lasts about seven weeks. The eggs are laid singly, usually on the woody parts of the food plant or on nearby leaf litter. They overwinter as full-formed embryos in the egg, and hatch in March. The larvae, unlike those of the adonis blue, feed mainly in the evening and at night. Active larvae are invariably attended by ants, except during the first instar. These ants are attracted by sweet secretions exuded by scattered pores and a posterior honey gland. Larvae rest during the day beneath stones or at the base of their plants, and are sometimes buried in small earth heaps by ants; Prideaux once found eight individuals in one *L. flavus* cell (Donisthorpe, 1927). It is often said that ants carry the young larvae to suitable food plants, but there is no good evidence for this, and the belief apparently arises from Donisthorpe's (1927) observation that one larva was dragged a short distance when introduced to a captive ant nest. The pupa also produces secretions (Malicky, 1970), and it is almost certain that it too is buried and tended by ants in the wild.

Marking experiments suggest that chalkhill

blues form predominantly self-contained populations, although the odd male may stray miles from a breeding area. Such strays account for our records away from chalk and limestone.

The chalkhill blue can breed over large open continuous areas, often laying on isolated plants. However, it seems reluctant to cross discontinuities such as valleys, and nearby separate hillsides probably support quite distinct populations (Frazer, 1961, 1977) [R. Leverton; M. G. Morris]. The chalkhill blue is much more tolerant about where it can breed than is the adonis blue; it usually uses all the horseshoe vetch in a locality, regardless of the aspect (Thomas and Merrett, 1980). Females will also lay on plants growing in a range of vegetation heights.

Populations fluctuate greatly from year to year (Frazer, 1961, 1977), although some sites consistently support higher numbers than others. Examples of medium sized populations are a colony of roughly 18,000 adults in two hectares in Wiltshire [M. G. Morris], and about 5,000 (males only estimated) in just over one hectare in Kent (Frazer, 1962). Most populations are clearly much smaller than this. The best sites are usually south-facing downs which contain abundant horseshoe vetch. Some have had a lightly cropped turf [M. G. Morris; R. Leverton]; others were closely grazed (Crane, 1972) [W. Shreeves].

Although the British range of the chalkhill blue extends 100 kilometres further north than that of the adonis blue, it still occurs only in the southern half of the range of horseshoe vetch. For many years the most northerly known colony was on a road verge near Ancaster in Lincolnshire, but the site was destroyed around 1970. Today it is still a highly characteristic butterfly of old calcareous pasture from the Chilterns southwards.

Extinctions have occurred wherever pasture has been ploughed or improved; losses were particularly severe on flatter land, such as Salisbury Plain (Lipscombe and Jackson, 1964). By the 1970s, very little of the English chalk existed as unimproved grassland; what remained was mainly on steep slopes and non-agricultural land, such as army ranges. These sites are rarely grazed by stock nowadays and rabbit grazing is much lighter than before myxomatosis. Unlike the adonis blue, the chalkhill blue can survive in abandoned pasture, but only so long as horseshoe vetch remains abundant. Unfortunately, this low-growing perennial is eventually eliminated, or at least drastically reduced in tall grassland, though it may be maintained in abundance by light or periodic cropping. Many colonies of chalkhill blues have become extinct or declined on over-grown ancient grassland in the past thirty years, for example in the Cotswolds (Muggleton, 1973) and Kent (Frazer, 1977). Crane (1972) vividly described the decline of one famous colony at

Millhill, Sussex. Once, perhaps 50,000–100,000 adults regularly flew over tens of hectares of short close turf which was yellow with horseshoe vetch in May. Since myxomatosis, the area has become dominated by coarse grasses, and in 1971 only twelve males were seen in the main eight hectares, although occasional vetch plants were still well distributed, submerged by tall grass. Just one 'small patch' had been mown, and, there only, horseshoe vetch was common and fifty to sixty males were seen.

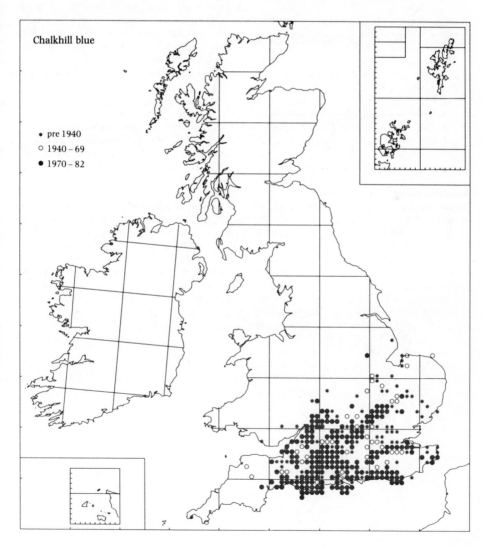

Chalkhill blue

• pre 1940
○ 1940 – 69
● 1970 – 82

ADONIS BLUE

Lysandra bellargus

The brilliant colour of the males and the occurrence of colonies in open grassland make the adonis blue one of our most conspicuous butterflies. It is also one of the best mapped, for since it has become a rarity it has been much sought by entomologists, and it was the subject of three intensive surveys in the 1970s.

Like its close relative the chalkhill blue, adonis blue larvae feed only on horseshoe vetch. This restricts colonies to calcareous grassland. The young stages also have a close association with at least two species of ant: *Myrmica sabuleti* and *Lasius alienus* (Thomas, 1983a). The larvae produce sweet secretions from their second instar onwards and this continues throughout the pupal stage. Larvae are tended incessantly by ants and are buried in protective earth cells when they rest overnight or moult. Pupae are treated similarly; some have been found deep in the brood chambers of ant nests. It is not certain, however, that ants are an important factor in the distribution and survival of colonies.

The adonis blue reaches its northern European limit in Britain. Colonies have been recorded only from the southern part of its food plant's range here and, not surprisingly, occur with increasing frequency towards the extreme south. They are very locally distributed, and mapping by ten-kilometre squares gives an exaggerated impression of their abundance. Few squares have contained more than one or two populations, each occupying a small fraction of the grassland that contains horseshoe vetch. In most localities breeding has been restricted to the same small area since records began, and marking experiments show that

adults very rarely leave their sites, although there are descriptions of local expansion in years of unusual abundance. Nearly all breeding areas are on steep, south-facing slopes, and most consist of closely-cropped, unimproved, calcareous pasture. The females are very choosy about where they lay: they show a strong preference for horseshoe vetch which is both in very short turf and in sheltered sunspots, such as a rabbit scrape, a hoof mark, or the edge of a path. On sites with sward of variable height, egg-laying is virtually restricted to local patches of vetch one to three centimetres tall (Thomas, 1983a). This, with the southern distribution of colonies, suggests that this butterfly requires a warm local climate.

Adonis blue populations are famous for their fluctuations: one in Dorset increased from under fifty to about 60,000 adults between 1977 and 1982. Declines may be equally rapid; Frazer (1961) documents the extinction of a Kentish colony just two years after it had contained an estimated 3,400 adults. A puzzling aspect of most extinctions is that they have rarely been preceded by any noticeable decline in horseshoe vetch or any obvious destruction of the site, which often continues to support the chalkhill blue. It is widely believed that a change from traditional sheep grazing to cattle is responsible for many extinctions, but this is not so. Most surviving colonies now breed on cattle grazed sites, including the largest colony in the country. Instead, it seems that a slight (perhaps temporary) relaxa-

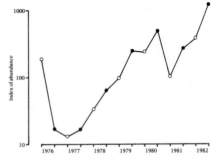

Changes in abundance of the adonis blue at Ballard Down, Swanage, a site in the Butterfly Monitoring Scheme. There was a sharp fall in numbers following the 1976 drought.

tion in the grazing intensity is the cause of many declines, whether through the loss of rabbits as in the 1950s, or because of the changing methods of farming on the downs. A survey of 106 former sites in Dorset showed that the butterfly had been lost from 90 per cent of downland where the height of the turf exceeded four centimetres, but survived in 80 per cent which had shorter vegetation (Thomas, 1983a). Monitored populations have also been consistently smaller on lightly grazed or ungrazed sites than where there has been heavy grazing. These smaller colonies are liable to extinction in a 'bad' year, such as 1977 after the drought.

In the past the adonis blue has been recorded from all the calcareous formations within its southern range, but it is now almost certainly extinct in the Cotswolds (Muggleton, 1973). A survey made in 1973 by R. D. Buxton and H. C. Connolly showed that adonis blues were present in about 10 per cent of known old localities, although in Dorset the situation was rather better (Thomas, 1983a). Occasional reappearances have been recorded recently in the Chilterns (Showler, 1980), Sussex (Edwards and Edwards, 1980), and Kent (Frazer, 1977), but the overall rate of loss in recent years has been dramatic. Particularly rapid losses occurred in the late 1950s and the mid to late 1970s. Occasional colonies still survive through most of its former range, but there were probably only seventy to eighty colonies left in the whole country in 1981. About half of these are in Dorset.

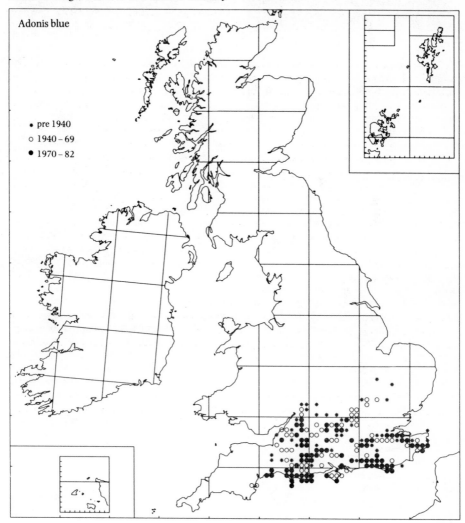

Adonis blue

• pre 1940
○ 1940 – 69
● 1970 – 82

MAZARINE BLUE

Cyaniris semiargus

The mazarine blue is one of four butterflies to have become extinct in Britain since the mid nineteenth century, but, unlike the large copper, black-veined white and large blue, it is not a spectacular butterfly and its history in this country is comparatively poorly known. It was first listed as a British butterfly by John Ray (1710) in his *Historia Insectorum*, and the last known colony, as distinct from record of an isolated individual, bred in Glamorgan until 1877. In the intervening years, the mazarine blue was caught in at least twenty-two counties, mainly in the south, and the occasional individual has been recorded in the present century. These are assumed (by us) to be releases and have not been mapped. However, adults were seen regularly and in numbers only in Gloucestershire (South, 1906), Dorset and Glamorgan. Many other old records are too vague to have been included on our map.

Because of the sporadic records of this butterfly in most regions, some entomologists questioned whether it might not be a rare vagrant from Europe, where it is common, rather than a British resident (e.g. Russell, 1943). However, the mazarine blue is not considered to be particularly mobile on the continent, and this theory was convincingly dismissed by Ford (1945) and Bretherton (1951b). It is more probable that established colonies were sometimes overlooked because the adults were flying among those of the very similar common blues or even silver-studded blues, and that other records of single individuals may have resulted from misidentifications, accidental escapes, or deliberate introductions of continental or British specimens. Such factors certainly account for many strange records of other rare butterflies, though we know of no documented example involving this species. There were, however, cases of imported specimens which were fraudulently sold as British as early as 1860, when the mazarine blue had become a marketable commodity (Bretherton, 1951b). This, too, confuses the records, and perhaps our map.

It seems likely that colonies of the mazarine blue occurred in small discrete areas in several regions during the first half of the nineteenth century, but were regularly visited only if they were easily accessible. It is easy to forget how few entomologists there were at that time and, in particular, how restricted were their movements. For example, that much greater and commoner prize, the large blue, was not discovered in its most famous collecting grounds – the Cotswolds and the Atlantic coastline of Cornwall and Devon – until the 1850s and 1880s, respectively. Thus, although C. W. Dale (1886) described the mazarine blue as 'common in meadows' in Dorset up to 1839, and his father J. C. Dale discovered at least six colonies in that county, of which four were within ten miles of his home, J. C. Dale's only regular records are for the colony that bred on his doorstep, at Glanvilles Wootton. There, adults were noted in at least twenty-seven of the years between its discovery in 1808 and its presumed demise in 1847. In his famous diaries, J. C. Dale described the butterfly as 'common' in ten of those years, including 1808, and Bretherton calculated that 300 individual adults had been noted or caught, including twenty that were taken on 13 June 1825. This shows clearly that the butterfly occurred as a discrete, if small, colony that was resident at Glanvilles Wootton for at least thirty-nine years, and probably for many more before.

Bretherton also describes records of established colonies in Glamorgan: '. . . it was seen in plenty from 1835 to 1837 near Merthyr and again from 1871 to 1877 at Penarth and Llantrisant. There Evan John "took it every year and once saw about 20 in a field" – and, having invited his collector friends from Bristol, even caused the edges of the hay to be scythed in order to give them a better chance. There are also references to repeated captures near Hereford and in one or two other places.'

Little is known of the ecology of this butterfly, and no plausible or comprehensive explanation has been given for its decline from local rarity to extinction, although Chapman (1909) suggested that it might be related to changes in cutting methods of clover crops. Unlike our other extinct butterflies, it remains a very common insect throughout much of Europe, and is especially characteristic of hay meadows and unimproved, lightly grazed pasture. Its main larval food is the flowers of red clover, though other leguminous plants may also be used (Frohawk, 1934). Flowery meadows were widespread in Britain long after the extinction of this butterfly, and we shall probably never know why it disappeared.

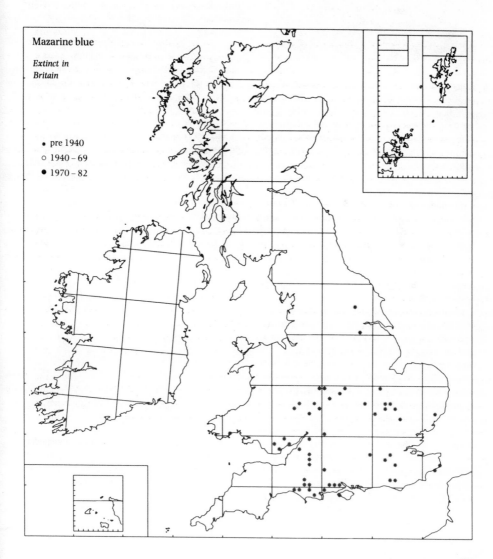

Mazarine blue

Extinct in Britain

• pre 1940
○ 1940 – 69
● 1970 – 82

HOLLY BLUE

Celastrina argiolus

Holly blue larvae feed on the developing flower buds of a variety of shrubs, and so this is our only blue which is found more generally in the sunny rides and clearings of woodland than in open grassland or heathland. It also breeds along hedgerows, in gardens – even those in the suburbs of large cities – and in urban parks. Often it occurs in isolated small colonies, for example centred on the churchyards of many of the Fenland villages of East Anglia, there being a virtual absence of suitable habitats in the intervening prairies [D. A. Ratcliffe]. There are two generations a year in most parts of the country, but in the north and west there may only be one. There is a suggestion that there are now two generations in Ireland, whereas until recently there was one (Baynes, 1964).

In spring the eggs are often laid on flower heads of holly, as its name suggests. Cultivated species and varieties may be used in gardens and parks, and sometimes support large populations. The butterfly lays freely on both male and female holly flowers [K. J. Willmott], which are on separate trees. This is very curious behaviour, as larvae on male flowers invariably die, for they are dependent on developing berries. The flowers of several other shrubs are also used, including dogwood, spindle, alder buckthorn and, in gardens especially, snowberry. In the south-west, and probably elsewhere, some colonies are supported entirely by gorse in both generations. Over most of Britain, by far the commonest food plant

for the second generation is ivy. The slug-like larvae, which are occasionally tended by ants, are particularly conspicuous on ivy berries, which bleed when bitten. Large numbers of the holly blue have built up in one small London park where walls, walks and beds have been planted with a mixture of different varieties of holly and ivy. The larvae may be parasitized, and are the only known host of a large and attractive ichneumonid wasp which kills large numbers on some sites.

This blue seems to colonize new areas frequently, increase in numbers for a few years and then decline and disappear. It is possible that a build-up of parasites could account for such a pattern of events, but there have been no population studies of this species. There must often, of necessity, be considerable movement of adults in successive generations to locate suitable food plants. The distribution map may suggest that it is more common than it actually is, for in any one year it may occupy only a proportion of the squares in which it is recorded as present. There seems to have been a more permanent withdrawal from the north-east of England.

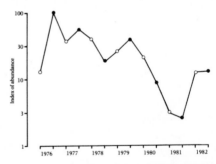

Changes in the abundance of the holly blue, 1976–82, as shown by data from the Butterfly Monitoring Scheme.

The monitoring scheme data show a considerable decline in the period 1976–81. This is probably a normal fluctuation, as there is no reason to believe that its habitats are under any serious threat.

Flight periods of the holly blue at five sites in England in 1979, and at one site in three different years.

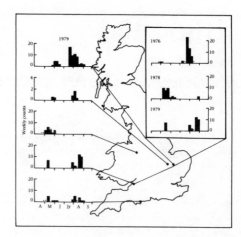

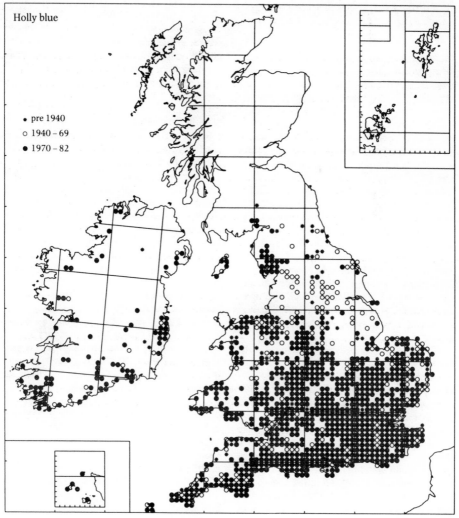

Holly blue

- pre 1940
- 1940 – 69
- 1970 – 82

LARGE BLUE

Maculinea arion

The large blue is presumed to be extinct in Britain. It was one of the great prizes among early entomologists because of its beauty, its rarity, the remoteness of its sites, and the inability of anyone to breed it in captivity. The discovery in 1915 of its dependence on ants added an extra cachet. Few species have been more assiduously hunted or more extensively documented. But the record is extremely confusing; some genuine sites have been kept secret, fraudulent ones have been claimed, and misidentifications have been made by hopeful entomologists. Spooner (1963) has made a detailed study of old collections, diaries, and the literature.

The first colony of any size was found by Bree (1852) at Barnwell Wold, Northants, in 1837. Perhaps six other colonies were discovered in the district, and large numbers of adults were caught regularly up to 1859, when about 200 were taken during a cold wet summer. The butterfly has not been seen in Northamptonshire since.

In the 1850s, colonies were discovered in the Cotswolds. In all, thirty-three sites have been recorded from these hills (Muggleton, 1973). Although still locally common in the early 1950s, these had declined to one by 1960, and this was ploughed up three years later.

The other main areas for the large blue were in the south-west of England. It was discovered along the south Devon coast in 1856, between Bolt Head and Bolt Tail. The last definite record for this area was in 1906. Another colony was found inland, near Ashburton, in the late nineteenth century. This disappeared at the turn of

the century, but about five sites were found nearby in 1930–60. All were very small, but one colony lingered on into the late 1970s.

The most famous colonies in the south-west were on the North Atlantic coast between Tintagel and Clovelly, where about thirty-four colonies have been recorded. The large blue was first noted by C. W. Dale at Clovelly before 1889, and the butterfly remained abundant south of Bude until about 1920. Contemporary accounts indicate that extensive areas became very overgrown with gorse. However, the butterfly survived on most sites, and was common on several in the early 1930s until another severe decline occurred. It again just survived, and small numbers were recorded as late as 1963.

The large blue was discovered on at least three sites north of Bude in the 1890s, but this area did not become well known until the 1940s. The butterfly was found to be quite widespread and sometimes abundant, but by 1963 it was restricted to thirteen sites (Hunt, 1965). The last became extinct in the early 1970s.

There have been a few other genuine records of the large blue in Britain. An enormous number of dubious claims have also been made. We have checked all records; the only ones on the map about which there is doubt are those at Dover (eighteenth century) and Winchester. One much quoted example from the Hebrides in the 1930s almost certainly originated from a hoax (Campbell, 1975; Thomson, 1980). No new site has been confirmed since 1961, and the last known colony was lost in 1979.

Large blues form discrete populations (Hunt, 1965; Thomas, in press). Individuals vary in their markings within any colony and there is also regional variation. The most distinctive were those from south-east of Dartmoor, which, on average, were smaller, darker, and more heavily spotted than elsewhere.

The fascinating life cycle of the large blue was discovered in 1915 (Chapman, 1915; Frohawk, 1934; Purefoy, 1953), but little was known about its ecology until the 1970s (Thomas, in press). Adults emerge in late June and early July, slightly earlier in the Cotswolds (Muggleton, 1974). Females lay their eggs singly on the flower buds of wild thyme. The larva first feeds on the flowers and developing seeds and then, after a final moult, falls to the ground at dusk and waits to be discovered by a red (*Myrmica*) ant. The larva produces an attractive secretion, and after being 'milked', rears up on its prolegs. This causes the ant to pick it up and carry it into its nest, where the larva feeds on ant eggs, grubs and prepupae. It then hibernates, and resumes feeding in spring. The pupa is formed inside the nest, where the adult emerges and crawls to the surface to expand its wings.

Any species of *Myrmica* will adopt the large blue, but only *M. sabuleti* and *M. scabrinodis* occur in significant numbers in the dry grassland where thyme grows. Only inside *M. sabuleti* nests do enough larvae survive for a colony to thrive, and the butterfly is dependent on this ant.

About half of Britain's ninety recorded sites have been effectively destroyed, for example by ploughing or afforestation. Most others contained abundant thyme when the large blue was lost, but, in every case except one, *M. sabuleti* had disappeared. In Britain *M. sabuleti* flourishes only in a very short turf on warm slopes. Many extinctions of the large blue coincided with the development of scrub, and the loss of rabbits has been a major factor in this. It is simple to reverse this trend by heavy grazing, but this was discovered too late. Good conditions have been re-created on a few sites so that reintroduction from continental stock remains a possibility.

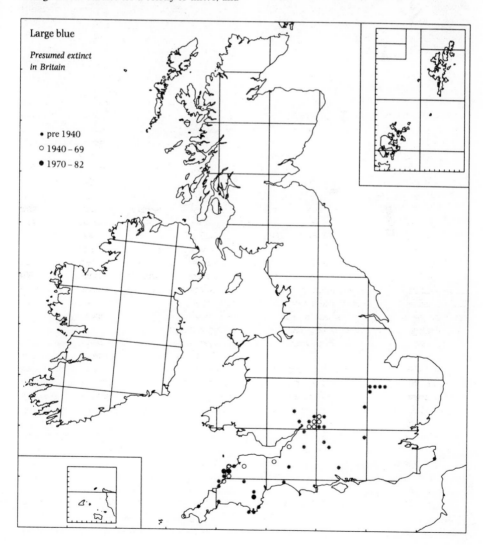

Large blue

Presumed extinct in Britain

● pre 1940
○ 1940 – 69
● 1970 – 82

DUKE OF BURGUNDY

Hamearis lucina

This attractive butterfly has apparently declined considerably in recent years; our records certainly do not suggest that it is common in woodland over the southern half of England, as Frohawk indicated in 1934.

Adult Duke of Burgundies fly in mid to late May and early June, having overwintered as pupae. They generally form extremely small localized colonies which are quite easy to overlook. The males congregate in small, sunny nooks among open scrub, or in glades and clearings, and each establishes a small 'territory', usually at the junction of two rides or paths. The same spots are often occupied year after year, each male perching on tall vegetation about half a metre above the ground. Shreeves (1979) found a marked male in the same territory after a five-day interval. From these spots they sortie after any intruding butterfly or other insect of similar size, in search of a virgin female, which is mated with little or no courtship.

The females lay their eggs on the larval food plants, cowslip (*Primula veris*), and primrose (*P. vulgaris*). Cowslip is much more commonly used, although there are a few colonies that breed entirely on primrose. K. Porter studied one of these, in Bernwood Forest, Oxford; egg-laying occurred in discrete areas near the male territories and females showed a very strong preference for laying on the largest leaves of the largest primrose plants available. These tended to be fairly well exposed plants growing along ditch edges and in rough herbage; females largely ignored very exposed, small-leaved primroses in mown, open rides, and also small but large-leaved

plants in deep shade. In addition, they ignored all apparently ideal plants growing in rides that ran from north to south, perhaps because of restricted sunshine on these rides.

Such truly woodland colonies of this butterfly are rather unusual in Britain, although not on the continent; more breed here in scrubby areas on chalk, where cowslips are almost invariably used, even if primroses are also common. Again, they very rarely lay on small plants growing in open short turf, and larvae from the few eggs in this situation soon die because the plants wither before the end of the feeding period [M. Oates]. Instead, nearly all eggs are laid on large flowering cowslips, especially those that are slightly shaded, but not swamped, by taller grass in scrubby areas, or on plants growing in warm spots under shrubs. The round, translucent eggs are laid in small batches of from one to ten, but usually two to four, on the undersides of leaves, and are very conspicuous. Small areas with very few *Primula* can support a population. Although colonies are always discrete and small, tending to remain in the same place, the exact areas used for breeding may shift by small distances from year to year, subject to the availability of suitable plants. This is also true of woodland colonies which move to recently cleared areas.

The range of the Duke of Burgundy once extended to Scotland, where there are three old records. These colonies became extinct in the mid nineteenth century (Thomson, 1980). It is still locally common in the limestone country north of Morecambe Bay and in north Yorkshire, and until recently was frequent in many of the woods of Rockingham Forest on the chalky clays near Peterborough. It has now disappeared from most (but not all) of these. Colonies are commonest in wooded districts of the southern chalk, but are always extremely localized and there is evidence of decline in recent years; for example, M. Oates reports twenty recent extinctions but no new colonies appearing in other areas. This butterfly seems to have poor powers of dispersal, and it is likely that lack of suitable habitat near existing colonies is to blame for its decline: some woodland colonies have been completely shaded out, while others, in more open localities, have been eliminated by overgrazing. It is encouraging

that the largest known colony in Britain breeds
on a local Naturalists' Trust reserve.

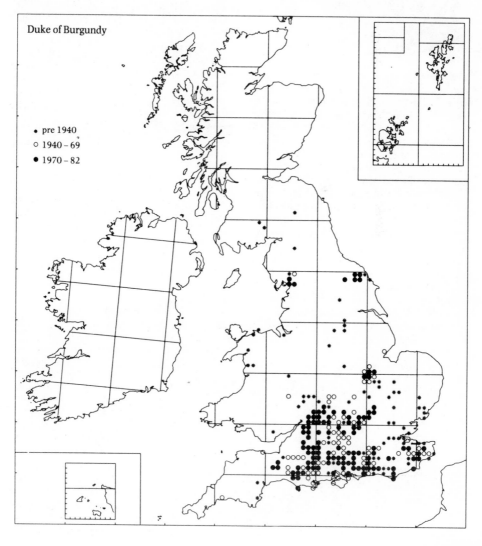

Duke of Burgundy

• pre 1940
○ 1940 – 69
● 1970 – 82

WHITE ADMIRAL

Ladoga camilla

The white admiral is very strictly a woodland butterfly, flying in late June and July in many woods in southern England which contain its food plant, honeysuckle. The eggs are laid on honeysuckle in shady rides or under light canopy, often quite distant from the sunlit areas where the males hold territories, for the white admiral is a powerful flier and ranges over large areas of woodland. The young larva causes characteristic feeding damage, which, in late summer, is very easy to find. It feeds from the leaf tip, but leaves the mid-rib of the leaf projecting and often uses this as a resting place and, perhaps, as a refuge from predators. Overwintering is in a hibernaculum formed from a honeysuckle leaf, usually the one on which it has been feeding, which is spun on to the stem. The larva feeds again in the spring, this time from the base of the leaves upwards, and pupates, suspended from a stem or leaf. The beautiful pupa is green with shining reflective patches, which make it very difficult to see in dappled sunlight.

In the early years of this century the white admiral was confined to a relatively small area in the extreme south, mainly in Hampshire and neighbouring counties. It then aroused considerable interest as it spread to occupy much of southern England, as far north as Lincolnshire, in the 1930s and 1940s. Since then there have been some losses, but it remains in many of the newly occupied woods. The spread in this century was, to some extent, a reoccupation of areas where it had occurred earlier in the nineteenth century. It seems quite possible that these expansions and retractions have happened several

times before. The expansion in the 1930s and 1940s has been documented by Pollard (1979) and shown to be related to weather. A population study in Monks Wood suggested that temperature in the late larval and pupal stages in June is important in determining annual population fluctuations. In warm seasons these vulnerable stages are of short duration, and mortality, believed to be mainly due to predation by birds, is low. In cold seasons development is slowed and losses are much greater. In the period of rapid expansion there was a series of years with above average June temperatures. It is likely that a population explosion during this period resulted in dispersal and colonization of new areas.

The Monks Wood study included the 1976 drought. A very large number of eggs were laid in the ideal sunny conditions. One rosette of four leaves carried seven larvae, with later-hatching individuals adopting side veins for their resting positions as the mid-ribs were occupied. Later the leaves dried up, larval mortality was extremely high, and in 1977 the number of adults was low.

In addition to the effects of weather, other factors may also have been involved in the spread of the white admiral. This species, unlike many other woodland butterflies, does not thrive in woods which are managed on a short coppice cycle, because there is insufficient time for the honeysuckle to reach a suitable stage of growth. The abandonment of coppicing must undoubtedly have substantially increased the carrying capacity of many woods for this butterfly, and so aided its spread.

Shaw (1981) has shown that the percentage of parasitized larvae is often high. It is possible that parasitism is sometimes important in the population dynamics of this species. In Pollard's study it was negligible. Counts are available from sites in the monitoring scheme, and these sites show a strong tendency for synchronous changes, which suggests that the influence of weather is dominant in determining annual fluctuations.

In the extreme south the future of the white admiral seems to be relatively secure. Little management of deciduous woodland is required, provided that there are some open sunlit areas.

However, in the New Forest, formerly a stronghold of this species, depletion of the food plant by pony grazing seems to have led to substantial reduction in numbers. Conifer plantations are often used, but perhaps only for a few years because of the rapid transition from open conditions to dense shade. In addition it is often the practice to remove honeysuckle, as a part of forestry management, because it may damage timber trees. Further north it is always possible that very cold early summer weather could cause extinction of populations.

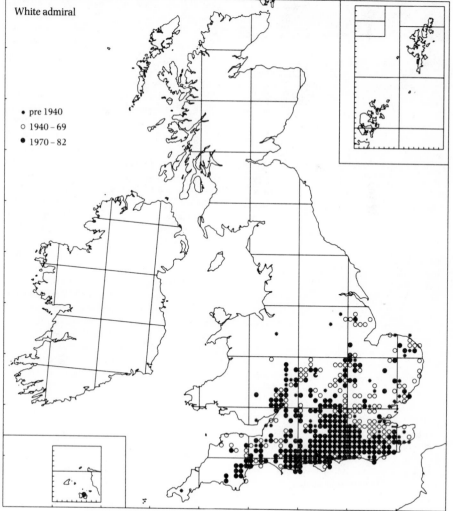

Flight period of the white admiral at five sites in England in 1979, and at one site in three different years.

White admiral

- • pre 1940
- ○ 1940 – 69
- ● 1970 – 82

PURPLE EMPEROR

Apatura iris

The sight of several male purple emperors soaring and 'battling' high above a tree-top is unforgettable. It is, nevertheless, remarkably easy to miss a colony, because most of the adult life is spent among the canopy of high forest. Males are more conspicuous than females because they periodically fly from their perching posts on 'master trees', and occasionally descend to puddles, excreta, or carrion. Consequently, our map for this butterfly is probably incomplete, especially as some recorders are reluctant to submit their records, believing it to be a much rarer species than is really the case. A few of our records may also be confused by the fact that inexperienced, but eager, entomologists sometimes mistake the glimpse of a high-flying white admiral for a purple emperor, but this does not seem to be a major cause of error.

The ecology of the purple emperor is still poorly understood, although much has been written about this butterfly. It occurs in heavily wooded districts and appears to breed at very low densities over large tracts of land. Consequently few, if any, of the woods in its stronghold (the west weald) probably support a colony on their own, but eggs can be found sparsely distributed on suitable sallow bushes in virtually every copse and spinney over wide areas [K. J. Willmott]. The adults congregate year after year on the crowns of particular prominent trees, or groups of trees, which may be a considerable distance away from the egg-laying sites; indeed, some Sussex woods famed for purple emperors contain little or no breeding habitat. Similarly, in Kent, Frohawk (1934) describes how the females regularly flew to the brow of a hill where they paired on a few oak trees, while their breeding ground was several hundred yards distant in the valley. This phenomenon of 'hill-topping' is well documented in America, where many species which breed at low densities over vast areas aggregate on hill-tops for mating (Shields, 1967).

Although the mated female purple emperors soon leave to lay their eggs, the males remain in residence, perching on particular twigs or even leaves, from which they sortie after females or seem to battle in rapid circling flights with competing males. There is much folklore about the 'master oak' which, in reality, can be a prominent tree of any species (Frohawk, 1934; Heslop *et al.*, 1964) [K. J. Willmott]. It is widely believed that the felling of a master oak results in the extinction of a colony. This is almost certainly untrue, but it may well be that the adults move to another nearby wood for mating.

Eggs are laid singly on the upper surface of sallow leaves. Goat or broad-leaved willow (sallow) (*Salix caprea*) is generally believed to be the only suitable species, but, in the weald at least, eggs are very often also laid on grey willow (sallow) (*Salix cinerea*) [H. G. Short] which is much harder to search. The situation rather than the species of plant seems to be the most important factor; a strong preference is shown for medium-sized to largish trees growing in sheltered, half-shaded situations, often round the edges of clearings and glades. Eggs are laid on the inner foliage of such plants. Most breeding occurs in young, fairly open woodland, regardless of whether the main crop is deciduous or coniferous. As the trees mature, breeding is largely restricted to sites with wide rides.

The larvae overwinter in the third instar on a silk pad, usually on the crotch of a sallow twig. In May, the full-grown larvae rest on similar silk pads on the uppersides of leaves, which they closely resemble. They wander and feed mainly at night, but nearly always return to the same pad to rest by day [R. Clarke]. The pupa is usually suspended from a leaf.

The purple emperor has declined in range during the present century. It has largely disappeared from the west and east of its former range, most notably from Kent. Unconfirmed reports strongly suggest that it still survives in Devon, and there is at least one colony in Nottinghamshire that we have not mapped. In the 1950s an egg was found on the first bush examined in a Suffolk wood where it had not been recorded for very many years [H. G. Short], again suggesting that small colonies are easily overlooked. The purple emperor still occurs widely in woods in the west weald of Surrey and Sussex, especially those on clays, but also in the wooded sandstone areas of south west Surrey and Hampshire. Colonies also occur in beech woods on the chalk of these counties. Elsewhere a few strong populations survive in Wiltshire, but it is ex-

tremely rare in Dorset, being confined to a few woods on the northern chalk. It is still seen regularly throughout the New Forest, but only in small numbers. Apart from the Nottinghamshire colony, its known northern limit is the east midlands forest belt which lies in the basin of clays between Oxford and Peterborough. It once occurred in all the woods in this region, but apparently became extinct in Cambridgeshire, Rockingham Forest, and other woods north of Salcey, Northamptonshire, about forty years ago. It still survives in Bernwood Forest to the south, and unconfirmed reports indicate that it breeds in several other woods in Buckinghamshire.

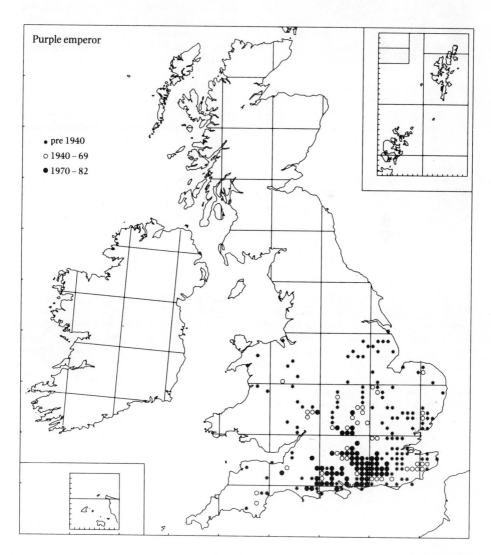

Purple emperor

• pre 1940
○ 1940 – 69
● 1970 – 82

RED ADMIRAL

Vanessa atalanta

The red admiral is one of our main migrants and so may be found in virtually any part of the country and in all types of countryside. It is often conspicuous among the butterflies on *Buddleia* flowers in gardens, and is certainly one of our most strikingly beautiful butterflies. It occasionally overwinters in this country, on tree trunks or sometimes in buildings or caves, but it seems likely that overwintered individuals make only a very small contribution to the numbers seen the following summer. The large fluctuations in numbers are almost certainly due to variations in the number of migrants which arrive each year.

The only important food plant is nettle, although related plants such as hop may occasionally be used. Females may lay on isolated plants or in large areas of nettle, always in sunny situations. The eggs are laid singly, usually on the terminal leaves, and each larva folds a leaf and feeds within it. The pupae are similarly formed within spun leaves. Compared with our other major migrant, the painted lady, which is more frequent in open situations, the red admiral is more often found in sunny spots in shady woodland. In the autumn the adults often feed on rotting fruit in addition to flowers, and in recent years they have been seen feeding on exudations from the trunks of elms dying of Dutch elm disease.

There is a general correlation between years of abundance of painted ladies and of red admirals, probably because good weather conditions for migration are likely to favour both species. However, the agreement is by no means invariable and it is possible for one to be abundant while the other is scarce (Williams, 1958). In recent years, and probably generally, the red admiral has been consistently more abundant than the painted lady. There is considerable evidence in this species for a return southward migration in the autumn (Williams, 1958; Baker, 1978) but, as with other butterflies, a full understanding of the nature and mechanism of migration has yet to be attained. Baker (1972a) has provided evidence, based on museum collections, that British individuals have a larger wing span than those caught in the Mediterranean region, as is also the case with the painted lady. This disparity in size may be because we have a large proportion of long-distance migrants, which may be expected to have large wings, but there is no direct evidence on this point. Baker considers it more likely that most of our immigrants have come only a short distance from the near continent.

There are probably, at most, two generations of the red admiral in this country, but the phenological data of the Butterfly Monitoring Scheme do not, as yet, reveal a clear picture. In any case, a relatively high proportion of records of this species occur in October, after the recording period of the monitoring scheme. It is clear that our common migrants still provide many unresolved problems for the next generation of lepidopterists.

Flight periods of the red admiral in different regions of Britain in 1980, and in one region in three different years.

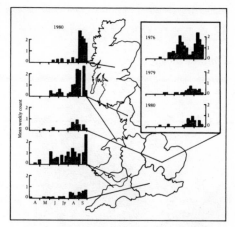

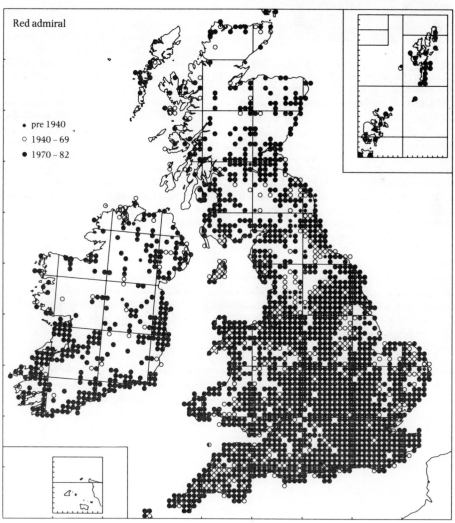

Red admiral

- • pre 1940
- ○ 1940 – 69
- ● 1970 – 82

PAINTED LADY

Cynthia cardui

As the painted lady is a true migrant, it may be found in passage in any part of the country. It overwinters in this country only very rarely or possibly not at all; captive adults are reported to die at temperatures of 5°C or less, unlike those of the red admiral which can survive at freezing point [M. J. Tucker]. In contrast to birds, which can be ringed individually, the study of butterfly migration is very difficult. No doubt because of this, there are relatively few facts and many conflicting views on the nature and range of migration in butterflies. Baker (1972a) considers that the movement of the painted lady is essentially short-range, with some individuals overwintering in the south and west of Britain and also some moving north from the near continent each year. A more usual view is that the painted lady

migrates over a much wider area, the spring individuals in Britain mostly coming from North Africa or southern Europe.

The occurrence of painted ladies in Britain has been recorded over many years (Williams, 1958). Large numbers occurred in 1892, 1903, 1928, 1943, 1945–9 and 1952. In 1980 two large migrations occurred, and these were probably better documented than any previously. A collection of observations has been published (Bretherton and Chalmers-Hunt, 1981), and the records of the Butterfly Monitoring Scheme also contribute to the overall picture (Pollard, 1982b). After a few early records in the west of Britain, a major migration occurred in early June, mainly in the west. It was particularly spectacular in the west of Wales and the western isles of Scotland. At the end of July a further large migration occurred, this time in the east. Individuals of this latter migration laid eggs, but the larvae must have perished with the onset of cold weather. There may have been a smaller third migration in the south-west in August. The arrival of migrants from the west in June coincided with westerly winds, which could have carried the butterflies round an anticyclone from Spain or North Africa. The migration from the east in July, with easterly winds, suggests an origin in central or eastern Europe. In 1982 the painted lady was again abundant, but there were no spectacular movements recorded. Their apparent continental or

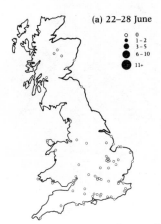

(a) 22–28 June

○ 0
● 1–2
● 3–5
● 6–10
● 11+

(b) 29 July–4 Aug

Counts of the painted lady at sites in the Butterfly Monitoring Scheme.

even trans-continental nature suggests that these migrations are more likely to be the result of dispersal of butterflies from 'outbreak' areas, with weather systems playing a major part in their direction and destination, than a directional flight comparable to that of birds like the swallow or swift. It is remarkable that there is some coincidence between years of abundance of the painted lady in Europe and America (Williams, 1958), but the reason for this is quite unknown. The distribution map shows that the large majority of sightings in the north of England, Scotland and Ireland are around the coasts.

The food plants of the painted lady include a range of species, such as mallows, nettles and even garden runner beans. However, thistles (*Cirsium* and *Carduus* species) are much the most usual larval food. The egg is laid singly on the upperside of a leaf, and the young larva moves to the underside where it feeds on the lower surface, protected by a silken web. As it grows larger, the larva constructs a conspicuous tent from leaves and silk. There are probably one or two generations a year in Britain, depending on the timing of the arrival of migrants. Because of its mobility, and because thistles are among the few weeds that commonly colonize improved grassland, the painted lady is perhaps better able to breed on modern intensively farmed pasture than is any other of our butterflies.

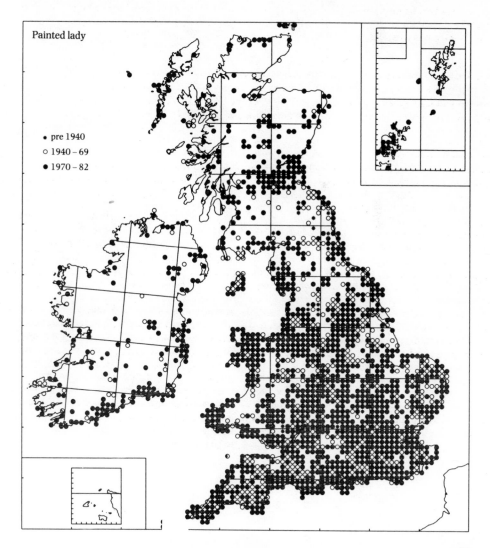

Painted lady

• pre 1940
○ 1940 – 69
● 1970 – 82

SMALL TORTOISESHELL

Aglais urticae

The small tortoiseshell is one of our most familiar butterflies and may be seen in a wide range of open situations. It is a frequent spring and autumn visitor to garden flowers, and often hibernates in houses or outbuildings.

The only food plants are the common nettle and the annual nettle. Adults of both sexes have a strong affinity for nettles, and even pair among them, deep down near the ground. The eggs are laid in large batches, usually 80–100 eggs but sometimes many more, under the terminal leaves. The females usually choose young plants, especially those growing in much more open places than those chosen by the peacock, comma and red admiral. The larvae spin a web over the food plant, in which they remain in aggregations until the final (fifth) instar. They may wander considerable distances to pupate, usually well away from the food plants.

Baker (1972b) has described the territorial behaviour of the adults. Like the peacock, they do not seem to form distinct permanent colonies in particular sites. Instead, they disperse through a region, using any suitable nettles they encounter for egg-laying, or flowers for feeding. Baker suggests that, on average, each butterfly probably moves a linear distance of 1–1.5 kilometres a day. Males bask and feed in the morning, and establish territories, or perhaps more strictly vantage points, in the early afternoon. These territories are near potential egg-laying sites, mainly along hedges or walls, but often also in more open situations. The males stay for one to two hours before moving on; they intercept passing butterflies in search of unmated females. In the autumn this behaviour is not shown, as the butterflies are solely concerned with feeding before hibernation.

The small tortoiseshell has two generations in the south, but only one in the north. Data from the Butterfly Monitoring Scheme suggest that in some years, in the south of Scotland, there are two generations, but in other years only one. It is possible that in southern Britain the first generation is partial, that is, some individuals develop quickly to produce midsummer adults and others more slowly to produce overwintering butterflies.

Small tortoiseshells fluctuate greatly in abundance, and provide a good illustration of the enormous potential for increase of many butterflies, given a period of good weather and adequate habitat. For example, in 1981 they were relatively scarce, but 1982 was a very good year, with numbers higher than previously recorded in the monitoring scheme and six times higher than 1981. In the longer term, there is no evidence that there has been any significant change in the overall status of this butterfly in Britain. It remains one of our most successful species, able to reach and breed on nettles almost anywhere in the country, including those growing in small isolated patches. Moreover, nettles are among the few butterfly food plants that have remained locally common in even the most intensively farmed areas; they may, indeed, have benefited from high applications of fertilizers. Nor, in these regions, is it likely that the small tortoiseshell has been harmed by the extensive spraying of insecticides; Moriarty (1969) found that adults caught in Cambridgeshire contained under one hundredth of the level of residues that was likely to be damaging.

Flight periods of the small tortoiseshell in Britain in 1979, and at one site in three different years. This species is often active in October, when we do not record.

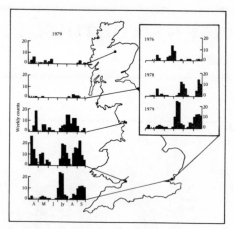

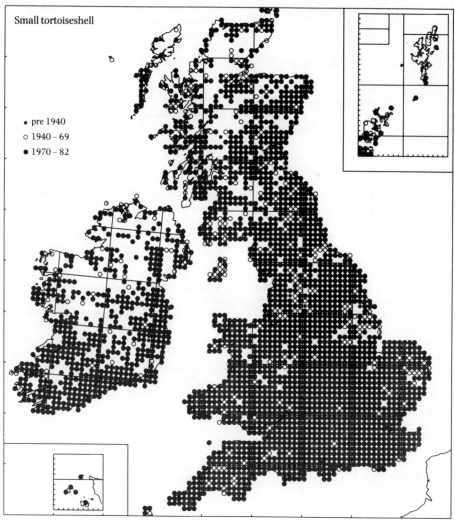

Small tortoiseshell

• pre 1940
○ 1940 – 69
● 1970 – 82

LARGE TORTOISESHELL

Nymphalis polychloros

Before its decline the large tortoiseshell was usually seen on the edges of woods, or along tree-lined lanes in wooded districts. It has one generation a year and overwinters as an adult. Most textbooks state that it hibernates soon after emergence from the pupa in midsummer, and that the adult is more often seen in the following spring. However, of the records submitted to the Biological Records Centre, summer sightings outnumber springtime ones by nearly two to one.

The eggs are laid in spring in large batches; Frohawk (1934) counted 212 eggs in one batch. They are usually placed round the tender terminal branches of large trees. Common elm or wych elm are mainly chosen, but sallows and willows are also used as, more rarely, are poplar, birch, aspen, whitethorn, cherry and pear (Frohawk, 1934). The young larvae spin a silk web over the young leaves, on which they feed. They remain together until full-grown, then they fall to the ground and crawl away to pupate.

The large tortoiseshell was last recorded in any abundance in 1948; there were then records from many countries. Nearly all recent reports are of single adults, and we suspect that these include a few misidentifications. The large tortoiseshell's conspicuous larvae are seldom recorded nowadays, although this was once one of the main ways in which the species was found. One or two sightings of an adult are still made in most years, but it is not certain whether these are residents, immigrants, escapes or deliberate releases. We have mapped all recent records that have been submitted, with these slight reservations about a few in the most recent date class.

The large tortoiseshell has been found widely through most of southern Britain, but its appearance has always been sporadic, even in strongholds such as the New Forest (Goater, 1974), Kent (Chalmers-Hunt, 1960–81), and East Anglia (Ford, 1945). The adults are highly mobile and do not seem to form discrete or permanent colonies, although they have established themselves and sometimes reached high numbers in certain woods or districts for perhaps a decade, only to disappear for a similar period. Chalmers-Hunt (1960–81) has meticulously collected records for Kent, and believes that it has been only a temporary resident even in that county.

Periods of local abundance have been roughly synchronized in different counties during the present century. At such times, occasional individuals are also recorded from many new localities. We illustrate this by records submitted to the Biological Records Centre. Our scheme began in 1967, and sightings from earlier years are pro-

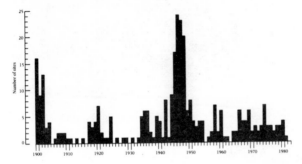

The number of different large tortoiseshell sites on the B.R.C. register in each year of this century.

94

gressively less fully represented. Thus the peaks at the turn of the century and in 1945–8 may represent periods of similar abundance for this butterfly. Anecdotal accounts suggest that similar fluctuations in distribution and abundance also occurred throughout the nineteenth century; the map should not, therefore, be interpreted as documentation of a progressive decline. Nevertheless, numbers since 1950 have been very low. During the past fifteen years there have been repeated (three separate) records in only three localities – in north Wales, Buckinghamshire, and Hampshire.

Some entomologists believe that the large tortoiseshell is merely a migrant to Britain which sometimes establishes itself in temporary colonies for a few years after arrival. Certainly it has been commonest during some of the great migrant years, notably in 1945–8 when extraordinary numbers of several migrants reached Britain. However, unlike some of these migrants, the large tortoiseshell survives our winters well, and the absence of records from Ireland also argues against major migratory movements. It seems likely that some breed here permanently, perhaps occasionally supplemented by immigrants. It is not known for certain, however, that any resident populations of large tortoiseshell survive. It is also feared that the chances of future re-establishments and resurgences may have been diminished by the recent loss of elms in southern Britain.

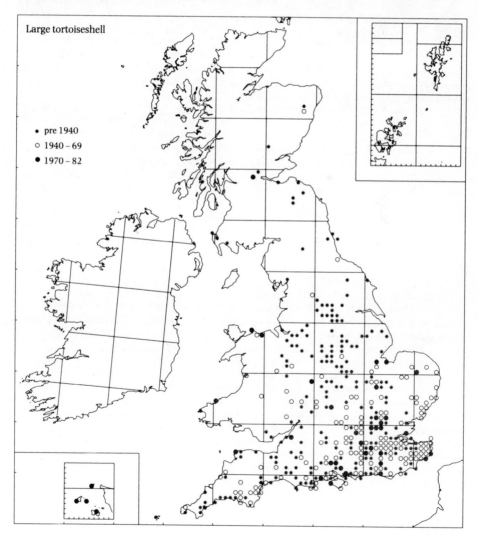

Large tortoiseshell

- pre 1940
- 1940 – 69
- 1970 – 82

PEACOCK

Inachis io

The peacock usually has just one generation a year; adults emerge in July and early August and are immediately conspicuous, for long periods are spent feeding at flowers prior to hibernation. There may be a small second emergence in September in southern England in very warm summers (e.g. Holmes, 1978). Peacocks are again seen on sunny days in March and April, when courting occurs, and when much time is spent in feeding and basking. Unlike the brimstone, which has a similar life cycle, there is a definite interval between the occurrence of spring and autumn individuals.

Although individual adults are often found feeding in gardens, and may be seen in most habitats, the peacock is predominantly a woodland butterfly. In spring, male 'territories' are established along wood edges, shelter belts and sometimes hedgerows, and females fly along these boundaries and are intercepted by the males for mating (Baker, 1972b). Egg-laying usually occurs during a restricted period in mid May, in more sheltered situations than those chosen by the small tortoiseshell and often on tall nettles. Baker (1972b), Davies (1978) and others consider that male butterflies show true territorial behaviour; that is, they defend areas against other males. Another possibility is that interactions between males are simply prolonged investigations, each individual trying to establish whether the other is a female. We recommend that the reader refer to the original papers. Each female lays her eggs

in large batches, and the larvae live gregariously and feed on nettle leaves. In summer, the newly emerged adult peacocks feed mostly in woodland rides, clearings and edges, as well as in gardens, and are particularly attracted by teasels, on which large numbers may gather. It is likely that most hibernation sites are also in woods, often in hollow trees.

The peacock is a highly mobile butterfly and does not form colonies with definable boundaries. Rather, individual adults fly between all the woody habitats in a district and egg batches are distributed between all suitable spots. Baker (1972b) found that in spring even the males often move on by half a kilometre or more each day, and only occupy a fixed spot for about four hours in the afternoon. Females probably cover much greater distances and, under some circumstances, the butterfly is truly migratory. Resident populations in southern Britain are probably reinforced in some years by immigrants from the continent, and a small reverse migration may also occur.

The conspicuous appearance, longevity, and behaviour of the peacock makes it one of our most comprehensively mapped butterflies. It is a common resident of all the southern half of Britain, except the Welsh uplands, but decreases farther north. In Scotland it is probably resident only in the west, and as far north as northern Argyll. Occasional breeding has been recorded in several other parts of Scotland; these records result from migrants which may cover large areas in some years, such as 1976, when they reached the Shetlands (Kinnear, 1976). However, the occurrence of migrants beyond Perthshire and the Firth of Forth is sporadic (Thomson, 1980).

There is no reason to believe that the peacock has declined in any part of Britain in recent years. Indeed, its present status and range in Scotland was attained only after an expansion which began in the mid 1930s and continued for the next twenty years. Before that it was established only in the south of Scotland, and was rare in most years. It has recently become much more abundant in the north of Ireland (ni Lamhna, 1980).

Flight periods of the peacock at five sites in England in 1980, and at one site in three different years.

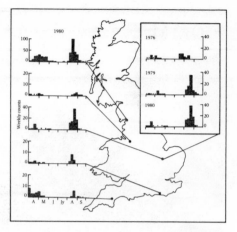

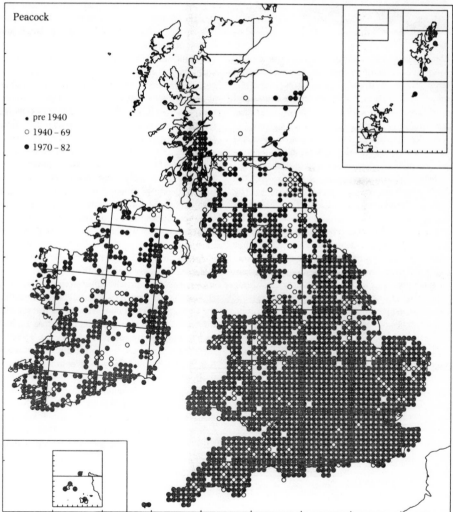

Peacock

• pre 1940
○ 1940 – 69
● 1970 – 82

COMMA

Polygonia c-album

The deeply and irregularly indented outline of its wings readily distinguishes the comma from all other British butterflies. The adults hibernate, sometimes in exposed positions on the trunks and branches of trees, and their 'broken' outline no doubt helps to conceal them.

Adults are nearly always found in wooded areas, where individual males establish 'territories' and perch for long periods on particular twigs or leaves at the intersection of rides, along the wood edges, in scrubby corners, or on nearby hedges. The greenish eggs are laid singly on the edges of the leaves of stinging nettle, hop, elm and perhaps some other related plants. Nettles are almost certainly the commonest food plant, but usually only those growing along hedges or wood edges are used. The distinctive larvae are white on the upper surface of the posterior two-thirds of the body and otherwise dark or reddish brown. The pupa, which is also very striking, with iridescent patches, is suspended from a plant leaf or stem.

The comma tends to emerge early from hibernation compared with other species that have overwintering adults, and individuals do not appear to live as long. There are two generations, but a proportion of individuals of the first generation are thought to go quickly into hibernation after they emerge in July. These hibernating individuals have more deeply indented wings and duller markings than those (known as the form *hutchinsoni*) which produce a second generation (Frohawk, 1934). The autumn emergence from this second generation is again of the overwintering form. The sequence of broods does not show up well in our monitoring scheme data, partly because numbers at any one site tend to be low and partly because the second generation extends into October, after the counts have finished.

The distribution of the comma has changed radically during the last century, but this does not show clearly in our map because a period of contraction was followed by one of expansion. The contraction appears to have been mainly in the second half of the nineteenth century. By the early years of this century, the comma had become restricted to the west of England and to Wales and was considered a great prize by collectors, more so indeed than the large tortoiseshell. In Sussex, for example, where the comma is now present in virtually every wood, there were only about six records of the species from 1830–1930 (Pratt, 1981). In the 1930s and subsequently, the comma has spread east, and to a lesser extent north, to occupy much of its earlier range. The details of these changes have still to be brought together, although the necessary information is almost certainly available in the entomological journals.

Although nettles seem to be the main food plant, it is possible that, like the white-letter hairstreak, the comma will suffer from the death of elms through Dutch elm disease. However, unlike the hairstreak, it will breed readily on the suckers that often regenerate after the main tree is dead and it will also breed on cut hedgerow elm. To date, there is no evidence that Dutch elm disease has been a harmful factor: the comma has been particularly abundant in the early 1980s and has even spread to new areas. In 1982 it was recorded for the first time at seven sites, in the Butterfly Monitoring Scheme, for which we have four or more years' continuous data. Four of these sites were at the northern edge of its present range.

Flight periods of the comma at five sites in England in 1980, and at one site in three different years. This species often flies in October, when we do not record.

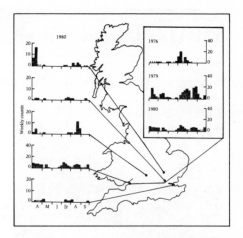

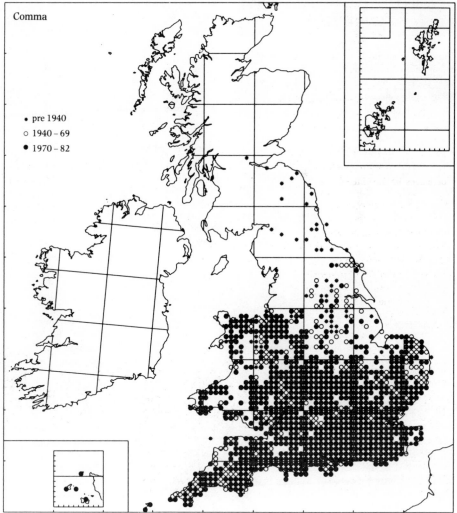

Comma

• pre 1940
○ 1940 – 69
◉ 1970 – 82

SMALL PEARL-BORDERED FRITILLARY

Boloria selene

This once common butterfly still has a wide distribution in Britain but is absent from Ireland. It emerges later than the similar pearl-bordered fritillary, although the two species usually coincide for a fortnight and often fly together in open woodland. When this occurs, the small pearl-bordered fritillary looks slightly the brighter and darker of the two, due partly to its freshness and partly to its deeper natural colouring. A safer way of distinguishing them is to examine the underwings: the small pearl-bordered fritillary has considerably more silver markings.

These fritillaries use the same larval food plants, mainly common dog-violet (*Viola riviniana*) in the south and marsh violet (*V. palustris*) in the north [K. J. Willmott]. Other species of *Viola* may be eaten. In many recent guides to butterflies *Viola canina* is given as the main food plant of this and other fritillaries. However, *V. canina* was the name often used in the nineteenth century for the common dog-violet (*V. riviniana*). The modern writers have copied the Latin name from the early lepidopterists and so introduced an error, for *V. canina* is now the heath dog-violet, a more local heathland species.

Despite a considerable overlap, the distributions of these closely related butterflies are not the same, either nationally or locally. Small pearl-bordered fritillaries are the commoner species in western, and especially northern, parts of Britain, whereas until recently, pearl-bordered fritillaries predominated in the south and east. On a local scale, the small pearl-bordered fritillary is more typical of wetter woods than those favoured by the pearl-bordered fritillary, and is very rarely found on really dry soils. The present species often occurs away from woodland in the west. Indeed, it is a characteristic butterfly of damp meadows, coastal cliffs, and moorland in the west from Cornwall to Scotland, although the woodland populations in these regions are generally larger.

Marking experiments indicate that the small pearl-bordered fritillary breeds in discrete, largely self-contained, colonies [J. A. Thomas], although Thomson (1980) suggests that the adults may be wide-ranging in some parts of Scotland. Large numbers can develop under certain habitat conditions, but most populations are fairly small in most years: an 'average' sized colony that we studied in Devon contained about seventy adults at the peak of the season, suggesting a total emergence of about 200 individuals.

The egg-laying females concentrate on locally warm areas within their site, where the ground cover is usually sparse and sunny [K. J. Willmott]. On finding a violet clump, the female becomes excited and either perches on it or flies a short distance away; she then bends her abdomen and lays an egg, so that it may or may not be under a violet leaf. The larva hides beneath leaf litter and is extremely hard to find (unlike that of the pearl-bordered fritillary, which basks openly). Feeding entails a brief exposure, ascending to bite the lobes off a violet leaf and then rapidly disappearing. Most larvae hibernate in the early fourth instar, in crevices among dead foliage, and resume feeding in the spring. In warm summers a few may not hibernate but form a small second brood.

The range of this butterfly has contracted in much the same way as that of the other 'common' woodland fritillaries. Some declines were reported at the end of the nineteenth century, and there has been a spate of local extinctions since the 1950s, particularly in the east. It is not known whether the contraction has been progressive or intermittent, with periods of partial recovery. Rapid as this decline has been, it has been generally overshadowed by that experienced by the pearl-bordered fritillary. The latter is now the rarer of the two species in many regions where it once predominated, for example in the weald of Surrey and Sussex, in Dorset, and in parts of Hampshire and the Isle of Wight. Away from the east of England the story is not entirely of losses. Thomson (1980) considers that the small pearl-bordered fritillary is commoner than formerly throughout Scotland.

A few large isolated colonies of the small pearl-bordered fritillary still survive in eastern and central England in open sunny woods and, especially, in the first five to six years of conifer plantations. The declines may be related to changes in the structure and management of most woodlands, as suggested for the pearl-bordered fritillary. It may have been adversely affected by drainage and other agricultural improvement of pasture, and probably by the decline of swaling (scrub burning) in the west, a practice which results in open rough grazings supporting a flush of violets. Nevertheless, this fritillary is still a fairly common insect in the west of its range.

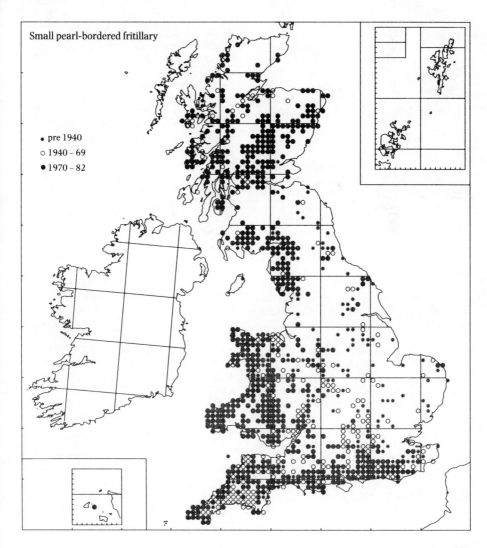

Small pearl-bordered fritillary

- pre 1940
○ 1940 – 69
● 1970 – 82

PEARL-BORDERED FRITILLARY

Boloria euphrosyne

This is the earliest of our fritillaries to appear, flying in May and June. Its main haunt is open woodland. The food plants are violets, and a number of species are used. In southern Britain common dog-violet (*Viola riviniana*) is the most important food plant, while further north marsh violet (*V. palustris*) is more commonly used.

The eggs may be laid on violets, but also on other plants and debris nearby. Often, two eggs are laid together. Young violets are preferred, especially if they are growing in sunny open situations in a wood, for example in depressions surrounded by bare ground. In Surrey and Sussex, where the species is now extremely local, it is still easy to find ten to twelve eggs per plant in these situations in certain woods; the best places to search are in freshly cleared blocks of old woodland and along the southern banks and ditches of broad, east–west running rides [K. J. Willmott]. In south-west England, breeding also occurs outside the strict boundaries of woods, along sheltered sunny hedgerows and along disused railway lines [M. S. Warren].

The spiny black larvae feed intermittently on violet leaves and, between feeds, leave the plants to bask openly on dead leaves. They often return to the same resting place repeatedly, and are quite easy to find in sunny weather. The larvae hibernate among leaf litter early in the fourth instar. They resume feeding in March or April, and pupate among low vegetation, attached to the under surface of a leaf. The butterfly normally has one generation a year in this country.

Like all our woodland fritillaries, the pearl-bordered has undergone a drastic contraction of range over the past 100 years. It was almost ubiquitous in English and Welsh woods in the middle of the nineteenth century, but the Victoria

County Histories and other local lists refer to a decline as early as the end of the century. This decline began in the north-east of England (where it was always more local) and in the east midlands. Despite this, Frohawk (1934), writing from Kent, could still describe this fritillary as being 'one of the commonest of our woodland butterflies . . . occurs in almost all the larger woods and forests throughout England and Wales'. Today, this is true only of parts of south-west England and south Wales, following a second major phase of extinctions in the 1950s and 1960s. During this period the species was lost from much of the south-east and East Anglia, making its disappearance from eastern England and south-east Scotland almost complete. This decline is still continuing: the vast populations that abounded in the young plantations of the New Forest during the 1960s are now greatly diminished, and the species has recently disappeared from most woods in Dorset. In Ireland it occurs only in the Burren, where it was discovered in hazel scrub as recently as 1922 (Baynes, 1964) and is still locally common.

A major factor in the contraction of the distribution of this fritillary has probably been the decline of coppice management of deciduous woodland, possibly exacerbated since the 1950s by the disappearance of the main herbivore of the ground flora – the rabbit – following myxomatosis. Old entomologists would agree with Frohawk (1934) that it preferred clearings 'where the undergrowth has been cut down for two or three years and the ground is carpeted with wild flowers such as the wild hyacinth, bugle, violet and primrose'. Unfortunately, most of our surviving deciduous woods now receive little or no forestry management. It is no coincidence that some of the only known populations now surviving in Kent (where it was generally abundant in woods only thirty years ago; Scott, 1950) breed in the Blean Woods complex, where commercial coppicing has been maintained (see Heath fritillary, page 114).

Young conifer plantations may provide good conditions for the pearl-bordered fritillary, but only for a very short period. After seven to ten years they are usually too shaded, although, before this, large populations may develop. Such large populations still exist in plantations in the west weald of Surrey and Sussex [K. J. Willmott] and in Bernwood Forest, on the Buckinghamshire/Oxfordshire border (Peachey, 1980), again suggesting that the virtual disappearance of this

butterfly elsewhere in these regions is due to local changes within woods rather than outside factors such as the weather or pollution. The major forestry planting operations of the 1950s to 1970s are now largely complete, and the cycle of cutting of conifers is too long, and the area occupied by the plantations is usually too large, to maintain the required patchwork of open areas.

While these changes in woodlands may explain most of the decline of this species, it is nevertheless surprising that the disappearance has been quite so complete in the east. It may be that management is less important in the naturally more open conditions of woodlands on impoverished soils in the west.

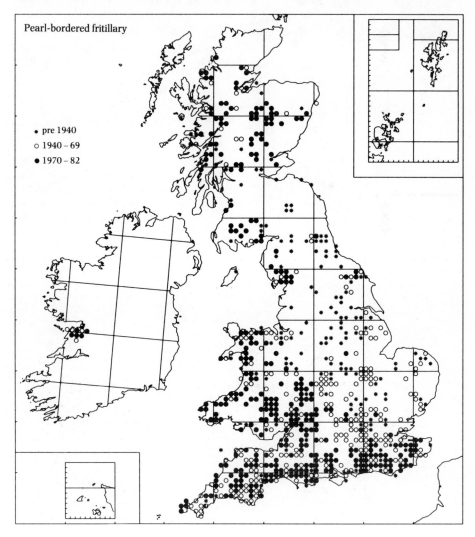

Pearl-bordered fritillary

* pre 1940
o 1940 – 69
● 1970 – 82

HIGH BROWN FRITILLARY

Argynnis adippe

During the last thirty years this large and attractive woodland fritillary has experienced one of the most dramatic declines recorded for a British butterfly. Although it was generally less widespread than the silver-washed fritillary, it nevertheless occurred in most of the larger woods of Wales and England in the nineteenth and the first half of the twentieth century, extending as far north as the Lake District (South, 1906; Frohawk, 1934). Thomson (1980) considers that the few Scottish records are very doubtful, probably mistakes for the dark green fritillary. The two species are very similar and there is a possibility of errors in their distribution maps. It is absent from Ireland.

The high brown fritillary is now a rare British butterfly, although it is still common in most woods throughout central and southern Europe. The British decline has occurred equally at all latitudes, but has been much more severe in the eastern half of the country. Nearly all the surviving colonies are in the west, and some of the largest are on the southern fringe of the Lake District, near its northern limit. Scattered populations also survive in Wales, and there is at least one large colony in the Wyre Forest. Further south it is perhaps slightly more widespread in Devon than the map suggests, and is still locally common in the extensive woodlands that fringe the southern edge of Dartmoor.

This butterfly's status falls sharply only slightly further east. Local extinctions are still occurring at a rapid rate, and it is clear, where detailed information is available, that our map gives an over-optimistic impression of its status in 1983.

It was once considered to be commoner than the dark green fritillary in Dorset (Dale, 1886), but is almost certainly now on the verge of extinction there. It is also very rare in Wiltshire, where it was still locally common in the 1940s and 1950s (de Worms, 1962), and it has perhaps disappeared from all the squares shown around Oxford, where it was locally common until the early 1950s (Peachey, 1980). In Warwickshire two specimens were reported in 1976 (but none since), yet it was 'not uncommon' in larger woods in the nineteenth century (Smith and Brown, 1979).

The picture is even bleaker in the eastern third of England, where it was apparently the commonest large fritillary until the early 1950s in Sussex (Pratt, 1981), parts of Hertfordshire, Buckinghamshire and Middlesex (Peachey, 1980), north Norfolk (in quite open scrub-grown grassland and heaths [D. A. Ratcliffe], and Essex (Ford, 1945). It was also 'generally common' in parts of Kent (Scott, 1950). A dramatic decline started in the early 1950s, and it is probably now extinct from all these counties and also from Cambridgeshire and Lincolnshire, apart from one known colony in east Sussex.

This decline has a similar pattern to those of other woodland fritillaries, although much more severe. No satisfactory explanation has been advanced, perhaps because very little is known about this butterfly's ecological requirements. The adults fly in mid June and July; our marking experiments suggest that they may cover fairly large areas of several hectares, but nevertheless form discrete self-contained colonies. The eggs are laid singly near the larval food plant, violets. It is likely that several violet species are used, but there is little positive information. The only violets present in the breeding areas of one large Devonshire colony we studied are common dog-violet (*V. riviniana*) and pale dog-violet (*V. lactaea*). That site consists of a well-grazed scrubby thirty-hectare hillside which is regularly burnt and is surrounded by extensive woodland. Fifty-five eggs were seen to be laid [J. A. Thomas]; the female always flew into the base of an isolated gorse bush, and crawled around probing twigs and leaf litter. The only egg that was actually found was deeply hidden on a dead bracken frond. The butterfly overwinters as an egg, and the solitary larvae feed by day on the spring flush of violet leaves.

Other surviving colonies in the Lake District and Wyre Forest also occur mainly in areas of open scrub, rough grass, and coppice among extensive woodland. In grassland, eggs are laid near violets shaded by tall grasses.

The high brown fritillary flourished in large coppiced woods, and there is little doubt that modern shady plantations are unsuitable. It is interesting that the dramatic decline of this butterfly started in the early 1950s in most regions, and it is possible that the loss of rabbits was also a factor, as we have suggested for the pearl-bordered fritillary. Rabbits have a considerable impact on the ground vegetation of woodland, and their disappearance at this time may have hastened the shading out of violets.

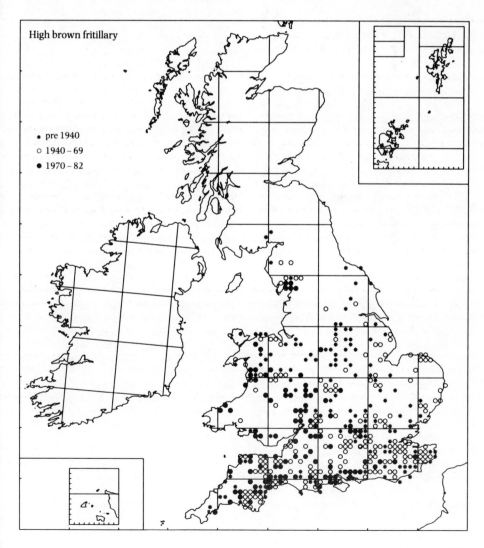

High brown fritillary

- pre 1940
- 1940 – 69
- 1970 – 82

DARK GREEN FRITILLARY

Argynnis aglaja

This is the most widely distributed of our three large fritillaries. It occurs as far north as the Orkneys, and on many other islands. Although a local species everywhere, the dark green fritillary is now the commonest of the large fritillaries in most counties except for parts of Devon, Somerset, Wales and Ireland. This is not to say that it, too, has not declined severely in many areas in recent years; rather that losses of the silver-washed and, especially, high brown fritillaries have been even more dramatic.

The dark green fritillary varies in appearance in different parts of its range. Irish specimens tend to be of a redder brown (Ford, 1945), and in Orkney they are much smaller and darker, so much so that some females appear to be almost black (Thomson, 1980). A separate subspecies, *scotica*, has been described from parts of Scotland. *Scotica* is more magnificent than the typical form, *aglaja*; it is usually larger, more darkly marked, and possesses greener underwings with more prominent silver markings. These beautiful butterflies predominate in most, but not all, of its localities in the Western Isles and in parts of north-west Scotland. There is, however, much local variation between island races, and populations may even differ in separate parts of the same island (Heslop-Harrison, 1946).

The fact that many local races have evolved and co-exist in nearby areas, and that a permanent population is restricted to a small island such as Lundy, suggests that this butterfly is not quite as mobile as is popularly believed. The adults are fast and powerful fliers, but marking experiments suggest that most individuals remain in a rather limited area throughout their lives [A. C. Morton]. However, they may wander from their breeding sites to feed, for example, on thistles in nearby woodland rides.

Breeding sites are usually distributed patchily within any locality and occupy only a small proportion of the land. The commonest areas used are rough broken ground or fairly open unimproved grassland, such as occurs along sea cliffs and dunes, downs, heaths and moors. Extensive woods which contain large areas of grass, scrub, and broad rides may also support small colonies, but this butterfly is not typical of the freshly cut coppices that are so favoured by the other violet-feeding fritillaries.

The dark green fritillary lays its eggs singly in July and August on herbs and debris near clumps of large violets in open grassland or, as Frohawk (1934) noted, deep under shrubs in scrubbier areas. The young larva eats its eggshell and then enters hibernation. It emerges in March to feed on the violet leaves until June. The solitary larva is very mobile and generally inconspicuous. It hides beneath patches of violets, emerges in sunshine to bite off the lobes of the leaves, and then disappears again, leaving highly characteristic leaf damage. Colonies occur on a wide range of soils and evidently use different violet species on different sites. In open calcareous grassland, large patches of hairy violet (*Viola hirta*) are the commonest food plant, but the early dog-violet (*V. reichenbachiana*) is also eaten. Thomson (1980) and K. J. Willmott state that marsh violet (*V. palustris*) is the main food in Scotland.

The best breeding sites of the dark green fritillary known to us are unimproved grassland, five to fifteen centimetres tall, which is lightly or spasmodically grazed or suppressed by sea spray. Populations tend to be small, but large numbers occasionally develop, for example, in the first years after intensive grazing of pasture is abandoned. There were many local increases in the late 1950s, following myxomatosis. More recently, one monitored population has prospered on a five-hectare 'island' of unimproved grassland in a region of intensive agriculture, over a period when other dark green fritillary colonies declined. Unfortunately, on many sites, both violets and the dark green fritillary are shaded out or greatly reduced fairly soon after the abandonment of grazing, as rank grassland and scrub develop. There is, however, at least one inland site where ungrazed grassland (on poor soil) has continued to support a large population [M. G. Morris].

These changes in the relative suitability of individual sites seem insignificant in comparison to the destruction of habitat that has occurred in most former localities in England. This has been caused by widespread improvement of grassland for agriculture by ploughing, seeding, herbicides and fertilizers. Together with the food plants of many other butterflies, violets disappear when old pasture is improved. Remaining populations

occur mainly on steep slopes, where cultivation is difficult. These areas still support small colonies of the dark green fritillary in most southern counties, with a few populations in the larger woodland complexes. These surviving colonies seem fairly safe, as do many that breed along the British and Irish coastlines, where farming is rarely intensive. Dark green fritillaries are also still widely distributed inland in poorer agricultural regions, especially in the south-west of England, Wales, Scotland and Ireland. However, many – probably most – of these populations will be destroyed if the improvement of marginal farmland continues.

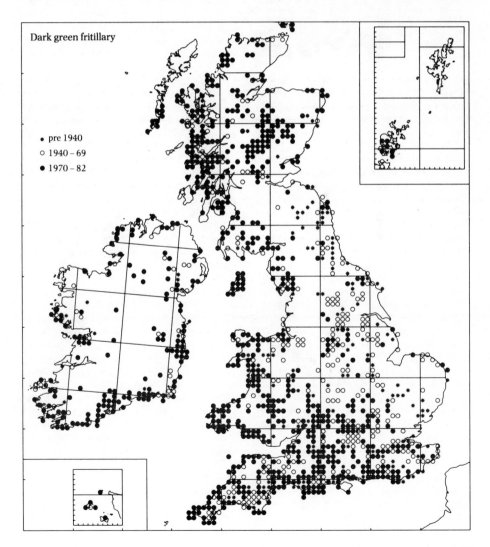

Dark green fritillary

* pre 1940
o 1940 – 69
● 1970 – 82

SILVER-WASHED FRITILLARY

Argynnis paphia

Until the middle of this century the silver-washed fritillary was a common butterfly in most of the larger woods of Ireland, Wales and the southern half of England, and often extended into small copses and, in the west, along hedgebanks. Now, like the other woodland fritillaries, it is a declining species.

Up to about 15 per cent of females in the New Forest may be a beautiful green form, *valezina*; this form is most prevalent when the butterfly is abundant (Ford, 1945; Bone and Hardy, 1958). Similar ratios of *valezina* have been regularly recorded in a few other southern localities, or in particular years of local abundance, for example in several woods in Dorset in 1976. However, it is very unusual to find *valezina* in most populations in most years, especially in the west.

Local declines of silver-washed fritillary colonies were already being described during the first half of this century, although in some areas there were also years of increase and abundance, notably 1941 and 1942 (e.g. Marcon, 1980). Local extinctions became frequent in the 1950s and serious during the next two decades. Surviving populations have still reached high numbers in occasional years such as 1976, probably because of exceptionally favourable weather, but the overall trend has been of a severe decline for about thirty years, except in the west. Our map under-emphasizes these losses, for many colonies have disappeared since 1971 and recent records often refer to single sightings of this fairly mobile butterfly, particularly in 1976. The high brown, pearl-bordered and small pearl-bordered fritillaries have declined even more rapidly in central

England, and the silver-washed fritillary has usually been the last of this quartet to be lost from a wood. At present, this butterfly is probably extinct in Yorkshire, Lincolnshire, Cambridgeshire, Northamptonshire and Norfolk, and is reduced to a few small colonies in Kent, Essex, Oxfordshire and Warwickshire. It is still quite well distributed in the west weald of Surrey and Sussex, but, although some very large populations survive, most are diminishing and are already small (e.g. Pratt, 1981). The same is true of Hampshire, including the New Forest where the species was once extremely abundant (Goater, 1974). In Dorset the 'common' woodland fritillaries are at an earlier stage of decline: the high brown is virtually extinct, both species of pearl-bordered fritillary are distinctly local, but the silver-washed fritillary still occurs in most woods, although rarely in abundance and often sightings are of single individuals.

The other historical strongholds of this fritillary are in south-west England, Wales and Ireland. Populations appear to have been stable in these regions, and in mid Wales there has even been some expansion of range in the 1970s. The tawny adults are still a common sight in summer along lanes and hedgebanks in Devon and Cornwall; indeed, many recent records for these counties were obtained simply by driving slowly along the minor roads.

Adult silver-washed fritillaries emerge in early July, with little variation in timing throughout the British Isles. Marking experiments suggest that the adults form more or less discrete colonies, which breed over fairly large areas in particular woods but are also apt to wander into neighbouring woods and along lanes [J. A. Thomas]. Frohawk (1934) made detailed observations of egg-laying adults and of larvae. The female flies low over the ground until she finds an abundance of violets, then flies one to two metres up on to a tree where a few eggs are inserted, singly, into chinks in the bark. She then flies off to repeat the process. Similar observations have been made by K. J. Willmott, who also reports that the north moss-covered side of the trunk is invariably chosen, and that females lay their eggs in shadier areas than the other fritillaries (although heavy shade is always avoided). Up to fifty eggs per trunk may still be found on trees growing in diffuse light in recently thinned, quite closely-planted woodland blocks in the west weald of Surrey and Sussex. In Cornwall, females often lay among moss and twigs along hedgebanks [M. S. Warren]. The egg hatches after about a fortnight, then the larva immediately hibernates deep in a fissure. In spring it descends to feed by day on the tender young shoots and leaves, especially the leaf lobes, leaving the characteristic fritillary damage. The older larvae are very active and wander long distances between periods of basking in the sun.

Apart from these observations, no comprehensive study has been made of the ecology or habitat of this or the other violet-feeding fritillaries. It is not possible, therefore, to describe the exact causes of decline. However, as violets are suppressed by shade, it is likely that the almost universal abandonment of coppice management in our remaining deciduous woods has been the major factor. Preference for slightly shadier conditions than other fritillaries would also explain why this butterfly survived rather longer in many woods. Unfortunately, the prospects for the silver-washed fritillary's long-term survival in central and eastern England now seem to be very poor.

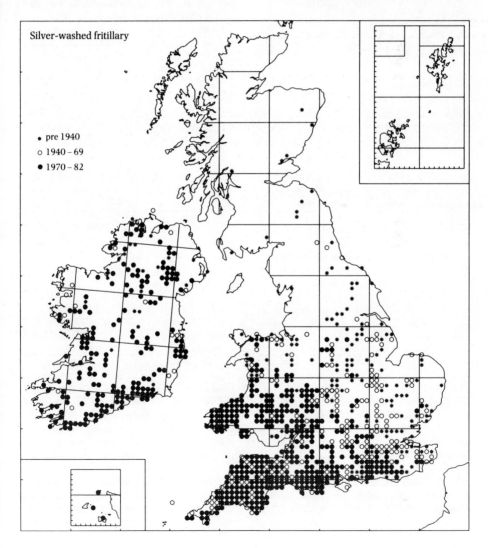

Silver-washed fritillary

• pre 1940
○ 1940 – 69
● 1970 – 82

MARSH FRITILLARY

Eurodryas aurinia

This beautiful fritillary was once locally distributed over most of the British Isles, but has now disappeared from many counties. The decline has been particularly severe since the 1940s and 1950s. Our map under-emphasizes this change because many ancient records are too imprecise to be plotted, while several 'post-1969' spots represent either a single colony which is now extinct or a recent reintroduction. Moreover, adults often stray during unusually warm weather or from areas of local abundance (Porter, 1981); we believe that several records made in 1975–6 do not represent established colonies.

The marsh fritillary is apparently extinct in the eastern half of its former British range, apart from the very few colonies that are being conserved on nature reserves. Probably the most eastern surviving unprotected colonies are on army ranges on the Surrey/Hampshire border. Another isolated colony exists on an Oxfordshire reserve. Two or three others occur further east in Sussex, but these are reintroductions (one from the early 1960s) to the county which was considered by Pratt (1981) to have been a British stronghold of this species in the early nineteenth century. We have not mapped known introductions.

Today the marsh fritillary survives in Dorset, Worcestershire and Cumbria, and there are still several populations in Wiltshire and Hampshire. Many colonies have also disappeared in southwest England. In Wales the species is still widely, but locally, distributed. Populations have apparently been stable in west Scotland (Thomson, 1980). This butterfly's distribution is almost certainly under-recorded in Ireland, but there is

no doubt that a severe decline is occurring there too (ni Lamhna, 1980). Irish and Scottish specimens have particularly vivid markings, and have been described as separate subspecies. However, this has been widely criticized because the marsh fritillary is extremely variable both throughout its range and on any one site in different years, depending on its abundance. Ford and Ford (1930) made a classic study of variation in one colony over a fifty-five-year period.

Declines are also reported throughout Europe. Indeed, the position of the marsh fritillary is now considered by the Council of Europe to be 'vulnerable' over the continent as a whole (Heath, 1981). Colonies breed on discrete sites in most years, where the adults fly in late May and June. Females each lay a batch of up to 500 eggs on the underside of a leaf of the devil's-bit scabious, the larval food plant. Large prominent plants are normally chosen (Porter, 1981). The young larvae spin a web on which they bask communally, forming a conspicuous black mass in which the temperature is maintained at about 30°C, even in weak sunshine (Porter, 1982). A denser hibernation web is spun just after the third moult. Larvae re-emerge in March and remain gregarious, moving from scabious to scabious, until their final, solitary, sixth instar.

A colony of the marsh fritillary can be supported on a small area of suitable habitat. Spectacular outbreaks of larvae have been recorded. An extreme case occurred in Fermanagh in the nineteenth century, causing questions to be asked in the House of Commons after villagers had to barricade their homes with peat bricks to keep out swarming larvae (Porter, 1981). A wide range of plants may be eaten during these outbreaks, but there is much starvation. Larval numbers may also be reduced by one of two specific parasites: *Apanteles melitaearum* in Scotland and Cumbria, and *A. bignellii* in the south. These wasps sometimes kill a high proportion of the larvae on a site, but by so doing may, paradoxically, reduce the colony's chances of local extinction by mass starvation, because excessive numbers are prevented from building up (Porter, 1981). Apart from population crashes caused by starvation, Porter (in press) attributed most annual fluctuations in numbers to the indirect effect of the weather. Warm conditions generally lead to more eggs being laid and fewer deaths among larvae from parasites and predators.

Devil's-bit scabious is a perennial that can be locally abundant both in boggy meadows and in calcareous grassland. Colonies of the marsh fritillary are unusual in the latter, probably because, on dry soils, the plant rarely produces the large prominent leaves that are essential for the larvae. Devil's-bit scabious grows more luxuriantly in boggy fields and moorland, which is where most marsh fritillary colonies are found. The host plant may grow in abundance in heavily grazed meadows, but the leaves are usually too small for the butterfly. On the other hand, egg-laying females

also avoid shaded plants in an abandoned sward. Similarly, colonies sometimes breed in new woodland plantations and along open rides, but rarely survive after the trees grow up. Some management of sites is clearly needed to maintain habitats and so conserve populations.

Unfortunately, suitable habitat is becoming increasingly rare. By far the greatest cause of loss has been the agricultural improvement of grassland by drainage, herbicides, fertilizers or re-seeding. Boggy meadows have suffered especially. Such improvement eliminates devil's-bit scabious and with it the butterfly. The long-term future of this local species is bleak outside the few nature reserves in which it breeds.

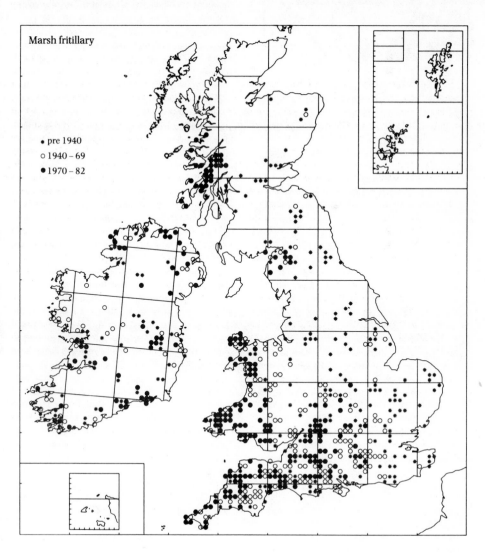

Marsh fritillary

• pre 1940
○ 1940 – 69
● 1970 – 82

GLANVILLE FRITILLARY

Melitaea cinxia

The Glanville fritillary is common and widespread in central Europe and occurs in most of the Channel Isles, where it breeds on rough ground, especially round the coast. Our records for these islands are probably incomplete.

The northern limit of this butterfly's range just extends into southern England. It was originally known from a few colonies on the Kent and Sussex coast, but these became extinct in 1857 to 1859 for reasons unknown. There are also eighteenth-century records of inland colonies; no specimen survives to confirm these, and Ford (1945) considers that they were probably erroneous, perhaps misidentifications of the heath fritillary. We have included these on the map but recognize that there is considerable doubt about them. Recent records from south-east Dorset appear to be escapes, or stray individuals blown across from the Isle of Wight. Several sightings have also been made in south Hampshire in the present century. Some may be stray adults that have crossed the Solent but most are undoubtedly escapes or introductions by entomologists who regularly visit the island and return with larvae for captive rearing. This frequently leads to release or escape of surplus stock. One introduction by Watson (1969) flourished on an abandoned railway line in the New Forest for seventeen years until the site was destroyed. At present we know of no colony on the mainland.

The Glanville fritillary was discovered on the Isle of Wight by Edward Newman in 1824. Numbers have since fluctuated between abundance and great rarity. A survey was made in 1979 of all former localities and other likely sites

(Thomas and Simcox, 1982). This confirmed Fearnehough's (1972) conclusion that colonies are now confined to the southern coastline of the island.

The boundaries of all breeding sites were identified in 1979 and counts were made of the larval nests. Larvae were found in twenty-eight one-kilometre squares. Marking experiments suggested that the adult butterflies can fly several kilometres from the main breeding centres, and occasional batches of eggs are deposited along the narrow strips of plantain that fringe the top edges of otherwise bare cliffs. As the coastal footpath follows this edge, it is easy to obtain an exaggerated impression of the butterfly's abundance. In fact, there were probably only twelve distinct colonies of the Glanville fritillary in 1979, with breeding in another six areas dependent on migrants from the major colonies. Large populations were found only on the undercliffs and chines (small valleys) to the west of its range, and the total population for the island in 1979 was about 4,350 'nests'.

Adults fly in June and early July. Eggs are laid in batches of 200 or more on the larval food plant, ribwort plantain (*Plantago lanceolata*), not sea plantain (*P. maritima*) as is given in most textbooks, but which was not found on any site in 1979. Larvae do, however, sometimes eat buck's-horn plantain (*P. coronopus*) when they exhaust their main food plant. The larvae live gregariously, spinning a conspicuous dense hibernation nest in late summer. In March and April, feeding webs, some supporting several hundreds of black bristly larvae with characteristic russet heads, are equally striking, spread out over the plantain.

The distribution of the Glanville fritillary in the Isle of Wight in 1979, plotted by one-kilometre squares.

The larvae eat enormous quantities of plantain, and the supply of this seems to be a major factor in determining the size and distribution of colonies. An abundant growth of plantain often develops on bare ground (especially on sandy exposures), created through landslips along the highly unstable cliffs, undercliffs and chines. A warm microclimate may also be needed, for eggs are rarely laid on the north-facing sides of chines. Females lay mainly in areas of fairly sparse vegetation where high densities of small young plantains have developed. However, suitable patches of ground soon become overgrown, and colonies depend on the regular creation of fresh habitat through slippage, even though this causes many

nests to be lost to the sea in certain years. Large populations once occurred on flatter, more stable land, such as around Binnell Bay, but these sites became overgrown after myxomatosis had killed the rabbits, and their present small colonies probably depend on regular influxes of migrants. For the same reason the inland chalk ridge of the Isle of Wight, which once supported a few colonies, is now also unsuitable [M. G. Morris]. Although the crumbling undercliffs will probably ensure the survival of the Glanville fritillary, some of the larger chines are threatened by holiday development. Fortunately, two-thirds of all larval nests (in 1979) occurred on sites owned by the National Trust.

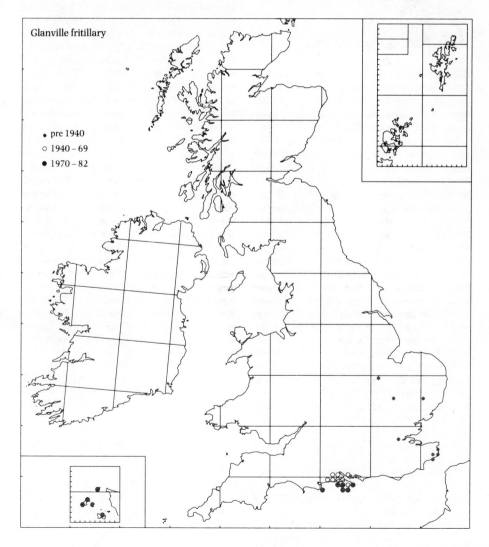

Glanville fritillary

• pre 1940
○ 1940 – 69
● 1970 – 82

HEATH FRITILLARY

Mellicta athalia

Despite its name, the heath fritillary is nearly always found in open woodland. It is a common butterfly of mainland Europe, but has always been extremely local in Britain and is now a great rarity. It has a curiously bisected distribution, occurring only in woods on poor soils in south-west England (Cornwall, Devon and Somerset) and the south-east (Kent, Sussex and Essex) in the present century, although there are a few ancient records from intermediate counties. Its range has been contracting steadily for at least seventy years: before 1910 it was known from fifty-one different ten-kilometre squares, but only from twenty-six in 1910–60, sixteen in 1960–70, and just six in 1980. Moreover, the real decline was undoubtedly severer than this, for recording has been much more comprehensive in recent years and particularly during the last decade when intensive surveys were made. The most recent of these surveys was made in 1980 (Warren *et al.*, in press) and showed that the butterfly was reduced to just five woods in south-west England, which supported six colonies, although two have since become extinct. It was slightly commoner in Kent, but was confined to only three of the woodland blocks in the Blean Woods complex near Canterbury. These contained twenty-five colonies, but twenty-one were small, with fewer than 200 adults on the day of peak numbers, and several colonies may merely have been offshoots of larger populations not viable in isolation. In all, the heath fritillary is probably the rarest and certainly the most endangered of Britain's resident butterflies.

The adult heath fritillary emerges in late May or early June in south-west England and can often be found well into July. The season is about two weeks later in Kent. Males are especially conspicuous, for they fly, rather weakly, around clearings and along rides whenever it is sunny, searching for mates. Eggs are laid in large batches, but the larvae soon split into groups of ten to twenty. They may be found basking on dead leaves in March and April. Although a conspicuous butterfly, it is fairly easy to overlook a colony, for most consist of low numbers and occupy only small pockets of their woods.

Breeding sites exist in sunny, open situations where the woodland is at an early stage of succession. The habitat differs somewhat in the two regions. In the east, larvae feed on common cow-wheat, and most breeding occurs in the diminishing areas where traditional coppicing has continued, or in nearby clearings that still contain young plantations. Cow-wheat is also used on one site in Cornwall, but the usual food plant in the south-west is ribwort plantain. Several other plants may be used in the south-west, including germander speedwell, which is especially important for the young larvae [M. S. Warren]. In 1980 the best sites in this region were former hay fields, adjoining old woods that had been afforested with young conifers and left to grow. One strong colony in the 1970s was on abandoned strawberry fields, and another on a disused railway through a wood.

Most breeding sites are small, discrete and ephemeral, and colonies wax and wane in them with great rapidity; it is not unusual for a population of thousands to build up in the two to three years after a clearance, only to be completely shaded out five years later. Colonies therefore move around their woods as suitable habitat comes and goes – 'following the woodman' as entomologists used to say. As a result, the butterfly has only survived in woods and complexes where new habitat has been generated continuously. The clearings must be near to existing breeding sites, for the adults have poor powers of dispersal. Unfortunately, few woods are managed in this gradual and piecemeal way nowadays, and coppicing especially is becoming uneconomic, threatening the butterfly's existence in Kent. Modern large high-forest plantations may provide ideal conditions for the first few years, but the entire wood may then be unsuitable for forty years or more while the crop matures. There is no known case of this weak-flying butterfly managing to recolonize an isolated wood naturally once it has been lost, although several reintroductions have been made to old localities which once again looked suitable. Some of these reintroductions have been highly successful, notably at Abbots Wood, Sussex (1935–55), and at Hadleigh Wood (1925) and Hockley (*c*. 1935) in Essex. Luckens (1980) has documented these and writes: 'At Hadleigh, especially, it took very well, and survived for over forty years. In its heyday it was so abundant that the larvae could sometimes be found on various cultivated plants,

such as *Antirrhinum*, in the gardens of houses near the wood … The colony became increasingly restricted, however, until its presumed demise in the 1970s.' No introduced colony was known to survive in 1983, and these have not been included in the recent date class on the maps. However, several reintroductions are planned for the next few years. These form part of an overall conservation programme for this species which, since 1980, has seen active protection given to nearly all known colonies. Most sites are now being managed to encourage large numbers of this butterfly, and early results are promising. It is probable that, at the eleventh hour, these actions have saved the heath fritillary from extinction in Britain.

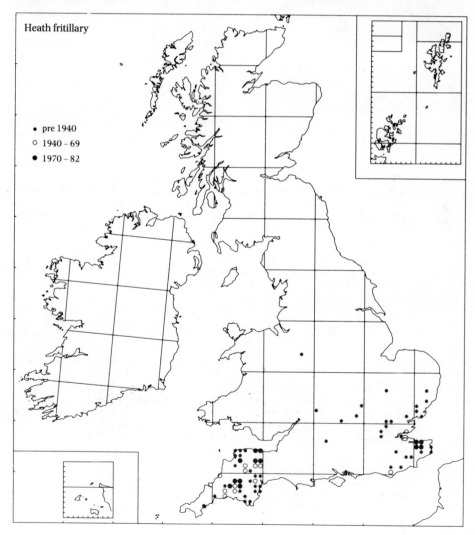

Heath fritillary

- • pre 1940
- ○ 1940 – 69
- ● 1970 – 82

SPECKLED WOOD

Pararge aegeria

This attractive woodland butterfly can be seen at almost any time between April and October. In the south of England and in Ireland it flies in woods, lanes, along hedgerows, and on scrubby cliff-tops, but elsewhere it is more strictly a species of shady woodlands. In fact, the speckled wood probably flies in shadier conditions than does any other British butterfly. The dark brown speckled wood (*P. aegeria tircis*) is the north and east European subspecies and is predominant in the British Isles. Two other British subspecies have been recognized, in the Isles of Scilly and in western Scotland (Dennis, 1977; Thomson, 1980). *P. aegeria aegeria*, which resembles the wall brown in colour, is the southern and western European subspecies.

The eggs are laid on a range of grasses. Most authors give cock's-foot (*Dactylis glomeratus*) and common couch (*Agropyron repens*) as preferred species, but the relative importance of the many species used is not known. The female is much more selective *where* she lays: shaded grasses, in woodland, hedgerows, or other scrub, are always chosen.

Joy is quoted by South (1906) as the originator of the generally held view that the speckled wood can overwinter either as a larva or a pupa and that, because of this, there are two distinct, although overlapping, spring flight periods, the first in April–May and the second in May–June. In a warm season each of these may give rise to further generations later in the year; in a cold season there may be only one further generation. This account is not fully accepted by lepidopterists

and there is a view (quoted by Thomson, 1980) that there is only one spring brood, followed by two others in simple succession. The data of Goddard (1962) and that of the Butterfly Monitoring Scheme support the first view, showing two overlapping flight periods which are too close together for the second to be the progeny of the first. Wiklund *et al.* (1983) has shown that in Sweden the larvae may have a summer aestivation (resting phase). If this also occurs in this country, as is likely, it further complicates the possible life cycle patterns.

The males perch in sunspots in woodland, which they appear to defend by skirmishing with other males which enter them. In one study these skirmishes were always won by the original occupant (Davies, 1978), perhaps because of his familiarity with the territory. The outcome of encounters between males was not found to be so predictable in a later study [T. G. Shreeve], in which perching behaviour was shown, in part, to be related to the need to warm up at low temperatures.

This butterfly has undergone major distributional changes, which have been documented by Downes (1948) in Scotland and by Chalmers-Hunt and Owen (1952) and Stroyan (1949) in south-east England. There was a period of retraction of range in the late nineteenth and early twentieth century, and after this the distribution in England and Scotland became disjunct and the speckled wood became absent or rare in much of southern England. In the 1940s and 1950s there has been a period of expansion, but parts of the north-east of England have not been reoccupied. The speckled wood remains scarce in most of East Anglia, apart from the newly afforested Brecklands. Some of this expansion may have been in response to the generally shadier conditions that have developed in modern woods. Certainly it is one of the few butterflies which may be common along rides in middle-aged conifer plantations or neglected coppices.

In recent years, the speckled wood declined sharply in abundance after the 1976 drought, but recovered very quickly, no doubt because it has more than one generation a year.

Flight periods of the speckled wood at five sites in England in 1980, and at one site in three different years. This species often flies in October, when we do not record.

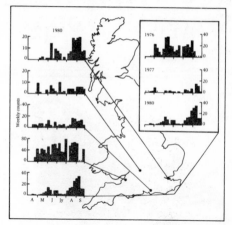

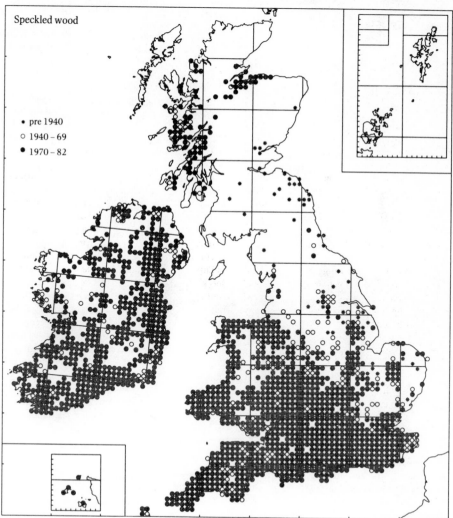

Speckled wood

- • pre 1940
- ○ 1940 – 69
- ● 1970 – 82

WALL

Lasiommata megera

The wall butterfly may frequently be seen perching on a patch of bare ground, or in a similar prominent spot. It is often common in a range of situations such as hedgerows, roadsides, woodland edges and, especially, open unimproved grassland. The first generation is usually very much smaller than the second, as shown by the data of the Butterfly Monitoring Scheme. In warm seasons there may be a small third generation in October.

The males both perch and patrol; types of behaviour with the same aim, the location of mates (Dennis, 1982c). Patrolling males fly actively in search of females; perching males sit and wait. Perching occurs more often early and late in the day, which suggests that, as with the speckled wood, it is related to a need to warm up by basking. Dennis (1982c) discusses other advantages and disadvantages of the two behaviour patterns in different circumstances.

On open grassland sites, the eggs are laid singly in warm sheltered depressions such as those provided by rock scree, hoofmarks, rabbit scrapes and the crumbling edges of paths. The eggs are sometimes placed on the exposed roots of grasses which protrude into the little sunspots [K. J. Willmott; M. S. Warren]. In open woodland and hedges, the eggs are more often laid on grasses which are sheltered by shrubs, or even on the shrubs themselves. The larvae feed on a range of grass species, especially tor-grass (*Brachypodium pinnatum*) and false brome (*B. sylvaticum*). Dennis (1983) has recently studied egg-laying by the wall butterfly in Cheshire; he mentions especially cock's-foot (*Dactylis glomerata*), wavy

hair-grass (*Deschampsia flexuosa*), *Agrostis* species and Yorkshire-fog (*Holcus lanatus*). He also observed that uniform areas of grass are not used and that small clusters of eggs may be found in recesses and overhangs of the type described earlier. As with other grass-feeding species, once details of behaviour and biology are known it becomes quite possible, and sometimes easy, to find appreciable numbers of eggs. Overwintering is usually in the larval stage, but according to Frohawk (1934) the wall may occasionally overwinter as a pupa.

There is a climatic limit to the range of the wall butterfly in Britain: it only penetrates to the south of Scotland although it is common along the Cumbrian coast. The northern limit has fluctuated considerably, with a major retraction in the late nineteenth century, particularly in the north-east of England and in eastern Scotland. In the last few decades it has recolonized many of these areas, as documented by Thomson (1980) and Dunn (1974). On a local scale, throughout its range, many of its former breeding areas have been destroyed by the intensification of agriculture, especially on chalk grassland where it can still reach high numbers if its habitat survives. In recent years the wall declined in numbers on monitored sites after the 1976 drought, but since then it has increased steadily, particularly in eastern England. The early appearance of the wall in eastern England in 1979, shown on our flight season map, is atypical and was not repeated in other years.

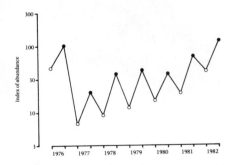

Changes in abundance of the wall, 1976–82, at sites in the Butterfly Monitoring Scheme. The consistent difference in size between the two generations is striking.

Flight periods of the wall at five sites in Britain in 1979, and at one site in three different years.

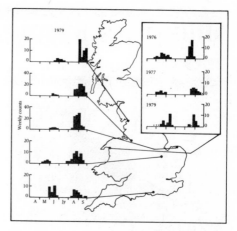

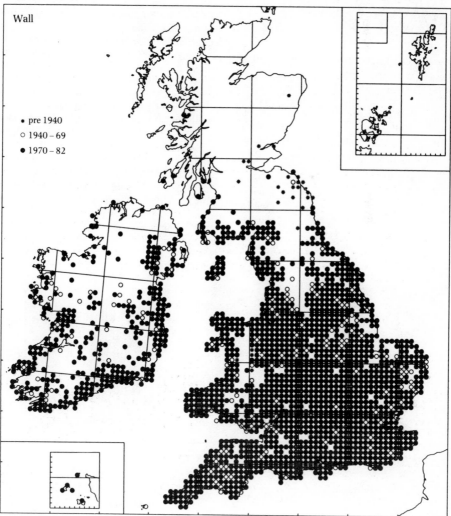

Wall

● pre 1940
○ 1940 – 69
● 1970 – 82

MOUNTAIN RINGLET

Erebia epiphron

The mountain ringlet is widely distributed at high altitudes on most mountain ranges of central and southern Europe, and is the only truly montane butterfly occurring in the British Isles. It was discovered in England near Ambleside in 1809, and the first Scottish specimen was taken in Perthshire thirty-five years later. It is now known from the central Lake District, from the Grampians, Inverness-shire south of Newtonmore, and from Ben Lomond. There are also references to colonies in north and south-west Scotland, but Thomson (1980) considers these to be doubtful. From Ireland there are three old nineteenth-century records, at Croagh Patrick and Nephin Beg in Co. Mayo, and Lough Gill in Co. Leitrim. These have not been substantiated in the present century, and in recent years their authenticity has been largely discounted (Redway, 1981).

Like other species of *Erebia*, the small mountain ringlet forms discrete, largely self-contained, colonies, most of which are isolated on their mountains from their nearest neighbour. The flight is rather weak and fluttering, typically just above the ground, and colonies usually occur in the same discrete areas year after year. There is much minor variation in the number of wing spots and in the extent of the fulvous bands within any population, and several subspecies have been described. Although specimens from Scotland tend to be larger than those in England [K. Porter], most taxonomists lump the British populations into one endemic subspecies, *mnemon*.

The only known food plant in the wild is mat grass (*Nardus stricta*), although larvae will accept other grasses in captivity. Females lay their large barrel-shaped eggs on the stems of mat grass in midsummer, and the butterfly overwinters as a larva in tussocks, which may be buried deep in snow for several months. Feeding resumes in late spring, and the flight period is from late June until the end of July, with considerable variation between years and at different altitudes.

The habitat of this butterfly is damp *Nardus* grassland, usually grazed by sheep or red deer. However, its distribution is very much more restricted than is that of mat grass swards, and it is quite unknown in the Pennines, Cheviots and southern uplands, where such grassland is extensive. Colonies in the Lake District occur locally down to 200 metres or less in good summers, but are mostly between 500 and 800 metres. In Scotland they have been found at sea-level, although most colonies occur between 350 and 1,000 metres and are commonest at 450–800 metres (Thomson, 1980).

Although this is one of our most localized butterflies, there is no evidence of any changes in distribution or abundance other than the normal annual fluctuations. Some colonies are very large – one studied by K. Porter contained 8,500–9,000 adults – and most in the Lake District are on National Trust land, where their future is reasonably safe. It is also well represented on Scottish nature reserves.

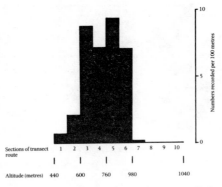

Numbers of mountain ringlets seen on a monitoring transect on Ben Lawers, Tayside, in 1977 to show the altitudes where maximum numbers occur [recorder, D. Batty].

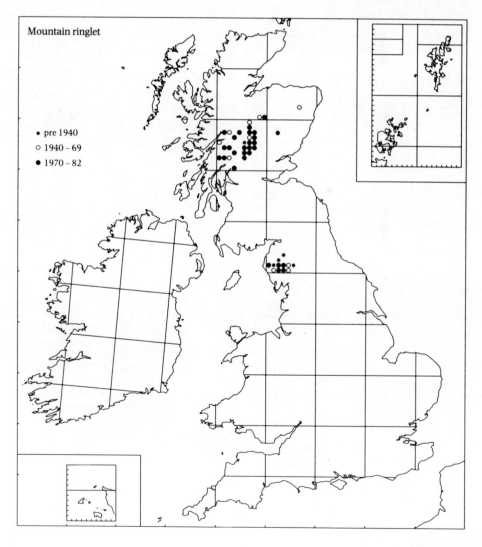

Mountain ringlet

- pre 1940
○ 1940 – 69
● 1970 – 82

SCOTCH ARGUS

Erebia aethiops

The Scotch argus is one of the most widely distributed of the many species of *Erebia* that occur in Europe, and is very much the commoner of our two British representatives. Unlike the mountain ringlet, our native populations do not belong to an endemic subspecies, although they differ slightly in appearance from European specimens. Within Britain, a distinctive dark race once occurred in Yorkshire, and populations in northeast Scotland have smaller, narrower and more angular wings, with narrower rust-coloured bands and fewer spots (Thomson, 1980).

In Scotland, this butterfly was first found in the second half of the eighteenth century on the Isle of Bute, and is now known to be well distributed in the Highlands, the Inner Hebrides, and in the southern uplands, except Berwickshire where it is extinct. In England it is now confined to two localities in Cumbria, although it was once abundant near Grassington, in west Yorkshire, from where it was last recorded in 1955 (Reid, 1955). The reason for its decline in this locality is not known; the habitat would appear to have changed little. It also occurred many years ago on the Durham coast and in Northumberland. It does not occur in Ireland.

The Scotch argus lives at lower altitudes than the small mountain ringlet, typically from sea-level to 500 metres in the mountains. Its usual habitat is moist *Molinia caerulea* (purple moor-

grass) grassland, especially where this occurs in warm valleys, is sheltered by wood edges or scattered scrubs, and where the grazing pressure is light enough to allow the grass to grow into tall dense tussocks. Enormous populations can develop in these situations, probably containing thousands or even tens of thousands of adults [R. L. H. Dennis]. Colonies also often occur in open *Molinia* grassland, sunny woodland and young forestry plantations. They are not found in shady woods.

The adult flight is stronger than that of the mountain ringlet. It flies mainly in full sunshine, although some activity is possible on warm, overcast days. Adults emerge in late July and August, occasionally surviving into September. Almost any available flowers are used as nectar sources. The males spend most of their lives perched just below the flower heads of *Molinia* tussocks, whence they sortie after any passing insect. Less frequently, they make patrolling flights; these are 'slow, scanning and weaving . . . generally below the grass-heads' [R. L. H. Dennis]. During these flights, they dip down into the grass to investigate any dark object, such as a dead leaf, that could be a female Scotch argus. The females fly less often and spend long periods resting, basking and feeding. When egg-laying, they crawl deep into the *Molinia* where they deposit their large eggs singly on the leaf blades. Plants growing in open situations seem to be preferred. In Cumbria, blue moor-grass (*Sesleria caerulea*) is the main food plant, as it may have been on other sites on limestone in northern England [R. L. H. Dennis]. The larvae feed by night on *Molinia*, or *Sesleria* leaves, and perhaps occasionally on other grasses such as *Poa*. During the day they rest deep in the clumps, where they also overwinter.

This butterfly seems to be surviving well over most of its British range, apart from the local extinctions that have occurred near its southern limit.

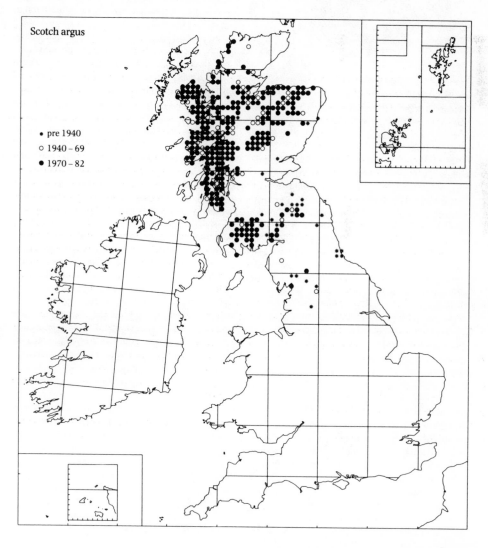

Scotch argus

- pre 1940
- 1940 – 69
- 1970 – 82

MARBLED WHITE

Melanargia galathea

The marbled white is one of the most abundant of all butterflies in central Europe. It is much more local in Britain but, nevertheless, our maps show that colonies are very well distributed in south-west and central England. It has not been reliably recorded from Ireland.

Marbled whites seem to occur in isolated populations (Paul, 1977; Morton, 1982). Towards the edge of its range, colonies often persist in particular fields, which may be quite small, for many years (Frohawk, 1934), although local shifts in distribution do occur (Blackie, 1951). It still flies in the same three fields on the North Downs near Dorking to which it was introduced in the late 1940s, and has only very recently spread at all into the many hectares of similar-looking grassland to the east and west along that scarp [K. J. Willmott].

The adult has a slow distinctive flight. Marking experiments indicate that a high proportion of those present on a site are visible (Paul, 1977; Morton, 1982). Some populations are obviously very large: one in Sussex was estimated to contain 1,069 adults at its peak (Paul, 1977). On the other hand, this butterfly is regularly seen only in ones and twos on many of its sites, and can clearly survive year after year at very low numbers. With a few exceptions, adult populations have remained remarkably stable on sites in the Butterfly Monitoring Scheme from 1976 to 1982.

Adults usually emerge in late June or early July and fly until mid August. The females have a curious method of egg-laying. They sit on tall vegetation with their wings open, pulsating the

abdomen until an egg appears at the tip. At this moment the female flies off, leaving the egg to drop to the ground. On hatching, the young larva immediately enters hibernation, hiding in a piece of dead grass (Frohawk, 1934). In spring, at first, it rests by day head down along a stem, but as it grows older it hides among the base of its grass clump, ascending to feed on the leaves at night (Tutt, 1905–14; Frohawk, 1934). Like most grass-feeding butterflies, it is not entirely clear which species are used in the wild. In Somerset, A. C. Morton found larvae feeding mainly on sheep's fescue (*Festuca ovina*), and Frohawk (1934) gives this grass as their favourite food. Frohawk also states that they eat other grasses, and most textbooks give Timothy (*Phleum pratense*) and cock's-foot (*Dactylis glomerata*). K. J. Willmott has often found wild larvae on tor-grass (*Brachypodium pinnatum*).

Most colonies occur on lightly cropped or ungrazed swards where the grass grows fairly tall. Populations can evidently be supported by quite small areas or strips of land, for example by road verges or along abandoned railways (Smith and Brown, 1979) and by broad rides in open parts of woods (Peachey, 1980). Similar high densities, and consequently much larger total numbers, breed on open unimproved downland, or in expanses of rough grass, such as along sea-cliffs.

The marbled white has a strong south-westerly element to its range. It is especially common on unimproved, mainly calcareous, grassland in Somerset, Dorset, Hampshire, Wiltshire and Gloucestershire, but is curiously scarce in south-east England. While it is well represented in the south-east on certain lengths of the South Downs, for example between Brighton and Eastbourne, it is virtually absent from long stretches of the North Downs. To the north, colonies are locally common in south Oxfordshire, but rare beyond this. It may be extinct in Cambridgeshire (the last sighting in Monks Wood was in 1976), and has declined severely on verges and wood edges in Warwickshire, where it was always extremely local, although this decline has been countered by its spread along recently abandoned railways and on waste heaps in that county (Smith and Brown, 1979). Our records indicate that a few colonies still survive in the Yorkshire Wolds, and reports suggest that it has increased in numbers there recently. Rafe and Jefferson (1983) provide details of its current status in Yorkshire and report that it is most abundant on south-facing slopes, as might be expected at the northern edge of its range.

As with most grassland butterflies, the number of marbled white colonies in Britain has clearly declined greatly in the present century – and especially since the last war – because of the ex-tensive destruction of natural grassland by ploughing, agricultural improvement, and other intensive forms of land use. This butterfly will undoubtedly decline further for the same reasons, but, in contrast to many butterflies, such as the adonis blue and the dingy skipper, the marbled white actually benefits from the relaxation of grazing on the few fragments of unimproved grassland that remain.

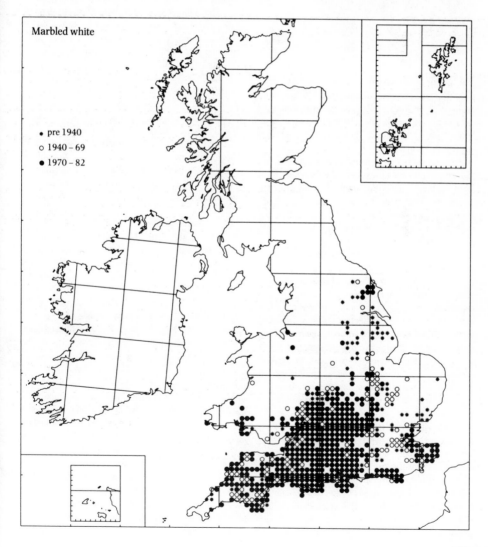

Marbled white

• pre 1940
○ 1940 – 69
● 1970 – 82

GRAYLING

Hipparchia semele

The grayling breeds on arid unimproved grassland throughout the British Isles. It has been recorded from many soil types, ranging from acid sandstones to chalk and limestone. Most sites have sparse vegetation, contain sheltered sunspots and all are extremely well drained.

Adult graylings are rather variable in size and markings, and as many as six subspecies have been listed from different parts of Britain in recent textbooks (Howarth, 1973; Dennis, 1977), although Higgins and Riley (1970) lump them all into the major west European subspecies *H. semele semele.*

Our marking experiments suggest that graylings form discrete colonies. One 'average' sized colony in Devon consisted of about fifty-five adults on the peak day of 1976, giving a total emergence of roughly 150 adults that year. These bred on about three hectares of south-facing shales. Other colonies have been recorded from much smaller areas, such as abandoned chalk and limestone quarries. Most seem to contain small numbers, although huge populations are regularly recorded from a few sites, such as the dry dune heaths of Tentsmuir Point in south-east Scotland.

Graylings have one generation a year. They emerge in early July with remarkable consistency throughout their range, except on Great Ormes Head where emergence is earlier (Dennis, 1972a). Their courtship behaviour has been recorded in a classic study by Tinbergen (1972) and colleagues. Graylings often settle on the ground or on low vegetation with the wings closed and tilted over to one side in a characteristic manner. It has been

suggested that this is to minimize the shadow and so aid concealment, but Findlay *et al.* (1983) consider that the main purpose is to regulate body temperature. The butterflies tend to present maximum wing area to the sun on cool days, and also early and late in the day when temperatures are low. The female lays her eggs singly, either directly on grass blades or on nearby debris. J. A. Thomas saw eighteen out of twenty-one laid placed on bristle bent (*Agrostis setacea*) on an acid site, and one laid on a sheep's-fescue (*Festuca ovina*) in calcareous grassland. K. J. Willmott has recorded eggs laid only on sheep's-fescue in chalk sites. On Lancashire sand dunes, Shaw (1977) found nineteen larvae feeding on marram grass (*Ammophila arenaria*) on the dry plateaux. The larvae can clearly feed on several different grasses, for none of the grasses occurs universally on the wide range of soils inhabited by the butterfly. The grayling hibernates as a young larva and resumes feeding in spring. It rests on the ground by day, ascending to eat at night. It pupates in early June by burrowing into the soil, where it excavates a small cell which it lines with silk.

In calcareous grassland this butterfly is particularly characteristic of abandoned quarries and sites that have skeletal, scree-like, soils. Some of these areas are very closely cropped, although it also breeds in taller sparse vegetation elsewhere. Colonies are particularly well distributed on sand dunes and cliffs along most of the Irish and British coastlines, including Lundy, the Isle of Man, and the Scottish Isles. It is a highly characteristic insect of dry southern heaths, where it may be found in most remaining areas, although a large proportion of its former sites have been destroyed by agricultural improvement (Moore, 1962). The steep calcareous downs on which it once bred have largely escaped such improvement, but the grayling was always more locally distributed on these and has been lost from most in recent years. Colonies were probably shaded out by the widespread growth of dense vegetation that followed myxomatosis; for example, at Porton Down, Wiltshire, M. G. Morris reports that it is still abundant, but only on areas grazed closely by rabbits. Elsewhere, the grayling seems to be holding its own well on its many scattered coastal

sites; it has become decidedly more restricted to
the coast in recent years.

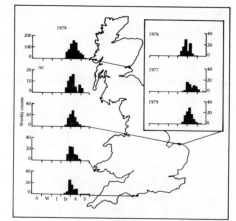

Flight period of the grayling at five sites in Britain and
Northern Ireland (a) in 1979, and at one site in three
different years. The synchrony of flight at far distant sites
is a feature shown by a number of other species.

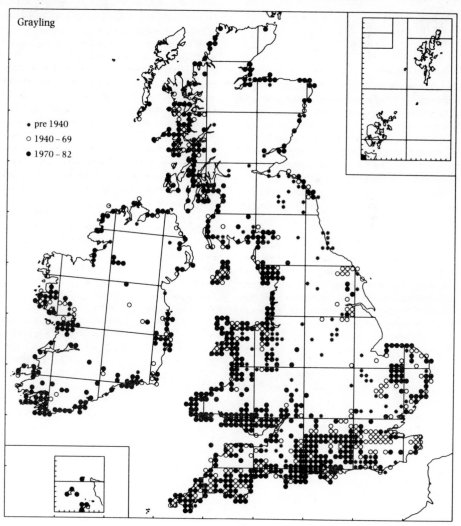

Grayling

- • pre 1940
- ○ 1940 – 69
- ● 1970 – 82

HEDGE BROWN

Pyronia tithonus

This butterfly, known also as the gatekeeper, is a common species of farmland in southern Britain. It flies in July and August along hedges, lanes, woodland edges and rides, and in scrub. Occasionally, it can be found in more open situations, such as among sand dunes and on downs, although even there it is almost invariably associated with scattered shrubs.

The eggs are laid singly in lightly shaded places, usually beneath shrubs. They may be deposited on grasses, which form the larval food plant, on the shrubs themselves, or even ejected over the ground vegetation in much the same way as those of the ringlet, meadow brown, and marbled white. A range of grasses is eaten by the larvae; there is little reliable information on any preferences except for K. Porter's observation that fine-bladed species such as fescues and bents are commonly used, and that of T. J. Bibby, who saw egg-laying on common bent (*Agrostis tenuis*) in Monks Wood. The larvae feed at night and hibernate when partly grown; there are two colour forms, green and brown, with the former normally more abundant. The sexes of the adults are very distinct in appearance: the males are considerably smaller and darker than the females. It is a sedentary species, forming local populations, although it colonized newly cleared rides in Monks Wood immediately after management.

There was some contraction of range in the north in the late nineteenth century. Thomson (1980) suspects that the old Scottish records were not established colonies, but vagrants or introduced individuals. It has almost certainly suffered from the loss of hedges and other intensification of agriculture in recent years. In spite of this, the hedge brown has spread back to parts of the Chilterns, east midlands and Yorkshire in the last decade. It is almost absent from London, and in this respect contrasts sharply with the closely related meadow brown. In Ireland it is restricted to the south-east, a fact which tends to confirm that its northern limit in England is a climatic one. Like the wall, it becomes increasingly coastal at its limits in Cumbria. It is often true that, as the limit of a species' range is approached, it tends to become markedly less abundant. However, the highest counts of the hedge brown in the Butterfly Monitoring Scheme are consistently at the scheme's most northerly site for this species, on the Lincolnshire coast.

Flight period of the hedge brown at five sites in Britain in 1980, and at one site in three different years.

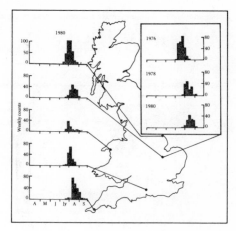

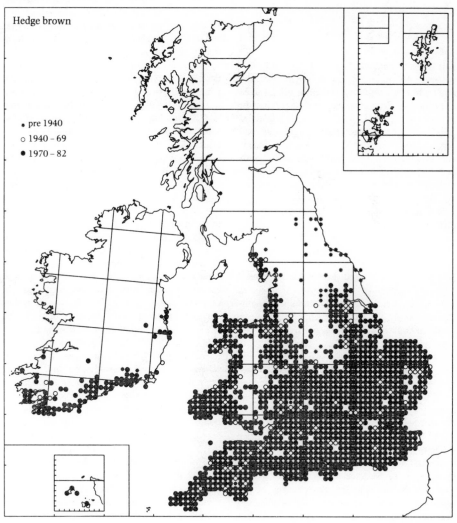

Hedge brown

- ● pre 1940
- ○ 1940 – 69
- ● 1970 – 82

MEADOW BROWN

Maniola jurtina

This species is probably the most abundant British butterfly. Although not as common as, say, the small white or small tortoiseshell in urban areas or in gardens, it is often extremely abundant in grasslands, on heaths and moors, in woodland rides and clearings, and along hedges and road verges throughout the British Isles. It is absent only in northern uplands and locally in the south in areas of highly intensive farming. Some of the highest densities are on potential building sites, awaiting development [P. M. Brakefield].

The meadow brown is well known to science through the classic studies by E. B. Ford and his colleagues on the variability in the number and arrangement of submarginal spots on the underside of the hindwing (reviews by Ford, 1975; Dowdeswell, 1981; and Brakefield, in press). There are regional differences in spot frequencies even, in some cases, where populations are contiguous, as in the famous boundary between southern English and Cornish spot types near the Devon–Cornwall border. Here there is, in some years, a change between the two types from one field to the next. The selective pressures responsible for the evolution of the spotting and for its variability are not well understood, but recently Brakefield (in press) has suggested that the spot pattern deflects the attention of bird predators from the body of the butterfly. He further suggests that differences in the behaviour of males and females make them vulnerable to different types of predator attack and so are responsible for the different spot patterns of the sexes. Once these processes are fully understood, a much fuller interpretation of the ecological

genetics of the species will be possible.

The variability of the meadow brown, not just in spotting but in many other respects, is considerable. Several subspecies have been described and these have been discussed by Thomson (1973). In Britain four subspecies have been recognized, but there is considerable variation within these and there are also transitional forms and seasonal variation. The subspecies *splendida*, in the north-west of Scotland, is particularly attractive. As the meadow brown does not usually fly far from its breeding areas (Pollard, 1981; Brakefield, 1982), the development of local variation is not surprising.

The sexes differ markedly and were originally described by Linnaeus as separate species: the female is larger and has bold orange markings on the upper forewing. The adults fly over a long period, from late June or early July onwards. On some sites, particularly on chalk downs in southern England, the flight period is so long that individuals are on the wing until well into October. Sometimes it has been suggested that there is more than one generation a year, but this does not seem to be the case. Cribb (1975) has found that there is great variability in the size of larvae in spring and this leads to a protracted emergence period. At chalk sites, and elsewhere, where the grass grows tall but not too densely, the meadow brown may occur in enormous numbers.

Eggs are laid singly and may be placed on a grass blade or on other vegetation, but frequently they are simply ejected into the base of grass-dominated vegetation. This suggests, but does not prove, that the particular species of grasses on which they feed is not very important. P. M. Brakefield gives smooth meadow grass (*Poa pratensis*) as a preferred food plant, and it seems likely that fine grasses such as *Poa* and *Agrostis* species are used rather than coarse grasses. The larvae overwinter within grass tussocks but will feed by day in mild weather. In the spring they become nocturnal, perhaps when they reach a size that is attractive to insectivorous birds, or perhaps because in winter the nights are too cold for activity. They can then be found by searching or sweeping with a net in the late evening in mild weather. The pupae, which vary greatly in colour according to their situation [P. M. Brakefield], are in grass cover from near soil level to among the blades. Although the meadow brown is still extremely common, there can be little doubt that it has been eliminated from many former sites because of the agricultural improvement of most farmland. In eastern England, however, in the period 1974–82, there has been a tenfold *increase* in its numbers on sites in the Butterfly Monitoring Scheme, which is encouraging, although these sites are mainly reserves or forestry plantations.

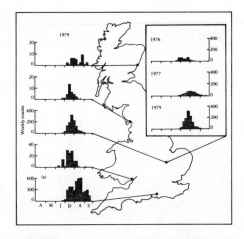

Flight period of the meadow brown at five sites in Britain in 1979, and at one site in three different years. Old Winchester Hill (a) is a chalk downland site where the flight period is very long.

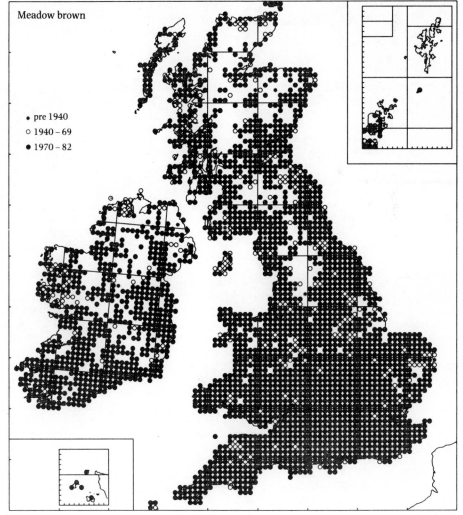

Meadow brown

• pre 1940
○ 1940 – 69
● 1970 – 82

SMALL HEATH

Coenonympha pamphilus

The small heath is such a familiar butterfly that it is often ignored by lepidopterists and much remains to be learnt about it. It occurs in un-improved grasslands, in situations as varied as wide woodland rides, open moorland, sand dunes, green lanes and road verges. It reaches its highest densities on coastal grassland sites and chalk downs; it is noticeable that on the latter it occurs almost exclusively in areas of short grass, as compared with the marbled white and meadow brown [M. G. Morris]. The eggs are laid singly on blades of grass, and a range of species is used. Most authors consider that finer grasses are used (e.g. Peachey, 1980), but as with some of the other grass-feeding species, the information available is scanty. *Poa* and *Festuca* species are usually quoted as the main food plants. Over-wintering is in the larval stage and there may be occasional feeding in mild spells of weather. The pupae are suspended from a plant stem.

The flight period and number of generations vary in different parts of the country. In the north of England and in Scotland there is usually just one generation a year, but in the south there may be two or three flight periods. The sequence of generations in the south is still uncertain, but that considered most likely is as follows (South, 1906). An early May–June emergence produces two types of larvae, slow developers and rapid developers. The slow developers overwinter as the late instar larvae and fly in May–June in the following year; the rapid developers produce adults in the same season – these adults fly in August and September and their progeny overwinter in early instars and produce further adults in July. Their offspring emerge in the next May–June. Lees (1962, 1965) has shown that there are genetic differences between individuals from the north and south of England as regards voltinism. Individuals from a southern population produced many more second generation butterflies than those from a northern population when reared under identical conditions. After some genera-tions in captivity there was selection for an in-creasing proportion of double-brooded butterflies. As these genetic differences between popula-tions suggest, the small heath is essentially a se-dentary butterfly. There is a limited amount of data from mark and recapture experiments which support this view (Pollard, 1977).

The small heath is widespread in Britain and does not appear to have changed its distribution significantly over the last century, although in many areas the number of sites for the species has probably declined considerably because of agricultural improvement. While it is rarely as abundant as the meadow brown, it is perhaps even more widespread, as it is more commonly found at high altitude. However, in Ireland it appears to be the less widespread of the two species.

Flight periods of the small heath at five sites in Britain in 1979, and at one site in three different years. The succession of generations is complex, except at some upland sites, where there is a single annual generation.

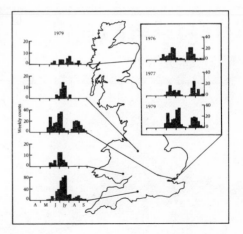

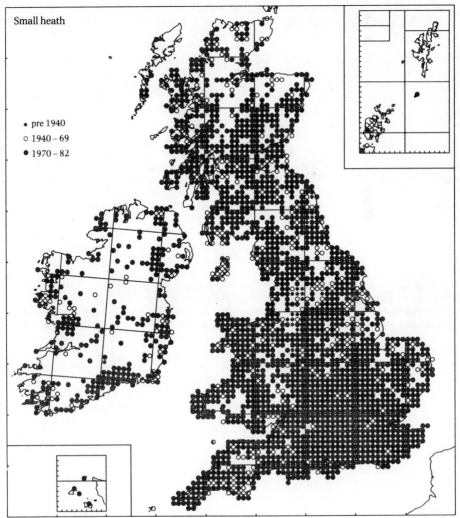

Small heath

- pre 1940
- ○ 1940 – 69
- ● 1970 – 82

LARGE HEATH

Coenonympha tullia

The large heath occurs, mainly in local colonies, in central Wales, northern England and southern Scotland, and is a local and uncommon, although widely distributed, butterfly in Ireland. It becomes much more frequent in the northern half of Scotland and breeds on many of the isles, including the Outer Hebrides and Orkney. It is almost certainly absent from the Shetlands, despite two references to its presence there in the nineteenth century (Thomson, 1980). Its world distribution includes much of central and northern Europe, Asia, and northern North America.

This is one of our most variable butterflies: two plates in Ford's (1945) *Butterflies* illustrate the range of markings found in Britain. Different names have been given to many of the local forms, but the situation has been clarified by Ford (1945), Turner (1963), and especially Dennis (1977). In Orkney, the Western Isles, and the Scottish highlands, the adults tend to be very pale and have few and insignificant spots. These have been named subspecies *scotica*. Progressing south through the central lowlands to Cumbria in the west and Yorkshire and Lincolnshire in the east, the wings become darker brown and there are more spots on both sides. This is subspecies *poly-dama*. The cline continues into Lancashire, Shropshire and, before extinction, to Cheshire and Staffordshire. Here, the adults are very dark, have large distinct eyespots, and belong to subspecies *davus*. The cline is not, however, always a gradual or simple one from north to south: in the south-west of the large heath's range, in Wales, the form *polydama* again predominates, and in Ireland and in some of the Western Isles there is a mix-

ture within populations (Dennis, 1977). Moreover, the markings of different individuals vary greatly within any colony, and the predominant type may also vary from one year to the next. Thus the division of this butterfly into three subspecies in Britain is a nonsense, although the naming of forms is useful inasmuch as it indicates the general type found in different parts of the country.

Turner's (1963) marking experiments suggest that there is little or no interchange between nearby populations, and it is highly probable that most local colonies in the south of its range are effectively isolated from any other. Colonies may be large, even in the south: Turner's three neighbouring Welsh examples probably contained a total of 1,000–2,000 adults in 1961.

This butterfly has one generation a year, with a flight period from the middle of June, throughout July, and (in Orkney) to the end of August. It overwinters as a larva. One known food plant is the white-beak sedge (*Rhynchospora alba*), but this is absent from large parts of the large heath's range in Scotland and from many individual sites elsewhere, and common cottongrass (*Eriophorum angustifolium*) is often quoted as an alternative (e.g. Higgins and Riley, 1970). Thomson (1980) suggests purple moor-grass (*Molinia caerulea*) as a likely larval food in Scotland, but this has not been established.

Colonies of the large heath are confined to lowland raised bogs, peat mosses, upland blanket bog and damp acid moorland, from sea-level to at least 800 metres. The lowland raised bogs were once very widespread in north-west England, being estimated at 20,000 acres (8,000 hectares) in 1831 (Lewis, 1844), since when there has been continual and continuing reclamation for agricultural, industrial and urban development. Old records indicate that the large heath was widespread throughout much of Shropshire and Lancashire at the start of the industrial revolution; indeed, its earliest common name was the Manchester argus. The remaining localities in England are but fragile remnants of the large mosslands of the early nineteenth century. There have also been some losses in Wales, but Scottish extinctions have, so far, been minimal, al-

though peat cutting, drainage and afforestation
threaten (Thomson, 1980).

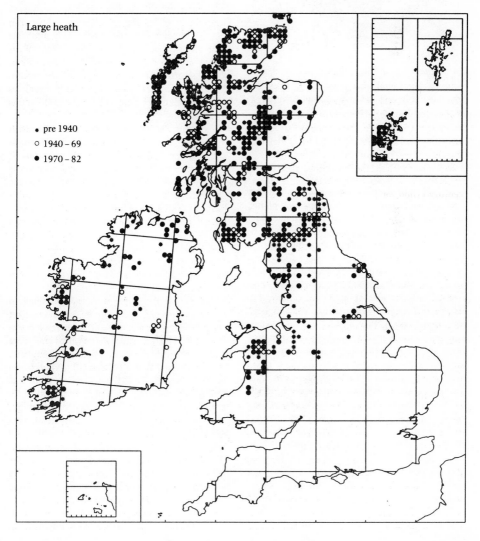

Large heath

* pre 1940
o 1940 – 69
● 1970 – 82

RINGLET

Aphantopus hyperantus

The ringlet is found most commonly in damp, sheltered lanes and shady woodland rides. In more northerly and westerly parts of its range it is often found in open areas of damp grassland in addition to more shaded areas. It has just one generation a year and flies in July and early August, often in cool overcast conditions. The ringlet appears to be very sedentary, occurring in small, well-defined, populations.

The eggs are dropped to the ground and the young larvae must locate their grass food plants when they hatch. There is some evidence that particular grasses are favoured: K. J. Willmott found several hundred larvae in a mixed grass sward, of which all but a few were feeding on one (unidentified) species. The highest densities were in wet areas where the grass grew to knee height. The larvae feed at night. Overwintering is in the larval stage and hibernation is incomplete, with some feeding during mild weather. After further feeding in spring and early summer, the larvae pupate at the base of vegetation in an insubstantial cocoon.

The range covers most of Britain, although there appears to be a climatic limit and the species is absent from the northern part of Scotland. The colour of the underside of the wings is ash-grey in Scotland but brown in southern England, where the butterflies are larger (Dennis, 1977).

In Ireland small individuals occur at high altitude in Co. Kerry (Huggins, 1960). There is a gap in distribution within its range, in the midlands, north-west and north-east of England, and there is some evidence that the ringlet was more widespread in these areas in the nineteenth century. There seems to have been a similar retraction around London (noted by Fenn, 1895) and in the south-east of Scotland. There is, therefore, some indication that declines have been mainly in industrial areas, but the nature of such an association, if indeed it is a real one, is not known. There has been speculation that some butterflies have been affected by atmospheric pollution, and the map of the ringlet distribution does resemble that of lichens affected by sulphur dioxide (Ferry *et al.*, 1973). However, it must be emphasized that in the case of butterflies there is no evidence of susceptibility to sulphur dioxide or other pollutants.

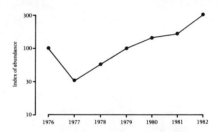

Changes in abundance of the ringlet, 1976–82, as shown by data from the Butterfly Monitoring Scheme.

The ringlet declined sharply in abundance in 1977, presumably because it was badly affected by the drought of 1976. Since then there have been five successive annual increases, taking numbers well above the 1976 levels. Its dependence on shelter is illustrated by its disappearance from a field in Monks Wood after scrub cutting (Pollard, 1982a), while species preferring more open conditions, such as the meadow brown and the grizzled skipper, increased in abundance.

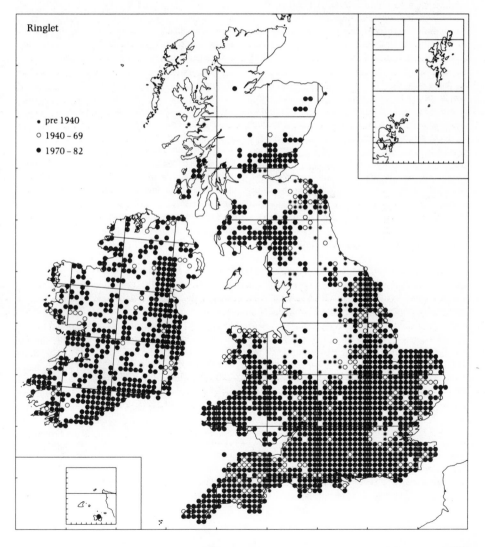

Ringlet

- pre 1940
- 1940 – 69
- 1970 – 82

THE PATTERN OF CHANGE

Climate and geology set limits to the maximum range which can be attained by our butterflies. The importance of these factors can be clearly seen in the map (opposite) showing the total number of species which have been recorded in each ten-kilometre square. Temperature is probably the most important component of climate; many butterflies are restricted to the south of England or to other localities, particularly on the west coast, with mild climates, even when their food plants have much wider distributions. The low summer temperatures are probably the main reason why the number of our butterflies is small compared with that of the continent. The effect of temperature may be on the butterfly itself, as we have suggested for the hedge brown, for example, or on its food plants, as with the brimstone. Geology interacts with climate: the harsh conditions of high mountain areas are unsuitable for most butterflies, and geology also influences distribution through the restriction of some food plants to specific soil types. The large number of species on the calcareous soils of the Cotswolds, the chalk downs and other areas can be quite clearly seen, and is partly due to this restriction of food plants. The changes in distribution discussed in this chapter must be seen against the background of these limits set by nature.

Even a cursory inspection of the maps in this book shows that the ranges of many species of British butterflies have contracted greatly during the last 150 years. During this time four resident species, the black-veined white, the large copper, the mazarine blue and the large blue, have been lost from Britain, and others are now quite close to extinction. It may be argued that all species of plant or animal are subject to continual changes in abundance and, often, changes of abundance are accompanied by changes of range. Even extinctions must be expected in nature from time to time. A few of our butterflies are at present expanding their ranges while many others are contracting. In this section we try to make sense of the recorded pattern of change. Is it part of the normal waxing and waning of species in response to fluctuations in environmental conditions, or a new and worrying general decline which is likely to result in a permanent impoverishment of our butterfly fauna?

In addition to the extinct species mentioned, other butterflies which have become much more restricted in range are the chequered skipper (extinct in England), silver-spotted skipper, wood white, brown hairstreak, small blue, silver-studded blue, adonis blue, Duke of Burgundy, purple emperor, large tortoiseshell, small pearl-bordered fritillary, pearl-bordered fritillary, high brown fritillary, dark green fritillary, silver-washed fritillary, marsh fritillary, heath fritillary and marbled white. Some of these species began to decline during the nineteenth century, but the timing of periods of rapid decline varies considerably. The wood white and purple emperor, for example, declined mainly in the early years of this century, but the woodland fritillaries, after a period of slow contraction, disappeared rapidly from large areas of central and eastern England during the 1950s and 1960s. Some species have had periods of temporary recovery: the wood white has very recently colonized some new areas of southern England and Ireland, some of the fritillaries flourished for a period in the 1930s and 1940s, and the large tortoiseshell was relatively abundant in the late 1940s. However, all of these species are now much rarer than they were 100 years ago, and many have recently shown accelerating declines; the maps often do not show the full extent of recent losses. In particular, this is true of the high brown fritillary which, together with the large tortoiseshell and the heath fritillary, is in some danger of extinction in Britain. Since 1969, our most recent date class, a number of other species have also disappeared from many areas. These species include the dingy skipper, grizzled skipper, white-letter hairstreak, brown argus and the grayling, at its inland sites.

A few butterflies which declined during the latter part of the nineteenth century have subsequently spread again to occupy much of their former ranges. This group of species includes the orange tip, white admiral, speckled wood, comma, peacock, wall and, to a lesser extent, the hedge brown. In the cases of the peacock and the orange tip, the former range seems to have been exceeded, but generally, as far as we are aware, the former ranges have not been reached in these re-expansions.

We have noted, so far, mainly major changes

in range, but these involve as many as twenty-eight of the sixty-two species we are considering. Some of the other species are migrants which, in any case, fluctuate violently in abundance from year to year, and others have shown minor range changes. Thomson (1980), in his comprehensive account of the butterflies of Scotland, records that eight species have become extinct there in the period which we are considering. Most of these eight we have mentioned as showing contractions of range, but Scottish losses also include the small skipper. The eleven species Thomson records as showing contractions of range include the large skipper and the ringlet, which we have not mentioned. We can conclude that a large

proportion of our species has changed significantly in range in the last 150 years; the evidence shows, however, that there has not been a rough balance of increase and decrease, expansion and decline, but that the overwhelming direction of change has been decline.

In addition to changes of range, there have certainly been striking changes of abundance within the current range of many butterflies. For example, the decline of the common blue in southern England perhaps matches or exceeds that of more obviously endangered butterflies, because of the loss of unimproved pasture, but these losses are not apparent on the distribution maps. Such declines in abundance are likely to

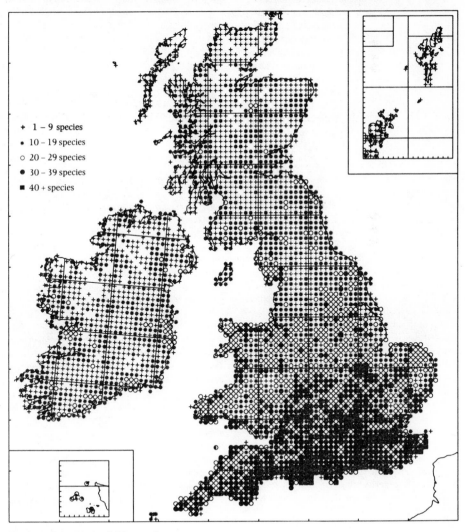

+ 1 – 9 species
* 10 – 19 species
∘ 20 – 29 species
● 30 – 39 species
■ 40 + species

Numbers of species recorded from each square.

Extinctions (date of extinction)	Major contraction of range	Contraction and partial re-expansion	Contraction and equal or greater re-expansion	Major expansion of range
Large copper (1851)	Chequered skipper	Comma	Orange tip	—
Mazarine blue (1887)	Silver-spotted skipper	Speckled wood	White admiral	
Black-veined white (c. 1925)	Wood white	Wall	Peacock	
Large blue (1979)	Brown hairstreak			
	Silver-studded blue			
	Small blue			
	Adonis blue			
	Duke of Burgundy			
	Purple emperor			
	Large tortoiseshell			
	Small pearl-bordered fritillary			
	Pearl-bordered fritillary			
	High brown fritillary			
	Dark green fritillary			
	Silver-washed fritillary			
	Marsh fritillary			
	Heath fritillary			
	Marbled white			

These major changes concern twenty-eight species. Thirty-four further species, including three migrants which do not usually overwinter here, have remained essentially stable over the period, although many of these species have declined in abundance within their ranges.

result eventually in contractions of range. Similarly, a much smaller number of species, such as the Lulworth skipper, have increased in abundance within their ranges but have yet to expand to colonize new areas.

The information available for butterflies is more complete than for any other group of insects because butterflies have always attracted the interest of naturalists. Apart from their beauty in the adult stage, butterflies, as we said in the Introduction, are likely to be typical of an enormous number of insects which feed as larvae on plants. It is also reasonable to suppose that other groups of insects have suffered losses comparable to those of the butterflies, but we have less information about these. Certainly, the available information suggests that the bumble-bees have declined in the midlands and central southern England in a manner comparable to that of the butterflies (Williams, 1982).

The cause of loss of some butterfly populations may be obvious; white-letter hairstreaks have been eliminated locally by the death of elms through Dutch elm disease, chalkhill blue colonies when areas of chalk down have been ploughed. The causes of other losses, such as those of the large tortoiseshell from most of the country or the total loss of the black-veined white and mazarine blue, when plenty of apparently suitable habitat remains, are complete mysteries. Clearly, in the light of our very incomplete knowledge of the biology of many species of butterflies, it is too much to expect that any account of the causes of loss of our butterflies can provide a complete explanation. In spite of this, we believe that, in broad outline, the causes of local losses and of the regional contractions in range of many species are clear.

There have been many thousands of words written on declines, both in the numbers of butterflies and in their ranges; it has been a source of concern to generations of naturalists. A very wide range of causes has been suggested: the most frequent have been the activities of collectors, the use of insecticides, and changes in the weather. It is now generally accepted that collecting is unlikely to have been important, except perhaps when a population has been reduced to very low numbers by other causes; in these circumstances collecting may just possibly tip the balance towards extinction, as has been suggested in the case of the large copper. Even this would only have been possible with the few species, such as the large copper and the heath fritillary, which are particularly vulnerable to collection. There are many species which marking experiments have shown would be virtually impossible to collect to extinction. Examples are the black hairstreak and the purple emperor, which spend most of their time high out of reach in the tree canopy. Insecticides are equally unlikely to have been a major cause of loss. They can certainly kill butterflies close to the target crops and perhaps sometimes in numbers, but the species involved are likely to be common and mobile, and will quickly recolonize from elsewhere. Research on the small tortoiseshell has suggested that butterflies away from the immediate spray area are unlikely to have been affected. Weather certainly has an impact on butterfly numbers, as we will discuss later, but we believe that the evidence clearly shows that the single main cause of change in the abundance and distribution of butterflies has been change and destruction of their habitats.

A wider perspective on our present butterfly fauna can be gained by looking much further back into its history. Butterflies moved north into Britain after the last ice age some 15,000 years ago. Dennis (1977) provides a full and fascinating reconstruction of the likely course of events, dispelling the idea, which was previously widely held, that many species had survived from the previous interglacial period and owed their present distribution to the pattern of survival. In fact no butterfly could have survived the severity of the last great ice age in Britain. As the ice receded, the weather was still harsh and the landscape treeless. The first butterfly colonists must have been open ground species, and would have included the handful of species which are now restricted to the north of Britain: the Scotch argus, northern brown argus, mountain ringlet and large heath, as well as the small copper, common blue and a few other hardy open ground species. After the last ice age there was a warm period, when many butterfly species would have colonized, and then a return to arctic conditions (about 11,000 years ago), when butterflies were again eliminated from all but southern England. It was after this that the colonization which resulted in our present butterfly fauna largely occurred. There are many intriguing questions which can be asked about the subsequent pattern of events. Why did some continental species apparently fail to colonize Britain? Is the absence of a particular species from Ireland or from other smaller islands because of a failure to colonize or later extinction after colonization? How can the disjunct distribution of the chequered skipper be explained? When did the British swallowtail become effectively isolated from the continental subspecies? Butterflies do not leave a significant fossil record, but there are clues to the answers to some of these problems, for example in the development of local races, and the reader is again referred to Dennis (1977) for a full discussion; our concern here is with the broad outline of events.

By about 5,000 years ago, woodland was well established over most of Britain. The advance of woodland was by no means a steady progression, but a series of advances and retreats, with the species composition of the woods changing radically as major climatic fluctuations occurred. There must also have been major changes in the distribution and abundance of butterflies, as at no time before or after the establishment of woodland can the situation have been static; we must suppose that climatic changes are continuing to affect the distribution of butterflies to the present day. In broad terms, however, we may speculate about the nature of the butterfly fauna of Britain, some 5,000 years ago, before man began to clear the woods and create his own landscape.

We cannot be sure of the nature of the primeval woodland, because there are now no woods in Britain which remain uninfluenced in one way or another by man or his grazing animals. We can assume that, on the richer soils at least, the canopy was generally closed, and unshaded areas were few and far between. The major open areas were probably along the flood plains of rivers, in a few larger expanses of low-lying wetland, in other poorly drained areas in the wetter parts of the uplands, and on the high mountains above tree level. The thin poor soils of the chalk and limestone and those of sandy areas now occupied by heathland vegetation were probably thinly wooded, as too would be the mountains close to tree level and coastal areas exposed to strong winds or to erosion by the sea. Otherwise the clearings would have been mainly temporary, created by the fall of a few large trees and soon disappearing as seedlings of new woody plants colonized them.

In such a wooded landscape, the relative abundance of our butterfly species would be very different from that of the present day. It is possible, and even likely, that some species were present which have since disappeared. There is some evidence for example (discussed by Allan, 1966) that the scarce copper *Lycaena virgaurea* once occurred in this country. Some of our species which are now common, such as the large white, small white and small tortoiseshell, must then have been rare. These species require not only open sunny conditions for flight, but are largely dependent on food plants provided directly or indirectly by man. The two 'cabbage' whites feed mainly on crop plants now, and we must suppose that they would have been dependent on crucifers growing in the rare woodland clearings, or in coastal habitats; the small tortoiseshell and a number of other related butterflies feed as larvae on nettles, which are very much 'followers' of man, thriving where he has disturbed and enriched the soil. In contrast, species such as the purple hairstreak, speckled wood and white admiral are very much species of mature woodland and must have been much more common in Britain before man destroyed most of the woodland cover and greatly modified that woodland remaining.

If we now jump forward to the middle of the nineteenth century, the start of the main recording period, the landscape had utterly changed. The wild plant species present were essentially the same, but now, especially in the lowlands, the countryside had been compartmentalized, divided into discrete units, for the convenience of ownership and exploitation by man. These units, hedged arable and grass fields, downland, heaths, managed wetland, upland pasture, parkland and so on, are often thought of as vegetation types, but they are essentially management units. Their characteristic vegetation is composed of species selected and managed for exploitation and, incidentally, others which found the conditions provided by man to their liking and so could thrive, sometimes in spite of man's attempts to remove them as undesirable 'weeds'.

For some butterflies, habitats created by man were almost certainly better than anything that occurred in the natural, largely woodland, landscape. Most of our butterflies have larval food plants which are associated with the early stages of the woodland succession or with permanently open ground; they are adapted to fly in light sunny conditions. Most managed habitats are maintained artificially in early successional stages, and so are likely to be suitable for a range of butterflies, provided that exploitation of a site is not so intensive that it reduces the vegetation solely to the few exploited plant species.

Individual butterfly species are now associated with particular land use types, for example, the chalkhill blue with chalk downs, because in these places they find a combination of conditions particularly suited to them. Some species are able to make use of two quite different situations: the chequered skipper occurs in damp pastures, usually in lightly wooded areas, in Scotland, and (formerly) on the edges and in the rides of coppiced woods in the east midlands of England; the green hairstreak occurs on both calcareous downland and acid heaths. Other species, essentially exploiters of disturbed ground, such as the small copper, can be found in a very wide range of open situations, while the large and small whites flourish in brassica crops in direct competition with man's interests.

The British butterflies are obviously species which can tolerate the climatic conditions of this country, although these conditions become increasingly marginal for butterflies as a group with distance north. Within this limitation, and that imposed by geology, it is clear that, just as the landscape is shaped by man, the characteristic butterfly fauna has been greatly affected by his activities. In the period from the mid nineteenth century to the present the same factor, man's impact on the landscape, has had an increasing influence on the distribution and abundance of butterflies.

As climate determines the limits of the range of many species, we must expect variations in climate to cause shorter-term fluctuations in abundance and also in range. There is good evidence that many species were adversely affected by the generally low summer temperatures in the latter half of the nineteenth century, when a number, as detailed in the accounts of individual species, declined in Scotland and northern England. Recent population studies suggest that butterflies suffer from poor summer weather in two ways. Low temperatures and lack of sunshine during the flight period reduce the time available for egg-laying, and low temperatures during the vulnerable late larval and pupal stages increase the duration of these stages and so the likelihood of their being taken by predators. From the 1920s into the 1940s there was a period of warmer than average summers, and many of the species that had declined earlier recovered the ground they had lost.

There can therefore be no doubting the important effect of climate on butterflies, whether acting directly on the insects, as described, or indirectly, through their food plants. Several major changes in the distribution of species undoubtedly have an important climatic component, such as that reported for the white admiral. Equally, it is certain that climate has not been the main factor in the recent declines in abundance and contractions of range of many species. Those butterflies which have declined include species with very different flight periods and life cycles, particularly overwintering stages. There has been a reduction in average temperatures since about 1950, but it is very unlikely that such diverse species would all be similarly affected by climatic change in the same general area of the country, namely central and eastern England, the area of most intensive land use. Virtually all of our butterfly species have wide continental distributions where they tolerate much greater extremes of climate than they encounter in central and eastern England. Where isolated populations do survive, such as those of the silver-spotted skipper in Kent and the pearl-bordered fritillary in Sussex, they may still be very large if habitat conditions are good. Equally, there is no shortage of the large and small whites in these same areas of England where their food plants – cabbages, sprouts and other brassicas – are grown extensively. Similarly, local species such as the Lulworth skipper and Glanville fritillary, whose habitats have been maintained or improved, have prospered. If any species are likely to be susceptible to cool weather, it is these butterflies of the extreme south. The causes of the declines are primarily the various ways in which man has changed the face of the countryside and so shaped the habitats available to butterflies.

Techniques of forestry and agriculture have been subject to continual change over the centuries, but the changes associated with the industrial revolution in the nineteenth century, and particularly those caused by the agricultural revolution of the mid twentieth century, have been more radical and more rapid than any that have gone before. Following the industrial revolution came the drainage of the remaining extensive wetlands and the displacement of wood as the major source of fuel and fencing, with the inevitable decline in the management of woodlands by coppicing, leading to the eventual replacement of many hardwoods with conifers. A more recent major change has been the cultivation or agricultural improvement of large areas of permanent pasture, moorland and heaths (in the uplands as well as the lowlands), sometimes through new drainage techniques, sometimes because modern farm machinery can operate on steep slopes, but more especially because fertilizers and herbicides can make inherently poor soils provide good arable crops or highly productive pastures. Two types of countryside created by centuries of traditional management had proved particularly suitable to butterflies, and consequently their loss has had particularly large effects. These are coppice woodland and chalk or limestone grassland. Changes in these habitats are almost certainly responsible for some of the more dramatic changes in butterfly distribution recorded in these maps.

Most of the woodlands that survived into medieval times in lowland Britain were managed by a form of coppicing. This management was essentially the regular cutting of small timber on a cycle of anything from about four to twenty years, depending on the use to which the wood was put. The main requirements were probably for firewood and fencing, while larger timber was often catered for by incorporating standard trees at low density. A large wood was divided into small units and one or more of these units would be coppiced each year. The patchwork of open areas and young growth so created was ideal for a number of butterflies, because their larval food plants flourished under the sunlit conditions. The chequered skipper, pearl-bordered fritillary, high brown fritillary, heath fritillary, Duke of Burgundy, and several other species were associated with coppiced woods. These are not all strictly woodland species, but the regular creation of open areas within the shelter of a woodland environment was ideal for them and some of the species no doubt also made use of unimproved grassland which frequently adjoined the woods.

Coppice products were replaced by coal for fuel, wire for fencing, and by other alternatives to wood; in the late nineteenth century this traditional management of our woods was already in decline. Now very little coppicing is practised, apart from that of sweet chestnut in Kent and East Sussex, a small amount of hazel in Hampshire and Dorset, and other small areas in various parts of the country, most of which are managed especially for nature conservation. Many of the ancient woods of Britain, which in some cases have been continuous woodland since prehistoric times, have now been cleared or converted to conifer plantations; others have been neglected and the coppice shoots have grown up to produce a dense shade quite unsuitable for the butterflies which formerly flourished there.

The decline of the butterflies associated with coppice woodland had begun before the end of the nineteenth century, as recorded in contemporary journals. The decline continued through this century, with short intervals when climatic conditions were particularly favourable, and it gathered pace in the 1950s and 1960s. In view of the history of the management of the woods which they frequented, this decline is hardly surprising, but it is perhaps surprising that the loss has been so complete in large parts of the east of the country.

The pattern of loss suggests that once a critical low density of populations is reached in an area, the final disappearance may be very rapid. The loss of the chequered skipper occurred so rapidly that, by the time entomologists realized it was in danger, it had disappeared from virtually all its sites in England. Although we do not fully understand the reason for these rapid losses, they are probably related to the fact that many butterflies are able to exploit individual areas of land for only the relatively short period that they provide suitable conditions, after which new areas must be colonized. If suitable new areas are too few and far between, the chance of colonization becomes remote and the species is doomed to extinction in that region. As we have discussed, some butterflies are very mobile and can even migrate across continents, but other species have surprisingly poor powers of dispersal and the distance between sites does not have to be very great to cause isolation; suitable new habitats within a few kilometres of existing sites may not be colonized. Artificial introduction of such species as the silver-studded blue, marbled white, black hairstreak, marsh fritillary and heath fritillary have often been spectacularly successful.

As might be expected, while some species have suffered from the abandonment of coppicing others, albeit a few, have benefited. The shady conditions of old neglected coppice are not suitable for most butterflies, but a few are able to thrive in them, provided some sunny area remain. The white admiral and speckled wood are such species, and it is likely that the substantial acreage of abandoned coppice helped them to spread during the fine summers of the 1930s and 1940s. In fact, the recent spread of the few species which require more shady conditions strengthens further our belief that habitat change has been of paramount importance in determining recent changes in the status of butterflies.

The conifer plantations which replaced some of the deciduous woodlands can, in their early years, support populations of a large number of butterfly species. They can indeed, then, be much richer in species than mature and shady broad-leaved woods, provided that the conifers are planted on old woodland sites and have a 'ready-made' ground flora. The benefit is not from planting conifers but from opening up the woodland. However, the cycle of cutting of conifers is very long, compared with coppice, and their shade is dense and lasts all year (except for larch); the abundant butterflies of the early years are soon lost. Experience of the wildlife of these plantations is as yet limited, and we do not yet know which species can survive in the rides through several crop cycles. The mown rides of many conifer plantations provide good conditions for some butterflies normally associated with grassland, but there seems little chance that the 'coppice' butterflies will find a permanent home in them. The extensive plantings of conifers in the uplands and elsewhere will undoubtedly have an impact on the abundance and ranges of some butterflies. Their sheltered and ungrazed rides have tall grassland which favours many species, although moorland butterflies such as the large heath disappear from the planted ground. It is possible that the recent success of the orange tip in the north is partly associated with these plantations.

Grasslands, in a similar way to coppice woodlands, are maintained at an early successional stage by regular management, in this case either by cutting, grazing, or perhaps burning. Areas managed in these ways for long periods acquire a large complement of species, both grasses and broad-leaved plants, and the invertebrates associated with them. The loss of these rich grasslands, by ploughing and re-seeding, by treatment with herbicides and fertilizers (favouring a few agricultural grasses), has greatly reduced the wildlife interest of farmland. Many grasslands on a range of soil types were rich in butterflies, but the grasslands of the chalk and limestone downs were, and are, of special importance.

The food plants of some butterflies are restricted to calcareous soils – horseshoe vetch (chalkhill and adonis blues), common rock-rose (brown argus), and tor-grass (Lulworth skipper) – while others are particularly abundant on them. The presence of these food plants, and an abundance of flowers, together with the varied slopes and aspects of the chalk downs, help to make them peculiarly suitable for butterflies. However, as with our other unimproved permanent grasslands, those surviving today are merely a small fraction of those present at the start of the recording period in the nineteenth century.

The survival of rich chalk grassland and its butterflies depends not only on the avoidance of destruction by ploughing or by heavy application of fertilizer and herbicides, but on the continuation of active management. Abandonment of grazing (or cutting) over a period results in a dense growth of rank grasses and scrub, which eliminates the food plants of many butterflies. The decline in grazing of the remaining fragments of chalk grasslands has for many years exacerbated the problem caused by actual destruction of areas. Again, as in the woodland situation, a few butterflies, such as the Lulworth skipper and perhaps the marbled white and some other grass-feeding butterflies, have benefited locally from the growth of rank grasses, but this benefit has been at the expense of the majority of our characteristic chalk butterflies. Unlike the few woodland species which benefited from increased shade, there have been no records of expansion of range of butterflies which thrive on ungrazed grassland, because these local benefits have generally been more than offset by total loss of other sites.

Several butterflies, both woodland and grassland species, appeared to decline particularly sharply during the mid to late 1950s. Weather or other factors could have been implicated in the timing of this decline, but the loss of rabbits, caused by the disease myxomatosis, was an important factor. Unimproved grasslands which were no longer grazed by stock had often been kept short by the high rabbit populations, but when these disappeared the effect on the vegetation was dramatic. For a year or two there was a great flowering of the downs and some butterflies, such as the dark green fritillary, became locally abundant, while others which needed very short turf, the adonis blue, large blue and silver-spotted skipper, disappeared from many sites almost immediately. Over the next few years other species, such as the chalkhill blue, and, eventually, even the dark green fritillary, declined as low-growing food plants were eliminated. It is not always realized that rabbits also greatly suppressed the growth of the ground vegetation of woodland, and even prevented clearings from developing into scrub and tree cover. In woods, as well as in grassland, the loss of rabbits could have been the final blow which caused the loss of many populations of butterflies. Many woodland butterflies feed on low-growing plants, such as violets, which are quickly shaded out by a dense ground flora.

We have selected woodlands and chalk grassland for special attention, but these are just examples, used to illustrate more general trends. Indeed, more unimproved grassland has survived on the chalk (3 per cent – Smith, 1980), where there are steep slopes which are difficult to cultivate, than in areas of flatter land, such as on the clay soils of the old county of Huntingdonshire (0.4 per cent – Mellanby, 1981). The general points made in connection with the woodland and chalk habitats are, however, applicable to other habitats, such as heaths, moors, fens, hay meadows, and other grasslands, and the same trends are evident. These trends are: the decline of traditional management of habitats rich in wildlife; the destruction of habitats; the isolation of remaining populations of many butterflies. The cumulative effect has been the loss of butterflies, in a few cases completely, in others at the periphery of their ranges. Northern species have tended to contract to the north and west, southern species to the south and west, in both cases to areas of less intensive land use.

A number of the best surviving examples of those habitat types which are particularly good for wildlife have been made into nature reserves. These have generally been very successful in conserving the plant species of special interest, but the conservation of butterflies has presented a very difficult problem. Coppice woodland, grassland, heathland, managed wetlands and other sites were good for butterflies because of the particular management that created them. A nature reserve is relatively easily (if expensively) acquired, but the problem of maintaining the necessary management, or of finding suitable alternative management, remains. So far, attempts to conserve populations of rare butterflies on nature reserves have had only modest success. It is very difficult, given the present state of knowledge of the ecology of butterflies, to ensure that populations remain large enough to make chance extinction, due perhaps to a combination of adverse conditions, including bad weather, unlikely. Final extinction is often, as in the case of the large blue, due to such a *combination* of unfavourable circumstances (Thomas, 1980b). Once such extinctions occur, the chance of natural recolonization of isolated areas by rare species is very small. There is therefore likely to be an increasing role for deliberate reintroduction of species to reserves as a conservation technique.

Although we have concentrated on the losses of butterfly populations, we have mentioned that there have been a few compensatory gains. In addition, there are a number of species, such as the hedge brown, small and large skippers, small heath, small tortoiseshell, green-veined white, and others, which can survive in uncultivated corners in all but the most sterile of arable prairies. Such species are probably not in danger of widespread extinction, within their climatic limits. It seems certain, however, that there will be further losses of more vulnerable butterfly populations over the next few years at local, regional and even national levels. It is also likely that some of the species we at present regard as ubiquitous will become much more scarce. We would guess, for example, that the common blue and perhaps the small copper will soon become rare in large parts of eastern England.

Already these maps are, to an extent, out of date. The post-1969 date class includes many local populations we know to be extinct. A close watch needs to be kept on our more local species; the rapid decline and extinction in England of the chequered skipper shows the speed at which losses can occur. Because of their short life cycles and highly specific requirements, butterflies are sensitive to change. Mapping and monitoring needs to continue to provide advance warning of species in danger.

There seems little prospect of maintaining sufficient habitats for many of our butterflies within our highly agricultural countryside, except in areas set aside for the purpose. If conservation of butterflies on reserves is to be effective we need to improve our knowledge of their ecology. Without such knowledge, and the means to apply it, another twenty years will see a further drastic decline in the butterflies of Britain and Ireland. Nor is the problem restricted to these countries; many parts of Europe are seeing similar declines in their butterflies (Heath, 1981). Nearly all our endangered butterflies have wide European ranges, but this does not mean that they have secure futures elsewhere.

REFERENCES

ALLAN, P. B. M. (1948) *Moths and memories*. London: Watkins & Doncaster.

ALLAN, P. B. M. (1966) Copper butterflies in the west country. *Entomologist's Rec. J. Var.*, **78**, 161–6.

ARCHER-LOCK, A. (1980) The white-letter hairstreak: *Strymonidia w-album* Knoch. *Entomologist's Rec. J. Var.*, **92**, 254–5.

BAKER, R. R. (1969) The evolution of the migratory habit in butterflies. *J. Anim. Ecol.*, **38**, 703–46.

BAKER, R. R. (1970) Bird Predation as a selective pressure on the immature stages of the cabbage butterflies *Pieris rapae* and *P. brassicae*. *J. Zool.*, **162**, 43–9.

BAKER, R. R. (1972a) The geographical origin of the British spring individuals of the butterflies *Vanessa atalanta* (L.) and *V. cardui* (L.). *J. Entomol. A.* **46**, 185–96.

BAKER, R. R. (1972b) Territorial behaviour in nymphalid butterflies *Aglais urticae* (L.) and *Inachis io* (L.). *J. Anim. Ecol.*, **41**, 453–69.

BAKER, R. R. (1978) *The evolutionary ecology of animal migration*. London: Hodder & Stoughton.

BAYNES, E. S. A. (1964) *A revised catalogue of the Irish Macrolepidoptera (butterflies and moths)*. Middlesex: Classey.

BIBBY, T. J. (1983) Oviposition by the brimstone *Gonepteryx rhamni* (L.), (Lepidoptera Pieridae) in Monks Wood, Cambridgeshire in 1982. *Entomologist's Gaz.*, **34**, 229–34.

BINK, F. A. (1972) Het onderzoek naar de grote vuurvlinder (*Lycaena dispar batava* Oberthur) in Nederland (Lep., Lycaenidae). *Ent. Ber., Amst.*, **32**, 225–39.

BIRKETT, N. L. (1957) Insects. In: *The changing scene*, **1**, 40–46. (Joint transactions of the Eden Field Club.) Penrith and District Natural History Society; Kendal Natural History Society.

BLACKIE, J. E. H. (1951) The range and distribution of *Agapetes galathea* L. *Entomologist*, **84**, 132–5.

BONE, Q., and HARDY, M. G. (1958) Some observations upon a polymorphic population of *Argynnis paphia* (L.) (Lep., Nymphalidae) in the New Forest. *Entomologist's mon. Mag.*, **94**, 114–19.

BRADLEY, J. D., and FLETCHER, D. S. (1979) *A recorder's log book or label list of British butterflies and moths*. London: Curwen.

BRAKEFIELD, P. M. (1982) Ecological studies on the butterfly *Maniola jurtina* in Britain. I. Adult behaviour, microdistribution and dispersal. *J. Anim. Ecol.*, **51**, 713–26.

BRAKEFIELD, P. M. (in press) The ecological genetics of quantitative characters in *Maniola jurtina* and other butterflies. In: *The biology of butterflies*, ed. R. I. Vane-Wright and P. R. Ackery. (Symposium of the Royal Entomological Society no. 11.)

BREE, W. T. (1852) A list of butterflies occurring in the neighbourhood of Polebrook, Northampton; with some remarks. *Zoologist*, **10**, 3348–52.

BRETHERTON, R. F. (1951a) The early history of the swallow-tail butterfly (*Papilio machaon* L.) in England. *Entomologist's Rec. J. Var.*, **63**, 206–11.

BRETHERTON, R. F. (1951b) Our lost butterflies and moths. *Entomologist's Gaz.*, **2**, 211–40.

BRETHERTON, R. F., and CHALMERS-HUNT, J. M. (1981) The immigration of Lepidoptera to the British Isles in 1980, with an account of the invasion of the painted lady *Cynthia cardui* L. Annexe III: The painted Lady (*Cynthia cardui* L.) in 1980. *Entomologist's Rec. J. Var.*, **93**, 103–11.

BROOKS, M., and KNIGHT, C. (1982) *A complete guide to British butterflies*. London: Jonathan Cape.

BURNS, J. M. (1966) Expanding distribution and evolutionary potential of *Thymelicus lineola* (Lepidoptera: Hesperiidae), an introduced skipper, with special reference to its appearance in British Columbia. *Can. Ent.*, **98**, 859–66.

CAMPBELL, J. L. (1975) On the rumoured presence of the large blue butterfly (*Maculinea arion* L.) in the Hebrides. *Entomologist's Rec. J. Var.*, **87**, 161–6.

CHALMERS-HUNT, J. M. (1960–81) *The butterflies and moths of Kent*. Arbroath: Buncle. (Published originally as supplements to the *Entomologist's Rec. J. Var.*)

CHALMERS-HUNT, J. M. (1977) The 1976 invasion of the Camberwell Beauty (*Nymphalis antiopa* L.) *Entomologist's Rec. J. Var.*, **89**, 89–105.

CHALMERS-HUNT, J. M., and OWEN, D. F. (1952) The history and status of *Pararge aegeria* (Lep. Satyridae) in Kent. *Entomologist*, **85**, 145–54.

CHAPMAN, T. A. (1909) Why is *Cyaniris semiargus* no longer a British insect? *Entomologist's Rec. J. Var.*, **21**, 132–3.

CHAPMAN, T. A. (1915) Observations completing an outline of the life history of *Lycaena arion*. *Trans. R. ent. Soc. Lond.*, **63**, 298–312.

COLLIER, A. E. (1959) A forgotten discard: the problems of redundancy. *Entomologist's Rec. J. Var.*, **71**, 118–19.

COLLIER, R. V. (1966) Status of butterflies on Castor Hanglands NNR 1961–1965 inclusive. *J. Northampt. nat. Hist. Soc.*, **35**, 451–6.

COULTHARD, N. (1982) *An investigation of the habitat requirements and behavioural ecology of the small blue butterfly, Cupido minimus Fuessly, in relation to its distribution and abundance in north-east Scotland*. M.Sc. thesis, University of Aberdeen.

COURTNEY, S. P. (1980) *Studies on the biology of the butterflies Anthocaris cardamines (L.) and Pieris napi (L.) in relation to speciation in Pierinae*. Ph.D. thesis, University of Durham.

COURTNEY, S. P. (1982) Coevolution of pierid butterflies and their cruciferous foodplants. V. Habitat selection, community structure and speciation. *Oecologia*, **54**, 101–7.

CRANE, R. (1972) Mill Hill-Shoreham. An example of

the deterioration of chalk grassland on the Sussex downs. *Newsl., Sussex Trust Nat. Conserv.* no. 38, 3–4.

CRIBB, P. W. (1975) The long emergence period of the meadow brown. *Proc. Trans. Br. ent. nat. Hist. Soc.*, 7, 96.

DALE, C. W. (1886) *The Lepidoptera of Dorsetshire.* Dorchester: Ling.

DAVIES, N. B. (1978) Territorial defence in the speckled wood butterfly (*Pararge aegeria*): the resident always wins. *Anim. Behav.*, 26, 138–47.

DEMPSTER, J. P. (1968) The control of *Pieris rapae* with DDT. II. Survival of the young stages of *Pieris* after spraying. *J. appl. Ecol.*, 5, 451–62.

DEMPSTER, J. P. (1969) Some effects of weed control on the numbers of the small cabbage white (*Pieris rapae* L.) on Brussels sprouts. *J. appl. Ecol.*, 6, 339–45.

DEMPSTER, J. P. (1971) Some observations on a population of the small copper butterfly *Lycaena phlaeas* (Linnaeus) (Lep., Lycaenidae). *Entomologist's Gaz.*, 22, 199–204.

DEMPSTER, J. P., KING, M. L., and LAKHANI, K. H. (1976) The status of the swallowtail butterfly in Britain. *Ecol. Entomol.*, 1, 71–84.

DEMPSTER, J. P., and HALL, M. L. (1980) An attempt at re-establishing the swallowtail butterfly at Wicken Fen. *Ecol. Entomol.*, 5, 327–34.

DENNIS, R. L. H. (1972a) *Eumenis semele* (L). *thyone* Thompson (Lep. Satyridae), a microgeographical race. *Entomologist's Rec. J. Var.*, 84, 1–11, 38–44.

DENNIS, R. L. H. (1972b) *Plebejus argus* (L.) *caernensis* Thompson. A stenaecious geotype. *Entomologist's Rec. J. Var.*, 84, 132–40.

DENNIS, R. L. H. (1977) *The British butterflies: their origin and distribution.* Faringdon: Classey.

DENNIS, R. L. H. (1982a) Observations on habitats and dispersion made from oviposition markers in North Cheshire *Anthocaris cardamines* (L.) (Lepidoptera: Pieridae). *Entomologist's Gaz.*, 33, 151–9.

DENNIS, R. L. H. (1982b) Patrolling behaviour in orange tip butterflies within the Bollin valley in north Cheshire, and a comparison with other Pierids. *Vasculum*, 67, 17–25.

DENNIS, R. L. H. (1982c) Mate location strategies in the wall brown butterfly *Lasiommata megera* (L.) (Lepidoptera: Satyridae): wait or seek? *Entomologist's Rec. J. Var.*, 94, 209–14 (and further part in 1983, 95, 7–10).

DENNIS, R. L. H. (1983) Egg-laying cues in the wall brown butterfly *Lasiommata megera* (L.) (Lepidoptera: Satyridae). *Entomologist's Gaz.*, 34, 89–95.

DONISTHORPE, H. St J. K. (1927) *Guests of British ants: their habits and life histories.* London: Routledge.

DONY, J. G., ROB, C. M., and PERRING, F. H. (1974) *English names of wild flowers.* London: Butterworths.

DOWDESWELL, W. H. (1981) *The life of the meadow brown.* London: Heinemann.

DOWNES, J. A. (1948) The history of the speckled wood butterfly (*Pararge aegeria*) in Scotland, with a discussion of the recent changes of range of other British butterflies. *J. Anim. Ecol.*, 17, 131–8.

DUFFEY, E. (1968) Ecological studies of the large copper butterfly *Lycaena dispar* Haw. *batavus* Obth. at Woodwalton Fen National Nature Reserve, Huntingdonshire. *J. appl. Ecol.*, 5, 69–96.

DUFFEY, E. (1977) The re-establishment of the large copper butterfly *Lycaena dispar batava* Obth. on Woodwalton Fen National Nature Reserve, Cambridge, England, 1969–73. *Biol. Conserv.* 12, 143–58.

DUNN, T. C. (1974) The wall brown butterfly. *Vasculum*, 59, 41.

EDWARDS, M., and EDWARDS, S. H. (1980) *West Sussex Wildlife Recording Group – butterfly report.* Midhurst: Edwards & Edwards.

FARRELL, L. (1975) A survey of the status of the chequered skipper butterfly (*Carterocephalus palaemon*) (Pallas) (Lep. Hesperiidae) in Britain 1973–1974. *Entomologist's Gaz.*, 26, 148–9.

FEARNEHOUGH, T. D. (1972) The butterflies of the Isle of Wight. *Entomologist's Rec. J. Var.*, 84, 57–64, 102–9.

FELTWELL, J. (1982) *The large white butterfly: the biology, biochemistry and physiology of* Pieris brassicae (Linnaeus). The Hague: Junk.

FENN, C. (1895) On the gradual disappearance of Lepidoptera from South-Eastern London and its neighbourhood. *Entomologist's Rec. J. Var.*, 6, 228–32.

FERRY, B. W., BADDELEY, M. S. and HAWKSWORTH, D. L. (eds.) (1973) *Air pollution and lichens.* London: Athlone Press.

FINDLAY, R., YOUNG, M. R., and FINDLAY, J. A. (1983). Orientation behaviour in the grayling butterfly: thermoregulation or crypsis? *Ecol. Entomol.*, 8, 145–53.

FORD, E. B. (1945) *Butterflies.* London: Collins.

FORD, E. B. (1975) *Ecological genetics.* 4th edn. London: Chapman & Hall.

FORD, H. D., and FORD, E. B. (1930) Fluctuations in numbers and its influence on variation in *Melitaea aurinia* Rott. (Lepidoptera). *Trans. R. Ent. Soc. Lond.*, 78, 345–52.

FRAZER, J. F. D. (1961) Butterfly populations on the North Downs. *Proc. S. Lond. ent. nat. Hist. Soc.*, 1960, 98–109.

FRAZER, J. F. D. (1977) The chalkhill blue butterfly (*Lysandra coridon*) at Burham Down, 1955–74. *Trans. Kent Fld Club*, 6, 71–74.

FRAZER, J. F. D. (1981) Roosting sites of blue butterflies. *Trans. Kent Fld Club*, 8, 149–51.

FROHAWK, F. W. (1934) *The complete book of British butterflies.* London: Ward Lock.

FUST, H. J. (1868) On the distribution of Lepidoptera in Great Britain and Ireland. *Trans. R. ent. Soc. Lond.*, 4, 417–517.

GARDINER, B. O. C. (1963) Genetic and environmental variations in *Pieris brassicae*. *J. Res. Lepid.*, 2, 127–36.

GOATER, B. (1974) *The butterflies and moths of Hampshire and the Isle of Wight.* Faringdon: Classey.

GODDARD, M. J. (1962) Broods of the speckled wood (*Pararge aegeria aegerides* Stgr.) (Lep. Satyridae). *Entomologist*, 95, 289–307.

GOSS, H. (1887) Is *Aporia crataegi* extinct in England? *Entomologist's mon. Mag.*, 23, 217–20.

GRAHAM-SMITH, G. S., and GRAHAM-SMITH, W. (1929 and 1930) *Pieris brassicae* L., with special reference to aberrations from Aberdeenshire. *Entomologist's Rec. J. Var.*, 41, 157–61, 173–80; 42, 1–7, 17–22.

GREEN, J. E. (1982) *A practical guide to the butterflies of Worcestershire*. Birmingham: Worcestershire Nature Conservation Trust Ltd.

HARPER, G. W. (1954) The macrolepidoptera of Inverness-shire–Newtonmore district. *Entomologist's Rec. J. Var.*, 66, 58–64, (further articles in this series 1955–68).

HAWES, F. W. (1890) *Hesperia lineola* Ochsenheimer: an addition to the list of British butterflies. *Entomologist*, 23, 3–4.

HEATH, J. (1967) Lepidoptera Distribution Maps Scheme. *Entomologist's mon. Mag.*, 103, 124–5.

HEATH, J. (1969) Lepidoptera distribution maps scheme, guide to the critical species. *Entomologist's Gaz.*, 20, 89–95.

HEATH, J. (1970) Provisional atlas of the insects of the British Isles. Part I. Lepidoptera: Rhopalocera (Butterflies). (Maps 1–57.) Huntingdon: Nature Conservancy.

HEATH, J. (1981) Threatened rhopalocera (butterflies) in Europe. Council of Europe. Nature and Environment Series No. 23. Strasburg.

HEATH, J. (1983) Is this the earliest record of *Lycaena dispar* (Haworth) (Lepidoptera: Lycaenidae) *Entomologist's Gaz.*, 34, 228.

HEATH, J. (ed.) (1976) *The moths and butterflies of Great Britain and Ireland*. Volume 1. London: Curwen.

HEATH, J. and SCOTT, D. W. (1974 and 1977) *Instructions for recorders*. Abbots Ripton, Huntingdon: Institute of Terrestrial Ecology.

HESLOP, I. R. P., HYDE, G. E., and STOCKLEY, R. E. (1964) *Notes and views of the purple emperor*. Brighton: Southern Publishing Co.

HESLOP-HARRISON, J. W. (1946) The geographical distribution of certain Hebridean insects and deductions to be made from it. *Entomologist's Rec. J. Var.*, 58, 18–21.

HIGGINS, L. G., and RILEY, N. D. (1970) *A field guide to the butterflies of Britain and Europe*. London: Collins.

HØEGH-GULDBERG, O. (1966) Northern European groups of *Aricia allous* G.-Hb: their variability and relationship to *A. agestis* (Schiff.). *Natura jutl.*, 13, 9–116.

HOLLOWAY, J. D. (1980) A mass movement of *Quercusia quercus* (L) (Lepidoptera Lycaenidae) in 1976. *Entomologist's Gaz.*, 31, 150.

HOLMES, J. W. O. (1978) A second brood of *Inachis io* (L.) (Lep., Nymphalidae) in 1976. *Entomologist's Gaz.*, 29, 42.

HOWARTH, T. G. (1973) *South's British butterflies*. London: Warne.

HUGGINS, H. C. (1960) A naturalist in the Kingdom of Kerry. *Proc. Trans. S. Lond. ent. nat. Hist. Soc.*, 1959, 176–83.

HUGHES, R. A. (1956) Denbighshire localities for the limestone race of the silver-studded blue. *Entomologist*, 89, 47.

HUGHES, R. A. (1960) *Plebejus argus caernensis* (Lep.) in Denbighshire. *Entomologist*, 93, 235.

HUNT, O. D. (1965) Status and conservation of the large blue butterfly, *Maculinea arion* L. In *The conservation of invertebrates*, ed. E. Duffey and M. G. Morris, 35–44. (Monks Wood Experimental Station symposium no. 1.) Abbots Ripton, Huntingdon: Nature Conservancy.

IRWIN, A. G. (in press) The large copper, *Lycaena dispar dispar* (Haworth) in the Norfolk Broads. *Entomologist's Rec. J. Var.*

JARVIS, F. V. L. (1958) Biological notes on *Aricia agestis* (Schiff.) in Britain. I and II. *Entomologist's Rec. J. Var.*, 70, 141–8, 169–78.

JARVIS, F. V. L. (1959) Biological notes on *Aricia agestis* (Schiff.) in Britain. III. *Entomologist's Rec. J. Var.*, 71, 169–78.

JARVIS, F. V. L. (1963) The genetic relationship between *Aricia agestis* (Schiff.) and its ssp. *artaxerxes* (F.). *Proc. Trans. S. Lond. ent. nat. Hist. Soc.*, 1962, 106–22.

JARVIS, F. V. L. (1966) The genus *Aricia* (Lep. Rhopalocera) in Britain. *Proc. Trans. S. Lond. ent. nat. Hist. Soc.*, 1966, 37–60.

JARVIS, F. V. L. (1969) A biological study of *Aricia artaxerxes* ssp. *salmacis* (Stephens). *Proc. Trans. Br. ent. nat. Hist. Soc.*, 2, 107–17.

JEFFERSON, T. W. (1958) The brown argus butterfly, *Aricia agestis* Schiff., in Great Britain. *Entomologist's Rec. J. Var.*, 70, 117–22.

JOHNSON, C. G. (1969) *Migration and dispersal of insects by flight*. London: Methuen.

KINNEAR, P. K. (1976) Unusual numbers of peacocks (*Inachis io* (L) Lep., Nymphalidae) in Shetland. *Entomologist's Gaz.*, 27, 137.

LAMHNA, E. NI (1980) *Distribution atlas of butterflies in Ireland*. 3rd edn. Dublin: An Foras Forbartha.

LEES, E. (1962) On the voltinism of *Coenonympha pamphilus* (L.) (Lep., Satyridae). *Entomologist*, 95, 5–6.

LEES, E. (1965) Further observations on the voltinism of *Coenonympha pamphilus* (L.) (Lep., Satyridae). *Entomologist*, 98, 43–5.

LEES, E. (1969) Voltinism of *Polyommatus icarus* Rott. (Lep., Lycaenidae) in Britain. *Entomologist*, 102, 194–6.

LEES, E. (1970) A univoltine race of *Pieris napi* L. in the Yorkshire pennines. *Entomologist*, 103, 260–62.

LEES, E., and ARCHER, D. M. (1974) Ecology of *Pieris napi* (L.) (Lep., Pieridae) in Britain. *Entomologist's Gaz.*, 25, 231–7.

LEMPKE, B. J. (1980) Insects from Cornwall, including apparently the first Cornish Lulworth skipper. *Entomologist's Rec. J. Var.*, 92, 189–90.

LEWIS, S. (1844) *Topographical dictionary of England*. Vol. 3. London.

LIPSCOMBE, C. G., and JACKSON, R. A. (1964) Some considerations on some present day conditions as they affect the continued existence of certain butterflies. *Entomologist's Rec. J. Var.*, 76, 63–8.

LONG, A. G. (1979) The return of the orange tip. *Entomologist's Rec. J. Var.*, 91, 16–17 (and further articles to 1981).

LUCKENS, C. J. (1980) The heath fritillary *Mellicta athalia* Rott. in Britain. Notes on distribution and ecology. *Entomologist's Rec. J. Var.*, **92**, 229–34.

MACKWORTH-PRAED, C. N. (1942) *Carteracephalus palaemon* Pallas (Lep., Hesperidae) in Inverness-shire. *Entomologist*, **75**, 216.

MALICKY, H. (1970) New aspects on the association between Lycaenid larvae (Lycaenidae) and ants (Formicidae, Hymenoptera). *J. Lepid Soc.*, **24**, 190–202.

MARCON, J. N. (1980) *Argynnis paphia* L. and *Limenitis camilla* L. in the New Forest in 1941/42. *Entomologist's Rec. J. Var.*, **92**, 277–9.

McNEIL, J. N., and DUCHESNE, R. M. (1977) Transport of hay and its importance in the passive dispersal of the European skipper *Thymelicus lineola* (Lepidoptera: Hesperiidae). *Can. Ent.*, **109**, 1253–6.

MELLANBY, K. (1981) *Farming and Wildlife*. London: Collins.

MERCHANT, A. J. (1956) *Plebejus argus caernensis* Thompson at Llanddulas and Rhyd-y-Foel. *Entomologist*, **89**, 234.

MOORE, N. W. (1962) The heaths of Dorset and their conservation. *J. Ecol.*, **50**, 369–91.

MORIARTY, F. (1969) Butterflies and insecticides. *Entomologist's Rec. J. Var.*, **81**, 276–8.

MORTON, A. C. (1982) The effects of marking and capture on recapture frequencies of butterflies. *Oecologia*, **53**, 105–10.

MUGGLETON, J. (1973) Some aspects of the history and ecology of blue butterflies in the Cotswolds. *Proc. & Trans Br. entomol. & natur. Hist. Soc.*, **6**, 77–84.

MUGGLETON, J. (1974) Dates of appearance of *Maculinea arion* (Linnaeus) (Lep., Lycaenidae) adults in Gloucestershire 1858–1960. *Entomologist's Gaz.*, **25**, 239–44.

NEWMAN, E. (1870) *The illustrated natural history of British butterflies and moths*. London: Allen.

OHSAKI, N. (1980) Comparative population studies of three *Pieris* butterflies, *P. rapae*, *P. meleta* and *P. napi*, living in the same area. II. Utilization of patchy habitats by adults through migratory and non-migratory movements. *Researches Popul. Ecol. Kyoto Univ.*, **22**, 163–83.

OWEN, D. F. (1976) Conservation of butterflies in garden habitats. *Environ. Conserv.*, **3**, 285–90.

PAUL, A. R. (1977) Some observations on the marbled white butterfly *Melanargia galathea* (L.). *Entomologist's mon. Mag.*, **112**, 127–30.

PEACHEY, C. (1980) *The conservation of butterflies in Bernwood Forest*. Foxhold: Nature Conservancy Council.

PEACHEY, C. (1983) White-letter hairstreak survey. *News Br. Butterfly Conserv. Soc.*, no. 30, 21–4.

PERRING, F. H., and WALTERS, S. M. (eds.) (1962) *Atlas of the British flora*. London: Nelson.

POLLARD, E. (1977) A method for assessing changes in the abundance of butterflies. *Biol. Conserv.*, **12**, 115–34.

POLLARD, E. (1979) Population ecology and change in range of the white admiral butterfly *Ladoga camilla* L. in England. *Ecol. Entomol.*, **4**, 61–74.

POLLARD, E. (1981) Aspects of the ecology of the meadow brown butterfly, *Maniola jurtina* (L.) (Lepidoptera: Satyridae). *Entomologist's Gaz.*, **32**, 67–74.

POLLARD, E. (1982a) Monitoring the abundance of butterflies in relation to the management of a nature reserve. *Biol. Conserv.*, **24**, 317–28.

POLLARD, E. (1982b) Observations on the migratory behaviour of the painted lady butterfly, *Vanessa cardui* (L.) (Lepidoptera: Nymphalidae). *Entomologist's Gaz.*, **33**, 99–103.

POLLARD, E., and HALL, M. L. (1980) Possible movement of *Gonepteryx rhamni* (Lepidoptera: Pieridae) between hibernating and breeding areas. *Entomologist's Gaz.*, **31**, 217–20.

PORTER, K. (1981) *The population dynamics of small colonies of the butterfly* Euphydryas aurinia. D. Phil. thesis, University of Oxford.

PORTER, K. (1982) Basking behaviour in larvae of the butterfly *Euphydryas aurinia*. *Oikos*, **38**, 308–12.

PORTER, K. (1983) Multivoltinism in *Apanteles bignellii* and the influence of weather on synchronization with its host *Euphydryas aurinia*. *Entomologia exp. appl.*, **34**, 155–62.

PRATT, C. (1981) *A history of the butterflies and moths of Sussex*. Brighton: Borough Council.

PRATT, C. (1983) A modern review of the demise of *Aporia crataegi* L., the black-veined white. *Entomologist's Rec. J. Var.*, **95**, 45–52 (and further articles 1984).

PUREFOY, E. B. (1953) An unpublished account of experiments carried out at East Farleigh, Kent, in 1915 and subsequent years on the life history of *Maculinea arion*, the large blue butterfly. *Proc. R. ent. Soc. Lond. A*, **28**, 160–62.

RAFE, R. W., and JEFFERSON, R. G. (1983) The status of *Melanargia galathea* (Lepidoptera Satyridae) in the Yorkshire Wolds. *Naturalist, Hull*, **108**, 3–7.

RAYWARD, A. L. (1907) Larvae of *Polyommatus icarus* and their connection with ants. *Entomologist's Rec. J. Var.*, **19**, 108–10.

REDSHAW, E. J. (1982) An early record of the large copper (*Lycaena dispar*) Haw. in Lincolnshire. *Trans. Lincs. Nat. Un.*, **20**, 119–20.

REDWAY, D. B. (1981) Some comments on the reported occurrence of *Erebia epiphron* (Knoch) (Lepidoptera: Satyridae) in Ireland during the nineteenth century. *Entomologist's Gaz.*, **32**, 157–9.

REID, W. (1955) Collecting notes, 1955. *Entomologist's Rec. J. Var.*, **67**, 281.

RICHARDS, O. W. (1940) The biology of the small white butterfly (*Pieris rapae*) with special reference to the factors controlling its abundance. *J. Anim. Ecol.*, **9**, 243–88.

ROTHSCHILD, M., and SCHOONHOVEN, L. M. (1977) Assessment of egg load by *Pieris brassicae* (Lepidoptera: Pieridae). *Nature, Lond.*, **266**, 352–5.

RUSSELL, S. G. C. (1943) *Cyaniris semiargus* (*acis*). *Entomologist*, **76**, 61–2.

SCOTT, E. (1950) *A list of butterflies and moths (Macro Lepidoptera) occurring in the neighbourhood of Ashford, Kent*. 2nd edn. Ashford: Headley Brothers.

SELMAN, B. J., LUFF, M. L., and MONCK, W. J. (1973) The Castle Eden Dene argus butterfly, *Aricia artaxerxes salmacis* Stephens. *Vasculum*, **58**, 17–22.

SHAW, M. R. (1977) On the distribution of some Satyrid (Lep.) larvae at a coastal site in relation to their Ichneumonid (Hym.) parasite. *Entomologist's Gaz.*, **28**, 133–4.

SHAW, M. R. (1981) Parasitism by Hymenoptera of larvae of the white admiral butterfly *Ladoga camilla* (L.) in England. *Ecol. Entomol.*, **6**, 333–5.

SHELDON, W. G. (1925) The destruction of British butterflies: a suggested remedy. *Entomologist*, **58**, 105–12.

SHIELDS, O. (1967) Hilltopping. *J. Res. Lepid.*, **6**, 69–178.

SHOWLER, A. J. (1980) The Reappearance of *Lysandra bellargus* Rott. in the Chilterns. *Entomologist's Rec. J. Var.*, **92**, 199–200.

SHREEVES, W. G. (1979) Territorial behaviour and the Duke of Burgundy fritillary. *News Br. Butterfly Conserv. Soc.*, no. 22, 12–15.

SMITH, C. J. (1980) *Ecology of the English Chalk.* London: Academic Press.

SMITH, F. W. (1949) The distribution of the orange tip butterfly, *Euchloe cardamines*, in Scotland. *Scott. Nat.*, **61**, 32–5.

SMITH, R., and BROWN, D. (1979) *The Lepidoptera of Warwickshire: a provisional list.* Warwick: Biological Records Centre.

SOUTH, R. (1906) *The butterflies of the British Isles.* London: Warne.

SPOONER, G. M. (1963) On causes of the decline of *Maculinea arion* L. (Lep. Lycaenidae) in Britain. *Entomologist*, **96**, 199–210.

STROYAN, H. L. G. (1949) Range changes in British butterflies. *Entomologist*, **82**, 210–11.

SUTTON, R. A. (1981) The ecology and conservation of the silver-studded blue butterfly (*Plebejus argus*) (L.) *News Br. Butterfly Conserv. Soc.*, no. 26, 37–9.

THOMAS, J. A. (1973) The hairstreaks of Monks Wood. In *Monks Wood, a Nature Reserve Record*, ed. by R. C. Steele and R. C. Welch, 153–8. Abbots Ripton, Huntingdon: Nature Conservancy.

THOMAS, J. A. (1974) *Ecological studies of hairstreak butterflies.* Ph.D. thesis, University of Leicester.

THOMAS, J. A. (1975) Some observations on the early stages of the purple hairstreak butterfly, *Quercusia quercus* (Linnaeus) (Lep., Lycaenidae). *Entomologist's Gaz.*, **26**, 224–6.

THOMAS, J. A. (1980a) The extinction of the large blue and the conservation of the black hairstreak butterflies (a contrast of failure and success). *Annu. Rep. Inst. terr. Ecol.*, 1977, 19–23.

THOMAS, J. A. (1980b) Why did the large blue become extinct in Britain? *Oryx*, **15**, 243–7.

THOMAS, J. A. (1983a) The ecology and conservation of *Lysandra bellargus* (Lep. Lycaenidae) in Britain. *J. appl. Ecol.*, **20**, 59–83.

THOMAS, J. A. (1983b) The ecology and status of *Thymelicus acteon* (Lepidoptera Hesperiidae) in Britain. *Ecol. Entomol.*, **8**, 427–35.

THOMAS, J. A. (1983c) A quick method of estimating butterfly numbers during surveys. *Biol. Conserv.*, **27**, 195–211.

THOMAS, J. A. (1983d) A 'WATCH' census of common British butterflies. *Jnl. biol. Educ.*, **17**, 333–8.

THOMAS, J. A. (in press) The conservation of butterflies in temperate countries: past efforts and lessons for the future. In: *The Biology of Butterflies*, ed. R. I. Vane-Wright and P. R. Ackery (Symposium of the Royal Entomological Society No. 11).

THOMAS, J. A., and MERRETT, P. (1980) Observations of butterflies in the Purbeck Hills in 1976 and 1977. *Proc. Dorset nat. Hist. archaeol. Soc.*, **99**, 112–19.

THOMAS, J. A., and SIMCOX, D. J. (1982) A quick method for estimating larval populations of *Melitaea cinxia* during surveys. *Biol. Conserv.*, **22**, 315–22.

THOMSON, G. (1970) The distribution and nature of *Pieris napi thomsoni* Warren (Lep. Pieridae). *Entomologist's Rec. J. Var.*, **82**, 255–61.

THOMSON, G. (1973) Geographical variation of *Maniola jurtina* (L.) (Lepidoptera, Satyridae). *Tijdschr. Entomol.*, **116**, 185–227.

THOMSON, G. (1978) *Aricia artaxerxes* (F.) (Lep. Lycaenidae) relocated in central Scotland. *Entomologist's Gaz.*, **29**, 1–2.

THOMSON, G. (1980) *The butterflies of Scotland.* London: Croom Helm.

TINBERGEN, N. (1972) *The animal and its world. I. Field studies.* London: Allen & Unwin.

TURNER, J. R. G. (1963) A quantitative study of a Welsh colony of the large heath butterfly, *Coenonympha tullia* Müller (Lepidoptera). *Proc. R. ent. Soc. Lond. A*, **38**, 101–12.

TUTT, J. W. (1905–1914) *British butterflies.* 4 vols. London: Elliot Stock.

WARREN, M. S. (1981) *The ecology of the wood white butterfly* Leptidea sinapis L. (*Lepidoptera, Pieridae*). Ph.D. thesis, University of Cambridge.

WARREN, M. S., (in press) The biology and status of the wood white butterfly, *Leptidea sinapsis* L. (Lepidoptera Pieridae) in the British Isles. *Entomologist's Gaz.*

WATSON, R. W. (1969) Notes on *Melitaea cinxia* L., 1945–1968. *Entomologist's Rec. J. Var.*, **81**, 18–20.

WEST, B. K. (1982) *Pieris rapae* and *Cardera draba* (Cruciferae) as a larval food plant. *Entomologist's Rec. J. Var.*, **94**, 72.

WIKLUND, C. (1977a) Oviposition, feeding and spatial separation of breeding and foraging habits in a population of *Leptidea sinapis* (Lepidoptera). *Oikos*, **28**, 56–8.

WIKLUND, C. (1977b) Courtship behaviour in relation to female monogamy in *Leptidea sinapis* (Lepidoptera). *Oikos*, **29**, 275–83.

WIKLUND, C., and AHRBERG, C. (1978) Host plants, nectar source plants and habitat selection of males and females of *Anthocaris cardamines* (Lepidoptera). *Oikos*, **31**, 169–83.

WIKLUND, C., PERSSON, A., and WICKMAN, P. O. (1983) Larval aestivation and direct development as alternative strategies in the speckled wood butterfly, *Pararge aegeria*, in Sweden. *Ecol. Entomol.*, **8**, 233–8.

WILLIAMS, C. B. (1958) *Insect migration.* London: Collins.

WILLIAMS, P. H. (1982) The distribution and decline of British bumble bees (*Bombus* Latr.). *J. Apic. Res.*, **21**, 236–45.

WORMS, C. G. M. de (1949) An account of some of the British forms of *Plebeius argus* Lina. *Rep. Raven ent. nat. Hist. Soc.*, 28–30.

WORMS, C. G. M. de (1962) *The macrolepidoptera of Wiltshire.* Salisbury: Wiltshire Archeol. & Nat. Hist. Soc.

We have also quoted from a number of unpublished reports. The following are reports produced for the Joint Committee for the Conservation of British Insects (a committee, organized by the Royal Entomological Society, on which many conservation organizations are represented): adonis blue (R. P. Burton, M. L. Connolly, 1973); chequered skipper (L. Farrell, 1973); Glanville fritillary (D. J. Simcox, J. A. Thomas, 1980); heath fritillary (M. S. Warren, C. D. Thomas, J. A. Thomas, 1981); silver-spotted skipper (D. J. Simcox, C. D. Thomas, J. A. Thomas, 1983). A number of reports were also produced on the large blue, for the Joint Committee for the Conservation of the Large Blue Butterfly: J. Muggleton (1975); P. Nevin (1975); M. G. Yates (1974). The Institute of Terrestrial Ecology has produced the following reports under contract to the Nature Conservancy Council: black hairstreak (J. A. Thomas, 1976); large blue (J. A. Thomas, 1976, 1977, 1978); monitoring butterfly numbers (E. Pollard, 1981). Finally, the following private manuscripts have been consulted: Scotch argus (R. H. L. Dennis, 1982); mountain ringlet (K. Porter, 1976); marsh fritillary (K. Porter, 1982).

Check List of butterflies, and their major food plants

Butterflies			Major food plants
Family	HESPERIIDAE		
Sub-family	Hesperiinae		
	Carterocephalus palaemon	chequered skipper	Brachypodium sylvaticum, Molinea caerulea and some other grasses
	Thymelicus sylvestris	small skipper	Holcus lanatus
	Thymelicus lineola	Essex skipper	Dactylis glomerata, Holcus mollis
	Thymelicus actaeon	Lulworth skipper	Brachypodium pinnatum
	Hesperia comma	silver-spotted skipper	Festuca ovina
	Ochlodes venata	large skipper	Dactylis glomerata and some other grasses
Sub-family	Pyrginae		
	Erynnis tages	dingy skipper	Lotus corniculatus
	Pyrgus malvae	grizzled skipper	Potentilla species and Fragaria vesca
Family	PAPILIONIDAE		
	Papilio machaon	swallowtail	Peucedanum palustre
Family	PIERIDAE		
Sub-family	Dismorphiinae		
	Leptidea sinapis	wood white	Lathyrus pratensis, L. montanus, Vicia cracca, Lotus corniculatus and some other legumes
Sub-family	Coliadinae		
	Colias croceus	clouded yellow	Trifolium species and many other legumes
	Gonepteryx rhamni	brimstone	Rhamnus catharticus and Frangula alnus
Sub-family	Pierinae		
	Aporia crataegi	black-veined white	Crataegus species, Prunus spinosa and other shrubs, including cultivated fruit trees
	Pieris brassicae	large white	Cultivated Brassica crops
	Pieris rapae	small white	Cultivated Brassica crops, Alliaria petiolata, Sisymbrium officinale and other crucifers
	Pieris napi	green-veined white	Cardamine pratensis, Alliaria petiolata, Sisymbrium officinale and other crucifers
	Anthocaris cardamines	orange tip	Cardamine pratensis, Alliaria petiolata, and other crucifers (flower heads)
Family	LYCAENIDAE		
Sub-family	Theclinae		
	Callophrys rubi	green hairstreak	Helianthemum chamaecistus, Vaccinium myrtillus, various legumes, flowers of various shrubs
	Thecla betulae	brown hairstreak	Prunus spinosa

Check List of butterflies, and their major food plants

Butterflies			Major food plants
	Quercusia quercus	purple hairstreak	*Quercus* species
	Strymonidia w-album	white-letter hairstreak	*Ulmus* species
	Strymonidia pruni	black hairstreak	*Prunus spinosa*
Sub-family	Lycaeninae		
	Lycaena phlaeas	small copper	*Rumex acetosa* and *Rumex acetosella*
	Lycaena dispar	large copper	*Rumex hydrolapathum*
	Cupido minimus	small blue	*Anthyllis vulneraria*
	Plebejus argus	silver-studded blue	*Ulex europaeus, Lotus corniculatus, Erica* species, *Helianthemum chamaecistus*
	Aricia agestis	brown argus	*Helianthemum chamaecistus, Erodium cicutarium*
	Aricia artaxerxes	northern brown argus	*Helianthemum chamaecistus*
	Polyommatus icarus	common blue	*Lotus corniculatus*
	Lysandra coridon	chalkhill blue	*Hippocrepis comosa*
	Lysandra bellargus	adonis blue	*Hippocrepis comosa*
	Cyaniris semiargus	mazarine blue	*Trifolium pratense* and some other legumes
	Celastrina argiolus	holly blue	Flowers of *Ilex aquifolium* and various other shrubs. 2nd generation mainly *Hedera helix*
	Maculinea arion	large blue	*Thymus drucei* (plus *Myrmica sabuleti* ant eggs, larvae and prepupae)
Family	NEMEOBIIDAE		
	Hamearis lucina	Duke of Burgundy	*Primula veris, P. vulgaris*
Family	NYMPHALIDAE		
	Ladoga camilla	white admiral	*Lonicera periclymenum*
	Apatura iris	purple emperor	*Salix caprea, S. cinerea*
	Vanessa atalanta	red admiral	*Urtica dioica*
	Cynthia cardui	painted lady	*Cirsium* species, *Carduus* species, a range of other herbs
	Aglais urticae	small tortoiseshell	*Urtica dioica*
	Nymphalis polychloros	large tortoiseshell	*Ulmus* species, occasionally various other trees
	Inachis io	peacock	*Urtica dioica*
	Polygonia c-album	comma	*Urtica dioica, Ulmus* species, and some other related plants
	Boloria selene	small pearl-bordered fritillary	*Viola* species
	Boloria euphrosyne	pearl-bordered fritillary	*Viola* species
	Argynnis adippe	high brown fritillary	*Viola* species
	Argynnis aglaja	dark green fritillary	*Viola* species
	Argynnis paphia	silver-washed fritillary	*Viola* species
	Eurodryas aurinia	marsh fritillary	*Succisa pratensis*

Melitaea cinxia	Glanville fritillary	*Plantago lanceolata*
Mellicta athalia	heath fritillary	*Melampyrum pratense, Plantago lanceolata, Veronica chamaedrys* and some other plants

Family SATYRIDAE

Pararge aegeria	speckled wood	Many grasses
Lasiommata megera	wall	*Brachypodium pinnatum, B. sylvaticum, Dactylis glomerata* and various other grasses
Erebia epiphron	mountain ringlet	*Nardus stricta*
Erebia aethiops	Scotch argus	*Molinea caerulea, Sesleria caerulea* and perhaps other grasses
Melanargia galathea	marbled white	*Festuca ovina, Brachypodium pinnatum* and other grasses
Hipparchia semele	grayling	Various grasses
Pyronia tithonus	hedge brown	Various, mainly fine-leaved, grasses
Maniola jurtina	meadow brown	Various, mainly fine-leaved, grasses
Coenonympha pamphilus	small heath	Various, mainly fine-leaved, grasses
Coenonympha tullia	large heath	*Rhyncospora alba,* and some grasses
Aphantopus hyperantus	ringlet	Various grasses

INDEX

MAKE A HARD HEART

Hearts are fragile
Delicate and sensitive
Easy to hurt
Always wanting what it can't get
Always ready for the next
Thrust of hurt
Would it be nice
If a heart was hard
No emotions
A piece of stone
That stays the same
No matter what happens
But, then
It won't be a heart
A solid residue
Of a life
So what if it is still a heart.

HOMELESS WITH A HOME

I have a home
But I am homeless
I have a home
But it is empty
I visit relatives (family)
But I am shut out
There is no place for me
In their homes
It is their home
And they have moved on
I visit loved ones
But their door is shut
I knock and knock
But their door is shut
I knock and knock
The door remains shut
Telling me
It is no longer my home
It does not belong here.

There are new occupants
To this hone.
I visit friends
But their rooms
Are occupied
By other friends
New and latest
I am now
A forgotten soul
A memory that
Must be forgotten
I wander home to home
And then return
To my home
And relax in its solitude
I am reflecting
I am homeless
In my home.

LIVING IN A DARK BOX

The dark box
Where I pass
My wasted life
Is fragile
The stained cardboard
Beaten
By rain, wind and sun
Is my home
A place of shelter
Where I exist
Surrounded by
Empty darkness
No windows, no doors
A place to reflect
On life and my life
As the box gets carried away
And dropped in the garbage.

AN ALIEN IN MY OWN PLANET

I stare at the faces
That walk the streets
Of our planet
I don't recognize them
They don't look familiar
They are all different
Aliens with no faces
No values
Greedy eyes
Shunning you
Hinting, why are you here?
You don't belong here
You have integrity, values, beliefs
Convictions, hope, faith, ambition
You are definitely not part of this world
Show me, clearly telling me
I don't belong here
I am alien in my own planet.

STANDING IN THE DUST

The caravan
Has passed me by
Horses and carriage
Spread dirt and dust
I stand alone
Waving my hand
Wondering
Why it didn't stop for me?
Why it ignored me?
Now I stand
With my baggage
When the next caravan will come
But until then
I stand and wait
In a dust storm
Hope and faith
My only diversion.

LAUGHING AT LIFE

I laugh at life
For what it has
Done to me
Life laughs at me
For what I have
Done to myself
We both laugh
At each other
The sense of humor
Makes living easy
No tears of laughter
Streak down our faces
Dripping on lips
With their salty taste
Awakening feelings
Of joy and sorrow
As our laughter continues.

LAUGHING AT LIFE (2)

I laugh at life
For what it has made me
Life laughs at me
For what I have become
We both laugh
At each other
For we are
Two of a kind
Both not knowing
How to live
Enjoying our follies and mistakes
Sharing the blunders
With a sense of humor
For that is all we have
To ease the pain
As we journey together
To our end
Full of laughter and joy.

LAUGHING AT DEATH

It was a dream
Or was it?
A knock, a jolt
An angelic figure
Beckoning me
I ask
    It is your time
    Death awaits you
I laughed
Is it a joke?
    No, I am here to take you
You got to be kidding
I still have dreams
    But, you had your chances
    And you blew it
So, what
It was my life
I did what I did
Right or wrong
Good or bad
You cannot change that
    But I can end
    It all for you
    Take you to a place
    Where you can
    Argue as much as you want
But, I don't want to argue
I want to live
And take my time
To decide
When I want to go
    You can't
    For I determine
    When you go
But who are you?
You just showed up
But, who are you?

You just showed up
At your whim
That is a joke
I don't even know you
Except that
You exist
And will come for me
Some day
It is okay
But I am not ready
I have
Visions of the future
That you
Cannot take away
So go away
  But, I can't
  For it is my duty
  To bring you
Why me?
  It was your turn
Who said it?
  Time
But, time never ends
It is perpetual
And I am in the middle
Of a new life
That will
Tell the world
That I was here
I made an impact
I left a legacy
So, leave me alone
For I need time
  I can't give you that
  Time may be perpetual
  But not for mortals
  You are mortal
  Just a speck
  In the dust
  No one will know

You ever existed
Or ceased to exist
I don't care
About anybody
It is me I have to live with
That is all that matters
I will go
When I am ready
So, leave me
Before I start laughing at you.

VICTIM OF SELF

I was born innocent
Everything was fun
Everyone was equal
Then I grew up
Learning from society
Dismantling the mask
Of innocence
For a new face of
Biases and prejudice
Changing one mask
For another
I lost myself
In this wilderness of life
Lost my innocence
I was
A victim of self.

EXIST TO DIE

Why do we exist?
To die for some
As Robert Browning, the poet, said,
    "Grow old along with me
    The last of life
    For which the first
    Was made."
And he was right
We exist for death
We do our song and dance
Perform for the world audience
And then the curtain falls
The final curtain
with no encore
The show is over
Time to call
It an end.

DREAMS ARE DREAMS

There are dreams
And there are dreams
There are dreams
That we yearn for
And there are dreams
That remain dreams
There are dreams
That come to us
While we are asleep
Howling through our subconscious
Into vivid images
Of space and time
That vanish
When we wake
Dreams are not reality
They are visions of a world
That we may not see
They are just dreams.

THE IMPERFECT LOVE

The beauty of life
Is that
It is so imperfect
The beauty lies
In its imperfections
In its unpredictabilities
In its vulnerabilities
For love has its wants
Its desires
But it does not know
How to achieve it
It flounders
In the ocean of expectations
Awakening reclamation
From stone walls
As it pounds
Our empty hopes
Not giving up
For love never gives up
It is a heart beat
That goes on
Until life ceases
Love is a heartbeat
That keeps on pounding
Until it finds a life
That it can live through
To a new world
Where it will meet love
Another love
To embrace life
For love and life
Are imperfect souls
Both wanting each other
But both eluding each other.

LUCKY TO LOVE

I would rather love
And lose
Than not love at all
Love is a divine gift
The feelings, the emotions
Make you alive
Make you feel
That you are
In the heart of God
In His bosom
Feeling
The highest form of expression
Feeling
That you are alive
Alive with love
And you can last
Through eternity.

THE DARK SIDE OF ME

We all have a dark side
I have mine too
In anger and frustration
I may think evil of some people
I may think life is unfair
I may not feel sympathy for some
I may feel that some people
Don't deserve good lives
I may feel that
Some evils get unpunished
But the dark side
Lasts a short time
The thoughts pass
Then I am back
To my normal self
Good and bad
A human.

THE END OF FLOW

I had a muse
I had ideas
The thoughts were flowing
Through the ink
Onto paper
Burning at things
Of the mind
Into unforgettable memories
As the ink dries up
The paper is blank
The writings stop
Life comes to a standstill
Having exhausted
All creativity
To live a life
Without words on a paper
A blank page
The end of flow.

SADDLING TWO HORSES

I ride two horses
At the same time
One of dreams
One of reality
It is dangerous
I perch precariously
Uncertain stability
Ready for a fall
A great fall
For dreams and reality
Never merge
Like two horses
My ride will always be dangerous
It is a ride that I must make
To reach
Where I must
For dreams to become a reality.

PATTERN TO THIS MADNESS

There is a pattern
To this madness
That I call life
My life
I live in a mad world
Among mad people
Where madness is normal
To the point
That my madness
Is now part of my life
Making mistakes
At every step of my life
For all the wrong reasons
But I am consistent
My madness is persistent
It is constant
It is there
A great pattern.

LOST HORIZONS

There is a world
I envision
A Shangri-La
Where a utopian world
Holds a perfect life
Where humanity is revered
Integrity worshipped
Love cherished
Friendship valued
It is a world
Across horizons
In the mountains
Away from
Dying societies
That self-destructed
In deceit and greed
Void of compassion
And snow-filled peaks
That watered
The fertile lands
Is barren
The heat has dried
All vegetation and life
Become wasteland
That once held
Fertile lives
Now stand desolate
Ravished by the
Greed of humanity
Plundering life
That sustains it
Disappearing horizons
Of hope
Until we are left
Alone and cold
No hope in sight.

IT IS JUST A GAME

It is just a game
Life
Sometimes you win
Sometimes you lose
Sometimes you just break even
Life should not
Be taken seriously
For we participate in it
Unwittingly and unwillingly
We are thrown in it
Like dice
We take our chances
We take risks
The dice
Determine our fate
All we can do is throw
If the dice are fair
They will decide our fate
But if the dice are tainted
They will control our fate
We don't know
What dice we will get
Fair or tainted
That itself is a game
A game in a game
We are pawns
That move with the dice
And we accept our fate
What gets through at us
We catch, we miss
The game goes on
And we must accept
That life is
Just a game.

RELIC OF THE PAST

Ancient virtues
Remnant values of the past
Treasures in dungeons
Beauty in antiques
Scars of wisdom
Washing of the wind
Carvings of nature
That is me
A relic of the past
That believes in value, integrity, beauty
In an unholy world
Inhabited by vacant souls
That walk around
As lifeless ghosts
Trying to imitate
Humans that have faded
Into oblivion
As I remain
A remnant of the past.

EMPTY VALUES AROUND

Values
Our honest beliefs
That give us dignity and individuality
Values and respect
To trust
Compassion for humans
Honesty in relationships
Is being eroded
And left behind
In the dust
People talk of values
As if they were commodities
For sale at cheap stores
Not knowing
That values are never sold
It is an inner virtue
That is the basis
Of all humankind
That is soundly ignored
Distorted by society
To save their own interest
Lying and deceit
Broken promises
Walking over people
Now is accepted as a norm
That we accept casually
For we are part of it
Why have values in society
When we don't have values
It is too much of a burden
It is easy to live
In an empty world,
With empty values.

WHERE IS HOME?

Where is home
To a traveler through life
That is constantly on the move
Searching for a place
Where he can rest in peace
And die with dignity
It is not a home
Where one lives
It is not a home
With a glamorous structure
It is not a home
Surrounded by relatives and friends
It is not a home
That gives you shelter
From heat and cold
It is not a home
Where you socialize and entertain
It is not a home
That protects you from the outside world
For the outside world is in shambles
In need of protection from itself
The home is
Where your heart is
Where you feel free and liberated
Where your energy is at its peak
Where creativity blossoms
Where the world seems tranquil
Where people are warm
Welcoming you as an individual
Is there such a place?
Is there such a home?
So I must continue
My journey to find
My true home.

EVERYONE FOR SALE

We get excited by
The sale signs
We love bargains
Even though we know
That sales are illusions
Attractions to spend our lives
For illusionary bargains
But it is not just
The goods or services for sale
People are for sale
There is always a price
For which we will sell ourselves
Our values, principles, dignity
For our safety or survival
For we must live
To leave a mark
Even a mark of disdain
There is a price
For which we will sell
Look at the politicians
Lawyers and public officials
Media and stars
Family and friends
Selling to save their souls
For materialistic existence
Even though
The soul is divine
It is not part of this shallow life
But we sell our souls
For instant gratification
For short term pleasures
In the end
We are all whores
Except, whores give pleasure
We don't.

FREEDOM TO DIE

Death is inevitable
It comes to us all
It is the only certainty
A "must" event for all of us
It comes
When it comes
So why not
Have
The freedom to die
Not avoid death
But to enjoy it
And die with dignity and class
In my own way
There is one choice
One freedom
That I must
Do it my way
At least die
The way I want
In pleasure
Savoring every last minute
Enjoying my life
With favorite foods and drinks
Music and books
Still growing intellectually
As life ebbs out of you
The divine luck
Slowly grinds your body and soul
To a halt
With dignity and grace
As you breathe
The last air of a decaying world
To leave on your terms
To end it with dignity
And your freedom.

FREEDOM FROM LIFE

Life is a cruel prison
That holds you until you die
Whether you are guilty or not
Because it thrives
On your helplessness
You are stuck with it
You are its cherished victim
To suck and bleed
Until you are dry and devoid
And then it throws you
To the vultures
To feed on you
Until not a remnant
Is left of you
Just a faded memory
Of a life
In need of freedom.

VICTIMS OF OUR CHILDREN

Our children
Are born through us
But are they our flesh and blood?
In a sense, yes
But, they are not our minds
Their minds are of a future
That we do not see
For that is not our world
We are of
Two different worlds
Though we are parents
Think that ours is the same world
But it is not
Our children
Are not our children anymore
They have moved on
While we are left behind
Victims of hope
That they will b like us
They will respect us
They will love us
That is an illusion
For we must realize
We are not them
We are not like them
We belong to a world
That died when we had our children
Soon they will leave
To start their nests
We are left alone
Starting the empty nest
The nest that we made for our children
Is now empty
Time to fly
For we are now
Victims of our children.

THE SYSTEM

The system
Is an organism
That feeds upon itself
For its survival
Creating mechanisms
To shield itself
With rules and regulations
That shout out outsiders and change
For change is a threat to a system
It wants status quo
Politics or public
Academic or non-profit
As organizations became systems
Organisms
Betraying their original goals
For survival
It is now just becoming a system
With its own rules and regulations
A living organism.

THE REPUBLIC

The republic, the state
Corrupt at the top
Rotten to the core
Using and exploiting
Its simple people
With lies and insecurities
Is a regime
That will meet its fate
At the last dust of lost societies
That imploded, self-destructed
To preserve the victors
Who served themselves
Not the people
For people are to be exploited
For their survival
The Machiavellian model
People are expendable.

THE POWER OF PEOPLE

The power of people
Is important
They are brainwashed
By politicians, by media
Manipulated, seduced
Because people are wanton
They don't read
Their knowledge is diminishing
They are exploited
For their ignorance
Divide and conquer
The power of the people
Is no more
Just an illusion
At the whims of the ruler or ruling class
Preying on ignorant people
Making promises they do not believe

THE CRUELTIES OF HUMANS

The cruelties
That humans inflict
On other humans
Is unbelievable
Indiscriminate killing
Mental and physical abuse
Callousness and neglect
Abandonment of responsibilities
Self-service and selfishness
Walking over each other
Ignoring compassion
Breeding in greed and avarice
Hurting children and elders
Where did we learn this
Not from God
But from other humans
Shallow and weak
We are evil.

THE AFTERLIFE

There is a world
That is waiting for me
At the other side of the universe
Where I will be truly me
A real person
I was supposed to be
In this life
A person I betrayed
I became a person
Prone to mistakes
Living shallow life
The afterlife
Is my redemption
To recover and recoup
My soul
That abandoned me
I searched
For meaning
In a desolate life
Shedding all my values
To exist in a carnal world
But, the afterlife
Is my home
To gain some respect
Within myself
To live a life
That I was supposed to live
A life
That will tell me
Who I am really
A person
Of substance.

A GOOD MAN

I am a good man
At least that is what I think
A good man in my eyes
Or a good man
In the eyes of others
But, then
What is "good"?
The fine line
Between good and bad
Is blurring
Depends on how
And who looks at it
I was born good
Pure and innocent
And then I grew up
In a polluted and corrupted world
Where survival and greed
Are the values
Of existence
As I struggle
To come out alive
From the grave
That I have dug for myself
Without dust
Clean and clear
Washed away
By my mistakes and blunders
To look at the mirror
Of life
As I face the eternal truth
Am I a good man?
I thought I was
I think I am
But only God and destiny
Are the ultimate judges.

RETURNING TO THE FIELDS

The fields
That I grew up in
Were full of life
Nature and nurture
Providing me
With all the ingredients
To live a rich life
The smell, aroma, food
Lush with water and flowers
I was part of it
It was part of me
We were one
A life in tune with nature
But then I left the field
To seek paths
In wilderness
And rugged mountains
I got lost
I stumbled
I got hurt
But I kept going
Searching for the fields
That I had abandoned
I yearned for soft earth
The gentle touch of nature
I want to return
To the fields
Where I can live
In open air
And be one again
At peace with nature
To embrace
The fields
Of my life.

THE LAST OF THE HUMANS

The humans
The endangered species
About to become extinct
Due to its own follies
Blunders and greed
Filling the environment
That sustains it
For instant pleasures
And self-gratification
Selling their souls
For greed and money
Where have all the humans gone?
Into an empty space of survival
Selling values, beliefs, integrity
Themselves
For a price
That is cheap
To anyone who will buy
Until there is nothing to sell
Just an empty shell
That is useless
Of no value
Then wonder
Who am I?
Stripped of all dignity
All divine gifts
Just a carcass
Of flesh and bones
That is wasting
To rot and decay
A feast of the vultures
The species
That came with a promise
Now nearing extinction
Destroyed by self
The last of the humans.

DREAMS OF A SOCIETY

A society
That is full of hope and dreams
Love and peace
Remains a dream
The utopian empire
Has crashed many times
As we struggle
To carve and existence
In a decaying world
Destroyed by hatred
While we still introduce
New humans
Into a dying world
Hoping that a
New society of perfection
Will emerge
Just to see our
Dreams crashing
As we continue
To give birth and kill
Hoping and failing
Dreams of a society
That fails to emerge
While we slowly
Fade into oblivion
And the dreams
Of a society
Just remain a dream.

DREAMING OF A RAINBOW

The rainbow
Spreading across the universe
Sparkling its brilliant colors
Across the sky
Inviting dreams and hopes
Of a dying life
Staring at a rainbow
That is just a mirage
At the mercy of
Sun and rain
Hoping that clouds
Don't cover the sky
And kill the dream
As the rainbow
Disappears
To be replaced
By an illusion of hope.

UNFIT TO LIVE

We live
We die
Some live better
Some live bad
Some are privileged
Some are not
And then there are those
Who are unfit to live
For they make mistakes
From the day they are born
And continue to do so
Throughout their lives
Piling one on top of another
Until the pile becomes a mountain
That crushes them
These are the people
Who are unfit to live
Unfit not because
They are born humans
Unfit because
Divine guidance is not with them
Luck deserted them at birth
Humanity trampled them
These are the people
Who are unfit to live
And to them
Life is a burden
That must be cast off
As soon as possible
To end the pain and agony
Of life
That is not worth living
For we are, I am,
Unfit to live.

THE HUMAN TOUCH

Humans have a touch
That destroys civilizations
Killing their own kind
For pleasure and greed
But, then
They don't stop at their own kind
They plunder
The earth
That gives them life
For they think
That their lives are limited
So they want to limit
Every nature's life
They kill rocks
 They kill plants
They cut through
Mountains and jungles
Destroying in their paths
In the name of progress
But more for their
Selfish pursuits
Of their short lives' gratification
Ignoring the earth
That gives sustenance
For they think
They own the earth
Not realizing
That they are useless against nature
They are vulnerable
They are useless
So, show humility
Let your touch be gentle
With respect
Make a human touch
A divine touch.

THE PATIENCE OF NATURE

Nature
Defines time
In its own terms
Nurturing it with patience
Creating rhythms and cycles
That move the world
As it carves
The earth
In its own vision
Creating mountains and oceans
Valleys and rivers
Color and shape
Slowly dripping
Gradually planting
Life and beauty
Into a desolate dangerous world
Hope that we will learn
From its caring patience
But, we humans
Live for a short time
For instant gratification
Making patience
Into a new virtue
As we come and go
While nature stops
Living through eternity
Specks of life
Forgotten and scattered
In the hands
Of nature.

MY MIND'S MIND

My mind
Has a mind of its own
It does not listen to me
It ignores me
It avoids me
It treats me with contempt
Brushing me aside
And making decisions
Without me in mind
It was not like that
I was in control
I learned, educated myself
Acquired knowledge
Nurtured my mind
Let it expand
Let it think
And then
It deserted me
It was too good for me
It made decisions
That hurt me
It made choices
That led me astray
Once we were one
Now we are aliens
To function without my mind
Floundering and existing
As my mind
Waved at me
From a distance
Bidding me goodbye
As I am left to
Fend off love without my mind
Just alone.

SUM TOTAL OF LIFE

As I tally
My assets and liabilities
Trying to determine
If I was profitable
Or a loss
I would be happy
To just break even
For I came from nothing
And will go into nothing
The assets I piled
Turned into liability
As they get
Fully depreciated
With no value left
And I was left
Without resources
As I fell into bankruptcy
And closed my life.

THE HUMAN ANIMAL

The human
Is an animal
With instincts for survival
Killing and stealing
To prolong life
But a human
Is an advanced animal
While an animal
Strives on basic survival
Humans rationalized
Survival by greed and lies
Killing for pleasure
Just to advance its case
Hollow as it might be
For the air of superiority
Permeates its being
For it can kill
Animals with weapons
Not with hands
For it is too weak
And the human
Is not even a noble animal
For animals serve a purpose
While humans
Exist for exploitation
Feeling superior
Just like the dinosaurs
Until nature
Can't stand it
And wipe the planet
Of humans
Making it pure and natural
Hoping a new species
Will emerge
That will make earth
A better place.

.

THE LAST OF THE BREED

I was bred
To respect people
Hold certain values
Follow principles
That uphold truth
Trust fellow people
And develop integrity
That is unquestioned
Learn and grow
For knowledge is power
And never ends
And that was my breeding
Given to me
By my parents,
Bless their souls,
Now I stand
Alone
In an empty village
Which is devoid of people
Who have left the town
In search of selfishness, greed and avarice
Shedding all goodness
That was ingrained in them
As they ride out
Storming dust in my eyes
Left alone
Reflecting on my bred
Lonely and alone
Wondering what happened
It was good
While it lasted
The last of the bred
That believed in something
That belief in life
Is worth living.

THE REMAINING DAYS

As I count
The remaining days
Of my wasted life
I wonder
When will it all end
How many days are left
What do I need to do
In my remaining days
Reflect on my past
Cry over my follies
Admire my achievements
Or just let it go
For I have lived
I cannot undo the past
It is over
The future -
Is a remnant of my past.

DREAMS OF A MAN

I had dreams
Of a wonderful home
Full of fun and family
Excitement vibrating through
Every pore
And then nature
Decaying the structure
Until it collapses in a heap
I stand alone
Pounded by rain and sun
Seeking shelter
In plants and fields
Scattering dreams
Sheltering illusions
Until reality sets in
And then
All I see
Is a hut
In the distance
A quiet place
Strong and silent
A place
Beckoning me
To give me solace
And peace
That eluded me
All my life
And now that hut
Is my home
A simple place
Where I can be at peace
And rest
Until the end beckons me.

WALKING IN, WALKING OUT

The curtain call
Time to enter
The stage.
Face the audience
Do my skit
Will they love it?
Will they detest it?
I don't know.
I enter the stage
Greeted with applause
For they have not seen
My performance yet
I respond
Just like a puppet
I sing and dance
Soliloquy and monologue
Crying and laughing
To the amusement
Of the audience
I get applauded
I get booed
But the show must go on
My performance ends
I have uttered
My last dialogue
It is over
I walk off the stage
Quietly and down
My game is over
Forgotten
As I unmask and wash
The artificial makeup
From my face
To be just me
Love's artist.

RISE FROM THE ASHES

The ashes
Scattered and scared
Gathered in the dust
Trying to carve
A life
Out of dead remnants
Igniting fires
Out of sparks
That burst into an eruption
To live and prolong
Life that died some time ago
But life does not die
The ashes are the skin
That must be discarded
For life to emerge
From its cocoon
To rise from its ashes.

THE FINAL FLAME

As the flame dies
It bursts into brightness
Emitting a myriad of colors
That announce its demise
Its final battle
Against life
As it loses its grip
But still fighting
To leave a message
That it won't die in vain
Even in its end moments
It will ignite the world
Brighten it up
For the last time
Before it plunges
Into eternal darkness
The final flame.

UNSHACKLING RESPONSIBILITIES

The end is near
The boat is heavy
I must lighten up
Unshackle the responsibilities
That I have carried
All my life
Bent with the burdens
I must straighten up
To be able to walk
Through the gates
Erect and proud
That I fulfilled my responsibilities
I am free
Of obligations
My conscious is clear
As I stand above the clouds
In full freedom.

MY LIFE IN THIS WORLD

My life in this world
Is full of contradictions
It keeps me alive
While it pushes me
Towards my demise
It gives me hope
Then it shatters my dreams
It soars to great achievements
Then crashes ferociously
It loves me
It hates me
It pleases me
It berates me
It amuses me
But, it is my life
I am in love with it
I will die within in.

THE HOME IS A PRISON

My home is my castle
Heavily stoned
That surrounds me
Keeps me warm
Protects me from the outside
While I breathe its stale air
I am comfortable
That is what I think
I am safe
That is what I believe
I am there
Because that is what
I believe is my home
But my home
Is also my prison
A self-imposed prison
That gives me a false sense of security
By keeping me inside
Shutting me off
From the outside world
In an artificial world
Of likes and dislikes
That are far from reality
But it is a home
A place of my own
Good and bad
A place where I belong
In my world
That is untouched by light and dust
Pure and simple
Far away from reality
But a place
That I must rest
A quiet prison.

RETURNING TO THE TRENCHES

I have wandered long enough
Searching for purpose
That still eludes me
I have climbed the mountains
Marched through the valleys
Still I remain
Where I started
Travelling all over
But remaining still
I must stay still
Stop the journey
Between the trenches
To regroup
To rethink
And start my journey again
With new hope and directions
Diving into a sunset of my choosing.

MISFIT TO THE END

I knew when I was born
That I was a misfit
In this world
Whether I was wrong for the world
Or whether the world was wrong for me
Maybe, I was born
In the wrong time
But me and life
May have known better times
But I continue to exist
Out of sync with the world
But never one with the world
And as my time
Draws to a close
I will leave it
Misfit to the end
From start to finish.

A PERFECT LIFE IN AN IMPERFECT WORLD

I live a perfect life
Full of mistakes and misjudgments
Gaining and losing opportunities
Just like a regular life
But it does not bother me
For I live in an imperfect world
Where my imperfections seem perfect
A world without values
Rampant competition and greed
Seeming normal
Accepted by the people is part of life
For we are as corrupt
As our leaders
So we are alright
Imperfection breeds imperfection
But I am alright
From imperfect
Perfect for an imperfect world.

LIFE OF A LONELY SURVIVOR

I have survived
A lonely life
In a miserable world
That exchanges values and principles
For hollowness and shallowness
To live a life
Of simple virtues and responsibilities
That means all of us
But, it is survival
That is proud
It had beliefs
It grew and learned
Even if it was lonely
It was worth it
For a lonely survivor.

MOTION OF SURVIVAL

The day starts
With an alarm
Nudging me
To face the world
Like any other day
The cycle of life
That continues
In perpetual motion
Killing time
Until sunset
Another day passed
Another day survived
As I rest thinking
What did I do this day
What did I accomplish
I stare at blankness
Ready to take on another day.

THE FINAL PAGES

The book is ending
But I do not know
The ending
A few pages are left
So what should I write?
A happy ending
A sad ending
Or, just a mystery
Of how life may end
And leave it to imagination
The final pages
Are the sum total of the book
What will it be?
Will it bomb?
But the pages
Are carved in stone
So, let it be
A memorable end.

IN SEARCH OF LIFE

I started my journey
At birth
In search of life
And as I near the sunset
I still search
I still haven't found it
It keeps eluding me
Maybe the life I seek
Does not exist
Maybe the life that exists
I do not want
We keeping missing each other
Like two trains
Passing each other in the night
Acknowledging each other
With a whistle
But never meeting
Just like the parallel
Tracks of the train
For if they meet
The train derails
So we travel
On distant tracks
Acknowledging and waving
Whistling and whimpering
Knowing that both are there
Apart but together
Existing but not together
Still searching for each other
And the search goes on
Until the day
When I find it
In eternity.

MY BLINDNESS

There was a time
When I could see everything
From near to distance
Left or right
Up or down
My eyes saw things
That others ignored
I had a clear view of the world
And I prided myself
That I was in touch with the world
What I saw
I could touch
Then came a night
A haunting night
When lightening stuck me
As I lay in a turbulent sleep
Awakening me with a jolt
I stood erect
I reached out
To touch
But my hands
Fell on empty spaces
People, places and images
Eluded me
My vision was tainted
I could only see
Part of life
Half of my life
Just disappeared
In a stroke
As I grope
To grasp things
I cannot see
Bumping into things
That should not be in my way
Waving to people
That I cannot see

Hoping they are there
Adjusting to life
In half a world
Forcing me to
Desert my territory
For unknown spaces
Where my blindness won't matter
Where I will not bump into things
Where my half world
Will be a full world
Looking at the world
With imperfect vision
Making an imperfect world
Look perfect
Keeping total imperfections
Away from me
As I continue
To hit unknown targets
Trying to live
A normal life
In a blind world
Then I realize
I am not blind
I am just fractured and defective
But still perfect
For a world
That is decaying from top to bottom
It is not me that is blind
It is the world
For I acknowledge my deformities
But the world goes on
Ignoring its frailties
Why blindness
Is a blessing.

THE CONTRADICTIONS OF LIFE

Every aspect of life
Is a contradiction
We are here
Why we don't know
We are born to parents
We don't choose
We hope life will be good
We walk toward it
Not knowing if it will happen
We love, we marry
Not knowing if it will work
We keep falling in and out of love
We are happy and sad
At the same time
Hope and disillusionment
Every aspect of life
Is a contradiction
It is just a life.

DREAMS OF A VAGRANT

Even vagrants have dreams
Eve wanderers have dreams
Even homeless men have dreams
For dreams are the only right
Of a human that is unique to him
The only thing
That he can call his own
A wish, a hope
Whether it happens
Does not matter
For it propels them
Toward a world
That they want
A world full of happiness
A world of honesty
A world of love and peace
For dreams are just dreams
Hope and faith
In the great goodness of mankind
That remains an illusion
But dreams
Are the spirit of survival
An elixir of life
A whirl of illusions
We cannot give in
Even as a vagrant
For in the true sense
We are all vagrants
Searching for meaning
In a meaningless life
Passing through
Dreams are the only hope
That keeps us alive
And searching for the truth.

THERE WAS A TIME

There was a time
When I thought
I was good
I controlled my life
I knew where I was going
I saw my future
My dreams were fulfilled
And I lived a happy
Healthy life
And destined to die a natural death
Surrounded by family and friends
Adoring and missing me
My lovers saddened and crying
It was a thought
A belief
That I aspired
It was a time
A time now lost
A time that does not exist
My future is uncertain
I am alone
Abandoned and alone
Shrinking beliefs
Lost lovers
A simple existence
With hope and expectations
Of a life
That I did not achieve
In this life
But it was a good time
A time, I thought
Was my own.

THE SLOW MASSACRE

Life ebbs slowly
Eroding each faculty
One by one
Diminishing desires and hopes
As it chips away
At our bodies
Slowing as
Pounding us
Until we get
Used to its blows
And gradually succumb to it
In sweet pain
Finding pleasure
In erosion
As we enter
A state of bliss and purity
The sweetness of a slow massacre.

UNSHACKLING MEMORIES

Memories are part of us
Whether they hold us back
Or propel us forward
Depends on how we deal with them
Unshackling memories is not easy
They are embedded in us
Haunting us in our dreams
Taunting us in our actions
Driving us to undesirable locations
Propelling us into space
Either to throw us into
A different orbit
Or let us crash
Vigorously to earth
Memories can be blessings
Or hindrance
But, it is best
To unshackle memories
That hinder you
For the past is over
It can never come back
Unless you allow it
For the future awaits you
That is where you belong
In a world
Where you create new memories
Memories that are pleasurable
Positive and peaceful
For you live in a world
That is yours
Uniquely yours
A world for you
For your future.

THE ANCHOR OF THE PAST

The past is an anchor
That holds us still
For that is safe and settled
While the waves of the ocean
Undulate beneath us
Wanting us to move
With the flow of nature
But the anchor holds firm
For it has its own
Score to settle
It thrives on firmness and control
That is its strength
But an anchor is just an anchor
A relic of the past
Whose job is to hold
According to the laws of nature
It must be severed
The anklet
That this anchor is
To our feet
Must be cut
Otherwise
It will pull us
Down into the ocean
Drowning us with memories of the past
That have lost significance
As we lay dormant
At the bottom of the ocean
Unless we break free
And let us flow with nature
To our destined lands
A future of our dreams.

THE COLLAPSING MONUMENTS

The fabric of our society
Is crumbling
The foundations
Of our institutions
That were built on
Values, freedom and hope
Are being eroded
By greed, corruption and incompetence
As we stare
Blindly and blatantly
At our collapsing monuments
Watching the decay with empathy
Helpless and ignorant
Warped by the
Onslaught of deceit and lies
Hurled at us
By our leaders and media
The corruption of corporations
Driven by greed
For short-term justification
At the cost of our
Long-term institutions of liberty
Eroding opportunities
Except for selected few
Who exploit the system
To preserve the few
While our monuments collapse
We just keep staring at it
Until all is left
Is a rubble of dust
That carries memories of a past society
That crumbled like
Many other great societies of the past
History repeats
And we never learn.

SERIES OF CHALLENGES

My life has been a series of challenges
That are thrown my way
By divine forces
Family, friends and society
I try to jump over obstacles
Like a runner over a hurdle
Trying to aim the jump
Over the wall
Sometimes clearing it
Sometimes bumping against it
Sometimes just falling
As I set to
Continue the race
The race of life
For which I was not prepared
Not coached or warned
As I struggle towards
The next hurdle
Just relying on my instinct
Guts and faith
As I crash
Through each challenge
One by one
Hoping that
It will be the last challenge
But life is not that kind
Challenges are interwoven into life
And I must unravel them
One at a time
Until there are no more challenges left
Just a straight race
Boring and straight
As I long for
The arrows of challenges.

THE FINGER OF FATE

I hold the finger of fate
As it guides me through life
Pointing me in unknown directions
Gently nudging me
To try alone
But I am afraid
To let go
For the few times
I did let go
I stumbled into unchartered waters
Where I was bruised and pounded
By invisible forces
Leaving me not dead but alive
Enough life
To recoup
And get up
To face another onslaught
Of life
But this time
I hold the finger of fate
And not letting it go
Trusting my life
To its will
For my schemes
Never worked
Now I hope
It will guide me
To my dreams
As I hold onto its finger
Tightly and gently
As I am led
Somewhere, some place
Where my destiny
Awaits me.

DECLINING

There was a time
When it was hard and erect
Ready to go places
Wherever there was a soft opening
Shimmering thrusts
Elating in its eruptions
Resting peacefully
And then ready to take on the world
It was a good life
Fun, joy and play
As it ages
And reflects
On its many adventures
It wonders
Was it worth it?
Wasting so much energy
On deserted terrains
Sowing seeds
On brown lands
Until the well
Grew empty
Drawing water
Became a chore
Holding pride
Diminishes
Not necessarily by choice
But life
The natural cycle
That cannot remain
On top forever
Men are devastated
Unnatural endowments
Play short-term tricks
Until you realize
It is over
And fun while it lasted.

SEARCHING

I am in search
Of life that continues
To elude me
I am in search of a world
Where there is peace and tranquility
And people live in peace and contentment
I am in search of a partner
That values me as a friend
And brings out the best in me
I am in search of friends
That accept me for who I am
Pushing me in the right direction with gentleness
I am in search of family
That is not overbearing and critical
Creating a nurturing environment for growth
I am in search of children
Who do not need me for their own purpose
Rather than respect me for what I did for them
I am in search of colleagues
Who value collaboration
Rather than snapping and back-biting
I am in search of service
That value you a virtuous
Rather than a necessary evil
For their growth and profit
I am in search of leaders
Who extol integrity and values
Rather than exploitation and manipulation
But, I am still searching
There has to be a place
Where one is at
Peace with oneself
In harmony with nature
Friendship with all
And so I embark
Searching.

AN ANCIENT MARINER

There was once
An ancient mariner
Who roamed the seas
In his dependable old boat
Visiting places and sights
On whim and impulse
Guided by instinct and guts
Experiencing life
With passion and excitement
Making friends with unknown souls
Sharing thoughts and feelings with strangers
As his boat
Flew over undulating waters
Propelled and pummeled
In all directions
It was a free world
Everything near
But nothing in sight
Just a floating journey
Searching for an abyss
That takes you
Into a new world
Whether it exists
The mariner did not know
He had faith
And enjoyed the journey
It didn't matter where it led
But it was an adventure
Of a free spirit
A journey we all should take
To be free from constraints
Just letting
Life, nature and destiny
Exist with each other.

GOING THROUGH THE MOTIONS

The sun rises
I wake up
I reflect on the upcoming day
Same routine
Survive to kill time
Going through the motions
Of living
But not living
Just existing
To kill time
And wait for the inevitable
The burdens of the past
The mistaken adventures
Have squeezed all life
Out of life
As each day becomes a burden
A load I must carry
To shed on the last day of life
The will to live
Dissipating with each day
Wondering how hopes
How dreams
Vanished into twilight
As I stand
Deserted and stranded
On a long terrain
Waiting for the vultures
Circling with anticipation
At my fall
To feast upon
A body
That outlived itself.

DEEPLY IN DEBT

I stare at my dwindling paycheck
Deep beneath the pile of debt
That surrounds me
The credit cards, the loans
With their hidden charges
Declining below
My income every month
The random offers of loans
To encourage more debt
The love of instant gratification
The seduction of material goods
Creating an illusion of happiness
That lives month to month
While we struggle
To get out of debt.

TO SPARK A DEAD LIFE

I lay in my coffin
The lid about to be closed
And piles of dust ready
To engulf me
But, I am not dead
I still have
Things to do
Dreams to fulfill
Adventures to sail
Challenges to overcome
I need a spark
To give life
To the dead
To become alive
And do all things
That I need to do
There is still time
I need a spark.

GOD'S OUSTSOURCING

Some time ago
Somewhere in the heavens
When God was about to make me
He decided it was too much trouble
But I was in the list to be made
So God decided
That my making should be
Outsourced
To cheap contractors
Who may do
An adequate job
On average people
For a fraction of the time
So, here I am
A defective individual
With faults and dents
Trying to carve an existence
From a imperfect world
Maybe my imperfections
Fit our world
Making mistakes
That are part of life
Body going through illnesses
As it streams toward its end
With creaking sounds
And frequent repairs
A cheap product
Of mass production
One of many
That will never amount to
Anything special
But to just fill a void
In a landscape of humanity
With imperfections of cheap labor
Of God's outsourcing.

GOD'S WARRANTY

When I was made
And sold to Earth
I came with a limited
Manufacturer's warranty
I performed well
In initial stages
I could walk and exist
And go through the motions
Of living
As I was programmed to do
But as my psyche
Aged
My body creaked
My mind slowed
I had to fend for myself
As my warranty had expired
I was on my own
Fixing myself
With screws and bandages
Trying to hold myself
Together in a tumbling world
I wish I had asked for
An extended warranty
To get Divine repair
Whenever I broke
Rather than taking myself
To crackpot repairmen
When God was self-indulgent
So now I am on my own
Repairing myself as much as possible
Avoiding repair garages
Longing for
Divine intervention
And a chance
To extend my warranty.

SO MUCH LOST, SO LITTLE TIME

As Robert Frost said,
    "The woods are lovely dark and deep
    And, have promises to keep
    And miles to go before I sleep."

I ponder at the sunset of my life
Surrounded by uncertainty and unfulfillment
Preparing for the end
But, not ready for the end
For I have unfulfilled dreams
That keep haunting me
Reminding me
That it is not over
I may have lost a lot
Maybe everything
But not myself
My hopes, dreams and faith
The end beckons me
With passion
Chastising me for my complacency
Reminding me
That my destiny
Is not over
My end will not come
Until I do
What I was sent to do
Leave a legacy
Of my thoughts
As I journeyed through life times
Capturing all
In the remaining time
And I have to promise
To me that my left
Is just the beginning
I have all the time in the world.

THE LIFE WRECKER

Is there an award
For people to wreck their own lives?
I will win it every time
For I am a master of it
I have done it too many times
In every aspect of my life
I have mastered the act
Not that I am dumb
Not that I am uneducated
Not that I have no knowledge
But it is just my brain
That seems to rationalize
Everything I do
Even turning absurdity
Into a reality
Telling me
That what I am doing
Is perfectly right
Shutting me away from reality
And plunging me
Into a box
That keeps me hidden
From what I should have done
I keep doing this
I build my mounting success
Then invite a wrecking ball
To slam into the structure
Grinding it into dust
As I search for sanity
Among the broken pieces
Ready to build
Another to wreck
I am the greatest
Life wrecker.

WHAT SHOULD I DO WITH ME?

Every morning
I look in the mirror
And see a faulty person
With cracks and imperfections
And now I wonder
What should I do with me?
I have choices
I can continue to live as I have
I can wait for my end
And accept the usual defects
I can change my course
To leave a legacy of my existence
Or just continue to stare
Every morning
Into the cracked mirror
I am confused
I do not know what to do
Accepting the blows of fate
As I get pummeled into the ground
Getting stronger with each blow
Building character
In a lifeless soul
To take on the challenges
That I will confront in the future
Is that I should do?
Face the future with dignity
And carve a world
That is my own
My own creation
Of love, happiness and contentment
That is my destiny.

A FAULTY STRUCTURE

I am built
On a faulty structure
With cracks in its foundation
And holes in its walls
That makes it
A dangerous architecture
About to collapse at any time
Just held together
By sheer will
To stand erect
As earthquakes shake it
Storms pound it
Termites gnaw at it
Hoping that the structure
Will become
An ancient monument
That will be admired
In due time
For its history of endurance
And resistance to natural laws
As it fought invaders
From within and without
Trying to leave a legacy
That time will appreciate
And admire a structure
For its ancient beauty
And carvings of time
And stories of a beautiful world
That once existed within its walls
Rich tapestries and loving stories
That once adorned it
With joyful music and culture
Now just a memory
Just a structure.

HURTING MYSELF

I am very good
At hurting myself
I think I owe it to me
I am sure
I have the right
Why let anyone outside hurt me
When I can do a great job
On me
I am my own worst enemy
Devastating my career
Blowing my relationships
Devouring my body
Messing up my dreams
Wasting opportunity after opportunity
I am my best enemy
I deserve an award
For doing an outstanding job
Of hurting myself.

THE TRAVELER'S JOURNEY NEVER ENDS

I left my home
Many years ago
On an unknown journey
That will take me
Over continents
Deserts and oceans
Over the mountains
To places I ha never seen
Meeting strangers who became friends
Finding relationships
That brought joy and sorrow
Enriching me
With knowledge about our world
Understanding people
I liked and disliked
Growing intellectually
On an unending
Quest for wisdom
And questions about the universe
That keep running away from me
And remaining unanswered
I look for hope
In desolate places
For in Divine guidance
As I walk paths
With no directions
That lead nowhere
Just a path
That continues my journey
To unknown places
In search of destiny
That will forever
Elude me.

ABOUT THE AUTHOR

Dan Khanna considers himself a traveler through life enjoying an adventurous journey. Dan was born in New Delhi, India. After he completed high school, at St. Columbus High School, Dan left India striking out for California via short stays in London, Montreal and Milwaukee, Wisconsin. Although his dream was to pursue a career in the arts, acting, music, and writing, a quirk of fate placed him in engineering college and pursuing a business management career, in which he excelled. Dan completed an undergraduate program in engineering, and a Master and Doctorate in Business Administration.

Dan worked in Silicon Valley's high technology firms and was a CEO and founder of several firms. He changed careers to be a professor. Now, he again is pursuing his dream in creative endeavors.

Dan is the quintessential Renaissance Man, whose interests span the gamut of the arts, sciences, history, social and political studies, classics and philosophy. His search for knowledge began in his early life where his father was the Chief Education Officer of Delhi and his mother was a Sanskrit scholar. Dan speaks English, Hindi, Urdu, Punjabi, and Gujarati.

As a child, Dan read voraciously, particularly enjoying novels, such as Sherlock Holmes, Agatha Christie, Earl Stanley Gardener, Ian Fleming's James Bond series and classic works of Shakespeare, Tolstoy, Dickens, Oscar Wilde, Thomas Hardy, and other writers. He was very interested in poetry and read English poems of Browning, Keats, Milton, Tennyson, and Frost, as well as, other poets, while mastering Urdu poetry. His intellectual interests including studying Western and Eastern philosophers, especially Socrates, from whom he learned questioning methodology employed in his research, lectures and seminars.

During his parochial education, Dan was interested in various sports: cricket, soccer and field hockey. His love for the arts and music was honed to a level that he performed in plays, movies and solo concerts.

Dan's present journey is devoted to creative arts and activities, primarily writing poetry, fiction and non-fiction books and plays, while continuing to acquire knowledge of diverse subjects. He has published one book and has written over twelve hundred poems. Dan has several non-fiction and fiction books in development.

Made in the USA
Charleston, SC
11 December 2016

CONTENTS

DEDICATION

This book is dedicated to the two mentors in my life:

Mr. Rasik Shah and Dr. Otto Butz.

They believed in me, encouraged me and guided me at the right time towards the right path. They referred to me as a phoenix, who rises from the ashes. I am eternally grateful to them. My life has been blessed by their presence.

God bless them.

ISBN: 0692802272
ISBN-13: 978-0692802724

C000099299

Glitter
in the
Dust

DAN M. KHANNA

tray at the end of the counter where we made our selection. I never bought chocolate, I went for quantity not quality, as much for your money as possible. Miss Moores was not the most patient of people, so if you didn't make your choice pretty quick she would rattle the tray, a clear indication to get a move on! This was never a problem for me, my choice was always the same - they were the new sweets called "chops, green peas, new potatoes". How I loved those sweets, you got a lot for your penny. Sometimes when we went in the shop Miss Moores would be reaching up to the shelves. She didn't wear glasses but her eyes were always screwed up, and in her thin red fingers, which always looked cold, she held a tiny bit of pencil and from time to time she would lick the end of the lead to make it work better. While we waited all you could hear would be the tap tap of the pencil on the counter and you had to wait till she'd finished.

One time I had a good look at Miss Moores; she was a small woman with her hair scraped back into a bun, and sticking out of the bun were always about three hair pins; how I longed to push these into her hair, but I wouldn't have dared, and while she was peering over her figures I had a good look at the wart that lay on her eyelashes hanging there by a piece of skin from her eyelids. It didn't bother Miss Moores, but it bothered me something awful. She must have liked me a little because she let me run the occasional errand for which I received sixpence. Well I ask you, sixpence for one errand! Miss Moores was my friend for life! So one day I decided to buy her a present. Down Commercial Road was Natty Whalley's shop, a small toy shop. I was a good customer at Natty's for my little rear end was always sticking up out of her bran tub Lucky Dip, from which you got a surprise present. Anyhow I chose a bright red pencil, long and slim, and back I ran as fast as my legs would carry me and presented my gift to Miss Moores, as her little pencil didn't work very well. Well, Miss Moores was visibly and audibly overcome. Dear Miss Moores I will remember you fondly always!

SUNDAY SCHOOL SERMONS

Sunday School Sermons was a very special day in our young lives for most children attended Sunday School. It was expected of you then to attend church, Band of Hope on Monday evenings and if you had a reasonable voice, and so wished, you would join the church choir. All these activities I took part in. The Sunday sermon was quite a large procession, the policeman right at the front, the scouts' band with banners waving; then all the tiny children walking together. This was the day when all new clothes were worn and it really was a lovely sight, for Mother's delighted in the dressing up of their children. There would be the Rose Queen, the Rose Bud, all the Sunday School Teachers, Sidemen from the

This little area was called the Croft. It was at the bottom of Commercial Road.
Waterloo Street is seen at the left side.

Mr Drinkwater's shop. It was such a busy shop. I would squeeze in to see what was going on.
I visited every day - what a little pest I was!

Church, Vicars and choir, congregation, and Mother's Union. It was always a good show on the Church's day.

There would be several stops for hymns, and of course there would be good crowds lining the pavement. I always knew where our Mother would be standing with the neighbours. It is always of that day that I have the clear memory of the look of love on her face; her eyes told us we were truly loved!

Much later on, I would then be about fifteen, I was in the sermons but as a chorister in the church choir - I remember being slightly bored, after all I was growing up fast. I couldn't wait to get to the South Park to meet the gang. I was into my interest of boys and had my first date with Peter Forbes Robinson - and has anything gone straight forward for me since! He was my first passion, not that he knew, and my first date, and if only I had not been so nervous, I would have enjoyed it so much more! There was not another date, let alone did we get around to kissing each other, so perhaps using the word passion is a bit strong; but you know what I mean, more of a fluttering feeling really!

MRS HAYCOCK RELIEF TEACHER

I would be in Standard 4, because I was in Miss Cornforth's class, and we learned that she had to go into hospital. In the school yard there was all kind of talk going on amongst the girls about how our teacher was going into hospital to have her eye taken out and put back again. This talk shocked me and I could not imagine how this could happen.

Whilst our teacher was absent we had a Miss Haycock. She was a big woman with Eton cropped hair, very dark and parted on one side with a slide on the side of her head. She had a stern face, and the strange thing about her was that she was a keen knitter and whilst she was taking arithmetic she did her knitting. She had a huge bosom and the knitting needles would be clicking away in front of her. I was sure Miss Swindells would not have allowed this. Then the lesson began, mental arithmetic which I was hopeless at. I just could not think quickly enough; those girls who thought they had the answer all had their hands up and if they had the right answer they would then leave the desk and stand by Mrs Haycock. Well, of course, in the rush of thinking, many girls got it wrong. I tried hard to keep up for I could not bear the thought of being left by my desk, so by more or less offering a number which was always hit and miss, I more often than not stood with the rest. I remember feeling so unhappy with this lesson and its teacher and I realise now she was not doing her job properly. She was taking the easy way out and doing what she liked best, knitting.

So the day Miss Cornforth came to visit us just to say hello, and we were told as she entered the classroom we must all clap our hands in welcome, no one clapped harder than I. We were all delighted to see her and we knew it would not be long before she was our teacher again, and what was more wonderful, she had both her eyes and was just as she always had been, beautiful!

WIRELESS

In the early thirties few people, at least in our area, had the luxury of cars or phones, and not everyone had radio, or wireless as they were called; much later on we did have a Murphy radio and it was Mother's and Dad's pride and joy. I remember it having a modern light wood case and it was regarded as a good set. As I was the errand girl, it was my job to take the battery to be charged which was a long way for me to carry. It was a square of glass with lead plates which were covered with acid; it had sort of tin arms and a wooden handle to carry it.

Dad used to say to me *"carry it straight, don't spill the acid".* Well I was very afraid of this, so I carried it with my arms outstretched, very tiring, as I made my way to Lucking's shop on Sunderland Street. It really was hard too for me and I hated this job.

THE LOLLIPOP

Outings like a day at the seaside had to be well organised, even saved for. Both men and women would join in this trip, but there were also all male outings if they were going to the races. Only the men seemed to go on these trips. But Mother and Dad joined in the outings from the Royal Oak on Commercial Road for this was their local. They would go to Blackpool, Menai Bridge, North Wales. All these were very popular and they would be taken around June which was the town's main holiday. I can remember peeping round the café corner watching this large bulbous blue bus standing outside the pub door! And seeing crates of bottles being carried on - no one died of thirst on those trips! Mother beckoned me to go to her but I was too shy, I was happy to watch from a distance to see them off!

From these outings they brought back presents for us. Once they brought a lollipop the likes of which I had never seen before. It was the biggest; large as my face, raspberry-coloured, on a long white stick and wrapped in shiny cellophane with a twist on top. Was I proud! So I paraded myself with my fruity phenomenon around Commercial Road, hoping everyone would see me. With hard work on my part, it took several days to demolish. My beautiful lollipop I will never forget.

This was probably taken on a pub trip. Mother is the one with the cross. Mrs Slater is on her right with her son Fred, and on Mother's left is Mrs Rutter. Dad and his brother Ted are at the back.

GOING TO THE CINEMA WITH GRANDMA

By the time I was 9 years I was in love with the films that were being shown at the cinema on Buxton Road. It had started long before that when I was about 6 with the tuppenny crush on Saturday afternoons, boys and girls queuing outside. What a noisy lot we were, boys pushing and shoving and cat-calling the girls, and being told by Mr Garlick we would not be let in the cinema until we quietened down. The only feature I remember was the "Clutching Hand", heavens above, how we all screamed when the dreaded hand reached out of cupboards, curtains, picture frames, grandfather clocks. We loved to be frightened really for we were all together, but really it didn't do me much good for I was very nervous really! And of course more often than not the film broke down, the lights came on and everyone stamped their feet and Mr Garlick came round with his very stern face *"Anymore of this and you're out"*, and everyone would more or less go quiet!

I was nine years when I started to go to the cinema with Grandma. Every Monday evening Grandma Hadfield, she was my Dad's mother, would go to the cinema. I would pester my Mother for the few coppers it took so I could go with her; it was not easy, I had to plead to go! More often than not I went as fast as my legs would carry me, but with Grandma I had to walk hand in hand sedately by her side. She was a very small, but very fat woman, shaped like a pear really with enormous hips, and always dressed in black, summer and winter. She wore a heavy serge skirt which went down to her ankles; in summer time she wore a silk coat which fluttered over the skirt almost to the bottom of the hem. She wore a tall black hat with a narrow brim and a black ribbon which hung over the hat. She also wore laced boots and to my young eyes she looked a strange sight.

Off we would go at snail's pace; I wanted to run and jump ahead but I didn't dare! Once inside the cinema, from her deep pocket Grandma would hand me four or five mint imperials. These would last me throughout the film; she always saved a few for Grandad, for they were good for his digestion! The only other sweets we had were Craven's butter mints of which I received three - these were a bigger sweet - and I love these mints to this day. Grandad always met us out and escorted us home. He was for sure the quietest man ever; he didn't speak, just puffed on his pipe, and with Grandma's arm through his, home we went.

In the summer time - it had to be a hot day - Grandma would sit outside the front door on Commercial Road eating ice cream from a cup, and if I was around she would give me spoonfuls. She would converse with the neighbours and say *"she's our Bert's little girl, bonny little thing"* or something like that. I remember I didn't like her talking to anyone for I wanted her all to myself! A strange thing happened when I was quite small, about 4 or 5 years old, when visiting Grandma, as I was saying goodbye to her she would always lift my dress and petticoat. I didn't like this, nor understand it, but when I told my Mother she said *"I know she's looking to see how clean I keep you; she needn't bother!"* I think there was no love lost between them, but I was loved by both, so it was OK by me.

CLARA MALINS CHEMIST SHOP

I would often go into the chemist shop if only to see the babies being weighed. They were put on the flat white scales in the large chromium scoop. The proud mothers placed their offspring on their muslin nappies. There was always a nice display of pure sweets in bottles of all shapes and sizes. All this was of great interest until I met Clara Malins! She was the Chemist's wife and she became my main point of interest, for Clara was colourful in every way. Her hair was bright yellow, a very pale skin, her nose was very large and hooked, small eyes which were quick and darting and a thin mouth. She wore bright red lipstick, and on top of her crisp white coat with pearl buttons she wore large bobble necklaces. She was very chatty, very dramatic, she waved her arms about whilst she was talking to someone, displaying her painted nails.

How many of us remember the babies feeding bottles, banana-shaped and popular in the 1930s; well I do for one! The glass was heavy, and the measured ounces were pronounced on the glass. There were two teats, one for slow flow and one for standard. Glass has been around for a long time but just what were the containers made of for babies in the Tudor times; quite a thought really?

Mr Malins was always at the back of the shop as he was the chemist. He was clever and popular, and was thought and said to be as good as a doctor. If you felt off colour, Mr Malins was sure to be of help to you. I have to say this was one shop where I was tolerated the least. Clara's eyes would really dart about when she saw me, she never said anything to me, but her look said "she's here again!" But whilst Clara was looking at me, I was doing the same thing to her! Clara was lively and colourful and I found her different to most of the female shopkeepers on Commercial Road, and she didn't have the normal accent I was used to hearing. What part of the country she came from I don't know, but with her arms waving about and her very special style of speaking with a slow drawl, for she pulled on her words and stretched out her sentences, all this made Clara Malins a pretty special person to me!

DEAN CROWDER GENTLEMAN

Mr & Mrs Crowder had their ladies & gents outfitters on Hurdsfield Road. It was a large shop and they sold all household goods too. Dean Crowder could not have known but he was my favourite male shopkeeper; for one he was handsome, so polite, very kind and thoughtful, and more than that he dressed so smartly. No matter who, he was always nice to everyone; when you went into the shop always he asked about your health, even at my young age he would say *"how are you Nancy today?"* and then speak of the weather, and then giving much thought and attention to your needs.

Now Mrs Crowder was quite different in temperament, she was very tiny, and her legs were rather bowed. She was rather like a little bird with her quick darting actions and you could be sure that whilst you were in the shop, she would make her appearance through the glass door, with its heavy cream curtain, her yellow duster over her shoulders. She would have a quiet firm word with her husband, talking at him rather than too him. She would then take note of your purchase, dart around the shop for a moment and quick as a flash she'd be gone through to their living area, and back to her housework.

When we moved to number 70, where we had a bathroom, what joy, we were back to back with Mr Crowder, and through his hard work he had turned the

Hurdsfield Road. Mr Nield's newspaper shop, then Davenport's Gents Hairdressers. The big window was Dean Crowder's. Mr and Mrs Etchell's house is next door.

Mr and Mrs Pearson's chip shop. Smythe Street leads off, where I walked with my basket of eggs.

long flagged yard into a lovely garden. They had four lilac trees, two purple and two white and every May we would be given a bunch from their trees. When he was not in the shop he was in the garden.

In my young eyes Dean Crowder was an ideal man; I wonder what he would have thought if he'd known of my adoration - hopefully he would have liked me more! My Dad only smoked Woodbines; if Mr Crowder had smoked, for sure they would have been Craven A in a long silver holder! And what's more he wore a heavy gold ring on his little finger. My Dad didn't!

MR AND MRS PEARSON'S CHIPSHOP

I believe at one time there were several chip shops near us, certainly two along Commercial Road and two on Hurdsfield Road; it was the latter two I knew, Pearsons and Parkers. Mr Parker ran his shop with his son and daughter Winifred. By now Winifred was a beautiful teenager, with a lovely face, flowing red wavy hair, and a super figure. I so admired her and hoped very much I too would look like her one day, and even today when I meet Winifred, with her youth long gone, she is still a lovely woman, that aura about her still and what's more, so nice to know! I have told her of my admiration for her; she was very embarrassed!

Now Pearson's chip shop was where I visited. The Pearsons were dedicated people to their work, they had to do things right. Their fish and chips tasted good, and there was always a snaking queue, and people standing with basins under their arms were quite the norm in those days. They sold minerals, cream soda - my favourite - dandelion & burdock, lemonade, Tizer, Vimto. These were on display on a high shelf all round the shop, no cold cabinets for cool drinks. In the window, on a huge willow plate, was the tripe, with a cut-out card which had U.C.P. in large letters, and underneath the opening hours of the shop. Another card announced "Fritters on Fridays, Savoury Ducks on Thursdays" and yet another card "We aim to please".

The fryer was huge, it took up the whole of the wall, with a mirror in the middle, four big pans, double-hinged with shiny aluminium lids that when opened filled the shop with steam. Mr Pearson ladled out the fish and chips whilst Mrs Pearson wrapped them up. She was kept so busy, all you would hear her saying was "salt and vinegar?" She had no time for conversation, and her hair was always damp on her forehead. In an alcove at the side was a flat topped gas cooker that held four black iron pans with long straight handles that held the steak and kidney puddings, suet and mushy peas. The best thing in the shop was to watch the potatoes being cut. I would squeeze into the corner near the large

The cross is the Elephant and Castle Pub. Our house was directly facing.

black handled chippers, where there were always two large enamel buckets, one holding the large white potatoes and the other to catch the chips. Sometimes it took several pulls on the handle to get the potato through, and the whole of the narrow counter, with the white tiles, would vibrate so much that the salt pot, which was made of tin, and very large and battered as if it had been dropped a lot, would go dancing along the counter and bang into the vinegar bottle.

Once this operation was over, off I would go, perhaps home to see what Mother was doing, or to go and play in the park. A whole new world opened up for me when I was seven; up until then I just played in Victoria Park, but then I became errand girl and, well, I became so curious, I found out I liked being with elders, watching, listening to them. I didn't talk much, I know that for sure. Mother would say to me *"Nancy keep out of the shops; you only go in when you are doing my errands!"* But I had found a new entertainment, and I did not heed her words because to my mind I had been a customer and would be so in the future; what was wrong visiting a shop when I had nothing to buy. And for sure I was in and out of shops like a rabbit out of a warren; only Clara Malins seemed to mind, and even she didn't complain, well not to me anyway! I was in love with life and its people! I just did not know it then!

LITTLE COUNTRY STORE

The Little Country Store sold just about everything. It wasn't very big, and if it looked cluttered, it was organised. Mr Drinkwater kept this shop with as I remember it, his son John. He was very popular with the farmers and country people. He had sacks of dried foods for all their needs placed in front of the counter, grain, meal, chicken feed, maize, and just about everything else that town people required as well. The space that was left was filled by a big black flat weighing machine, with the weights you had to put your hand through to lift - these were the potato scales.

On the big old fashioned heavy counter there was a large marble slab, and on it two porcelain saucers which held the butter and the cheese. It was good to watch Mr Drinkwater slap the butter into shape, he worked so quickly and expertly, in no time it was placed on greaseproof paper, and in an outer cover of brown paper. He was also noted for his cheddar cheese. He was a tall, rather thin man, quite bald, with a few strands of ginger hair, all he had left, stroked over the top of his head. He always wore a waistcoat and round his middle and down to his ankles he wore a thick white apron. The ties went round and fastened with a knot at the front, and he had shiny brown shoes with toe caps. His face was long and thin, and he had just one tooth in the upper part of his mouth which came down to his bottom lip, rather like a fang really! He was very partial to tasting his cheddar cheese; he would pick up the small pieces left on the marble slab whilst he was passing. The action would go like this; with the cheese in his mouth he would purse his lips together in a rather exaggerated way as if he was squeezing the liquid from it, then round and round would go his mouth. It didn't matter if you went into the shop morning, noon or night, Mr Drinkwater's mouth would be going round and round. There could not have been cheese in his mouth all the time, it must have been a nervous reaction.

Much later in life I found out he was a most interesting man, learned and well read, and I was told there was nothing he liked better, after he closed his shop, than to cycle into the country. How often have I wished that I had been old enough to have known him better! But as I was only a little girl, curious for sure, and always popping in and out, maybe he was fed up with me watching him from behind his many customers in any little space I could find! One day it happened, round the counter he came, the shop full of people, and in his hand he had a large round chocolate biscuit in shiny red paper. He patted me on the head and gave me the biscuit. Oh, the shame I felt! How could Mr Drinkwater do this, I was totally overcome with shyness. I couldn't even say my *"Thank you"*, and from that day on Mr Drinkwater got rid of me forever. I never returned to his shop! I only know I liked Mr Drinkwater, I never meant to be rude or a nuisance, and I shall never know what he thought of me! Perhaps as well!

BEN WRAGG

Ben Wragg was a butcher; he had a small shop on Mill Street. He was small in stature, wide of girth, a fat round face of high colour. He wore a blue striped apron and on his head a brown felt hat, with a low crown. He was a character of the kind you don't see today. No longer young, and his mode of travel, pony and trap, Ben enjoyed a drink after closing his shop and before he reached home. So Ben made a call here and a call there, and with his contacts he was sure of a bottle or two, even though, it was War time, and winter, and blackout.

Well one Sunday morning and early too, a very agitated Ben was knocking on our front door. Dad answered "Ere Bert," Ben said, *"Ave getten a bit of bother on. Last neet on me way wome, aye I lost a leg of pork; the bugger slipped o' back o' me trap, round Waterloo Street area, coz I'd had a few. I conna go askin questions, tha understands"* - meaning Ben dabbled in the black market. *"Wilt keep thi ears open; if tha knows who has it, tell'em fetch it back, and I'll share wiv'em"* - Ben wisely thinking half a leg better than none.

Dad didn't dwell on this salty problem too long. *"Ben, stop thi worritin, I'll tell thi what; get thi sel' round backstreets, gerup entries an get thi nose round back doors and if there's a bloody good smell, it's thi leg of pork some lucky bugger shoved in th' oven. Thou hasn't got a cat in hell's chance of gettin that back."* And we are sure he didn't. Poor Ben!

GRANDMA AND GRANDAD BOSTOCK

Mary Ellen Bostock and Joseph Bostock were my grandparents on my Mother's side. She was their only child. Early on in their marriage they lived in Macclesfield, but when work was short in the early thirties, Grandad found work at Newton Hyde, and here was to be their home for the rest of their lives. He was a weaver at the firm of J&J Ashton, where they made towels. Mother was left in Macclesfield with relations and close friends. Why I don't know, I could not have left my child, but that is what happened, and so she was raised mostly at public houses, in her Mother's relations keeping. The Royal Oak, Commercial Road, The Navigation, Black Road, The Cock & Pheasant, Bollington Cross. She rejoined her parents at about 12 years.

Grandma became an invalid and took to her bed at fifty years and was bedfast till her death. This of course made life difficult for her husband, but he was a gentle uncomplaining man - my Mother was to take after him in character. When my Mother married and had her family, she could only visit her parents on a fortnightly basis. I always wanted to be the one that Mother took, pretty selfish really but my eldest sister was at work, so my Dad looked after the two smaller children. I was more or less always the one who went with Mother on her visits. Whilst she was there of course she cleaned the house for Grandma, and there was always plenty to occupy me, always a present waiting for me, a pretty blue Celanese dress, the height of fashion, a doll's tea service in an enormous box; and a must was a trip to the cake shop mid-afternoon for my favourite cake called a top hat, or a sponge bun filled with confectioner's custard and topped with a small round sponge.

Sometimes I would ask for sweets and was seen across busy Ashton Road to the tiny sweet shop close by. Twin identical sisters ran this shop, they were both spinsters and by now quite old. They were extremely quaint, even eccentric really; they dressed the same, tiny patterned dresses with lace collars and on their head white cotton mop caps gathered with frilly lace. They were very chatty, they would say to me as I entered the shop *"here she is again, visiting Grandma and Grandad Bostock",* but because I didn't really know them I would just nod and take my sweets. I realise now, looking back, that, of course, these two sisters were special people, I was just too young to understand. One day I remember well; after my visit to the cake shop and carrying my cake I was followed by a large alsatian dog. All he did was follow me but I was so afraid of him I threw my cake at him and cried the rest of the way home to Grandma's. *"You didn't want it very much",* said Mother, *"to give it to the dog!"* Why didn't she realise I threw it away in fright. I didn't get another one, not that day at least!

When it came home time, Grandad would take us to the railway station. I can see him now, a tall, slender man, with a droopy moustache, he always carried Mother's basket filled to the brim with all the good things our Grandparents had given us - I suppose as a "Thank You" for her hard work at the house. Saying goodbye was difficult for me; "Nancy, give Grandad a kiss", but instead of going forward, I went behind Mother's skirt and because of the white droopy moustache I would not kiss him, and I never did. I was a much older child when I came out with a rather sweeping statement which I must have heard from somewhere. When asked again to kiss him I came out with the speech, *"it's not impossible, but it's highly improbable".* Grandad's head spun round, he looked angry and said to Mother *"Watch this one, Nancy".* I really did like my Grandad, it just had to be from afar!

ALBERT HULME COALMAN

Albert and Florrie Hulme lived next door to us at 70 Arbourhay Street. Florrie was a most unusual woman, and she and Albert did no get along very well at all.

For one thing the poor man got no peace from her at all, and all because of his work as a coalman. He of course brought quite a bit of dirt back home with him and Florrie found this very difficult to live with!

So on entering the front door, on top of the mat was a piece of newspaper; there Albert had to remove his boots. There was only one chair he could use and this too was covered with newspapers, seat and back. She really nagged him; anywhere where poor Albert might lose some coaldust had to get covered in newspaper; you could say it was a newspaper house.

Well as soon as Albert had his tea he would light his pipe, and as soon as was possible he would be off, out to the pub, where he would spend plenty of time. This also angered Florrie. All the neighbours secretly felt sorry for him - they didn't have a family and their poor marriage didn't bring them happiness, and really all because she was ashamed of his work. She wanted the neighbours to know just how clean she was about her house, so from morning to night she would be cleaning, and she made sure the neighbours saw her! Thursday night was known as bucket night, when the pavements, or the flags as there were known, would be scrubbed clean and also bleached. The steps of the house would be donkey-stoned. This was her night, she made sure she was the first out, and the last in, just to prove how particular she was.

Of course everyone was aware of her, and if she could get anyone at all to talk to, poor Albert's name was called black. Well one night Albert did not come home for his tea, he had been taken ill at work and landed in hospital with a burst ulcer. He was away from home for a fortnight, what a carry on, the whole street knew about poor Albert's plight and Florrie was quick to say she nearly ended in hospital with him, he caused her so much worry! Well Albert recovered and could not get over the treatment and attention he received in hospital. *"Just like a holiday"* he said, *"I enjoyed it very much"*. Poor Albert!

THE POACHER

There was a Mr Marsden who lived in our street. What he did during the day I don't know, but I do know that at night he became a poacher. I don't know what else he caught, perhaps for his own family needs, but he was very popular for his rabbits. Baby ones were 3d and adults were 6d. At our house you could be sure rabbit would be on the menu once a week, and always fresh and tasty.

Dad was an expert at skinning them and we children would all watch. He dressed the rabbits also for the neighbours who could not face the task - so dad was popular too, you could say.

Mr and Mrs Marsden were not Cheshire people for they came from

Yorkshire, with their distinct accents to prove it. They had one grown-up daughter, and she had a small son called Ronald, Ronnie for short - and short he was in stature, wirey with it too and top full of mischief. He was always in trouble for one thing or another. One day he posted his kitten through the letter box, the poor little thing screaming its head off. Ronnie felt his grandfather's strap, but no matter, Ronnie had to go on being Ronnie, he always followed trouble and trouble would follow Ronnie you could be sure.

One day he was taken to the Co-op - the main shop, corner of Sunderland Street and Park Green, selling all kinds of household goods from spoons to furniture, and also a ladies' and gents' outfitters. Whilst his mother and grandmother were intent on their purchases, Ronnie found himself inside the large shop window where the full size female models were displaying ladies underwear. Ronnie was quickly at work unscrewing the hands and arms leaving them like so many Venus de Milos. Not only that, but the passing public were being entertained by his antics. But his punishment wouldn't be too harsh from those two women who loved him so.

I don't know where he is now, but Ronnie Johnson you would not forget.

THE BASKET MAKER

Grandad Hadfield was my Dad's father and his name was Edward. He was such a quiet man, I don't remember him speaking much at all. He and Grandma were such a close and happy couple, they really just lived for each other. When Grandad died, Grandma died just three weeks later of a broken heart - she just did not want to go on without him.

I remember the present that Grandad gave me - a tin clockwork hen which when wound up would peck up and down on a plate. I thought it was wonderful!

For his living, Grandad was a basket maker, and he was a noted craftsman. He made the very large bread baskets they had in those days with rope handles. To get to his work place I would go down the entry at the side of Mr Marsden's house where it opened into a large yard where there was a brick bulding with the floor covered with straw. Here Grandad sat cross-legged as he did his work, more often than not with his pipe in his mouth. In I would go and I would sit facing him, also cross-legged. By his side was a long narrow zinc bath and this held the willow reeds that lay soaking in water to make them pliable for use.

And do you know, I didn't speak to him and for sure he didn't speak to me, yet it was always recorded that young Nancy had paid him a visit. For it seems, although I was here, there and everywhere, and only seven years old, in that tight community there was always someone's watchful eye on me. Mother would say

to me, *"And where have you been on your travels today?"* As if she didn't know
- she knew alright!

Commercial Road, which lies at the bottom of Hurdsfield Road, was my
world where I would look and watch, and listen, and absorb. And I was a happy
little soul - even if not everyone else was!

PARTIES

When I think about it I am quite sad for never once in my young life did I go to
a birthday party. Perhaps there were not so many held in those days. And being
such a sociable little soul, I would have loved the joy and excitement of it all.
Anyway there might have been the problem of taking a present, money being in
short supply. I had to wait 21 years for my own birthday party, held at home.

Of course there were the school parties held at Christmas, and the 1935
Jubilee of King George V and Queen Mary. The girls at school were all given
red, white and blue ribbons for our hair, and also we were given china mugs for
remembrance. I still have mine today! So bearing in mind these were the only
two parties I remember, is it any wonder I sought my social activity among
adults, and got myself that label from Clara Malins from the chemist shop, *"she's
here again"* - or that was the look on her face!

I suppose really I was like a female "Just William", and for sure about the
same age, slipping in one shop, and out of another, so curious. Heavens above
what was wrong with that, but now of course I can understand!

BAND OF HOPE

Around 1934-5 there was a little meeting of young people called 'The Band of
Hope' held at Daybrooke School on a Monday evening. I don't remember if it
was every week, or once a month; anyhow boys and girls together, an evening of
social time and more free than being at school. There was Mr Evans a lay
preacher from Hurdsfield Church, a dedicated worker in and out of the church,
and a young man, Mr Morlidge, he too was just as dedicated. These men were
at the Monday meetings. We started with a prayer and a hymn, but I cannot
remember much else that went on, although one Monday evening was to be
memorable for me and I'm sure for all the other girls and boys too! In walked
this very tall man and stood at a desk in front of us. He placed on the desk a glass
jar which I thought looked like a piece of brown leather in vinegar. What it was
was a human liver in some kind of spirit, and after our stern but kindly talk from
this tall stranger, who could have been a social worker, perhaps a doctor, we all
filed past this 'thing in the jar'. Well can you imagine 20 odd children making

noises and with tongues stuck out, nothing we had ever seen before, we were all impressed. Then leaflets were handed around for us to sign the pledge not to partake of alcohol. I for one couldn't wait to put my name down, for I was never going to have a brown liver, and then of course I proudly took home my pledge to my parents. Dad was the first to say *"Quite right, Quite right",* when no doubt his taste buds were looking forward to his regular allocation of the evil drink!

So for me it is a lasting memory, that Monday evening, and just all about alcohol, no talk about smoking, and of course, drugs not even heard of - so, so much more difficult for our young today! Is this the answer to catch them young whilst they are so impressionable?

COFFEE AT GRANDMA'S

As I have said before, because my sister Joan would be at work - she was by then 14 years and I was 7 - I wanted always to be the one who went to visit Grandma with Mother. The treat was the train journey and on arriving, a cake, or sweets, and a small present. This journey to Newton Hyde near Manchester was always exciting and took place about once a month. Grandma was bedfast with rheumatism. Her bed was in the large high-ceilinged kitchen and the purpose of the visit was for Mother to do the housework. And she worked very hard, so I was left to my own amusement.

I would wander around the house, and in the front room was my great joy, a gramophone. Set on a square of solid oak with a green baize turntable and a large horn, also green, it was called His Master's Voice. There were records that if dropped broke, and of course they were the old 78s. One of my favourite's was *'The Laughing Policeman'*; how I loved it, it was all I wanted to hear. No matter  how tired my poor Mother was she would struggle with the heavy music box for my amusement.

Also in the front room was a huge table in mahogany, a big fat leg in the middle coming down to three clawed feet covered in brass. I would sit under the table stroking the brass feet. There was also a black leather bound bible with brass clasp, and a family album with deep set pictures of people old and young in huge hats and funny dresses. So old fashioned, all these deep pictures had what looked like hand-painted flowers with each heavy cardboard page covered in tissue paper. So there was much to interest me, even at that early age.

When Mother had finished her work for Grandma she would make coffee for them both. I would get a sip from my Mother's saucer only when Grandma was not looking as she said coffee was not for children. I so remember the smell, it was good, it contained figs - it came from a tin called 'Blue Nun', and you can still obtain it today. Then from the table at Grandma's side, where she kept everything to hand, like all her medicines, out would come a small glass bottle with square shoulders and whatever it was, whisky, brandy, I don't know, it was poured into their coffee, and I could smell this also. So this was their treat, Mother and daughter - and grand-daughter!

Grand-dad would come home from work, a gracious kindly man, his adams apple would wobble up and down, and he had a heavy moustache. I didn't like this at all, and would not kiss him on leaving because of it. He would take us to the train station carrying Mother's basket full of goodies given by Grandma. In the years that followed, when Grand-dad had died in that very kitchen and with Grandma even more ill, then she came to live with us. And at her death Mother went back to the house at 46 Newton Road, Hyde, locked the door and left the house intact; everything, all the furniture, just as it always had been, Grandma's bed, the wonderful table and gramophone, the bible and album, all the household things. Mother just left and locked the door for the last time. Why she did this I don't know. I've never heard anyone do this before, but this is what happened, the year would be 1937-8!

ALBERT HADFIELD, COBBLER

When my Dad set up on his own as shoe repairer and needed his own premises, there was an old pub called the Bird in Hand, and he took over the small bar part, it could have been the outdoor sales as they had in those days. It was completely sealed off from the large main area of the pub and a very unusual family had taken the rest of the pub for their home. These people made a living with rag and bone, and whatever that kind of business produced. Dad said they were a rum lot and he knew many funny stories about them after they took over the old pub for their home!

The part that became Dad's shop, you entered through small double doors, then right facing was the very high and ornate bar in rose redwood - quite highly polished - and four steps up at the side took you to where Dad worked and had his machinery. He worked with his foot in a strap harness, the shoes fitted over a last. I would watch him throw a handful of tiny brass nails into his mouth, and then very quickly he would hammer them round the sole of the shoe. He also had a machine for stitching the repair work on the shoes, and he also hand-stitched shoes. I remember he would display these to dry on the outside step of the shop - I think he was rather proud of his work.

At the end of the week I would collect all the strips of leather, the cut offs, and tidy up for him. Also it was my job to take his rent every Saturday morning up Brunswick Hill to an accountant's office at the corner of King Edward Street, and this office had to be seen to be believed, it was one large room with bare boards. It was very quiet, all you could hear was the ticking clock, large on the wall. There were three men and one girl; to me they looked old men and did not speak or smile. The only noise apart from the clock was the scraping of their pens - they all had their own rather tall desks with lift up lids, and along one wall was a another complete fixture of desks with lift up lids. That office will always be in my memory - it was so very old fashioned.

The rent was paid in silence and duly entered into the rent book. It was one errand I did not enjoy, but after I returned, Dad would take me and treat me to a quarter of scone with cream and icing from the steam bakery. Of all the stories I heard Dad talk about, and there were many, one amused me very much about the people who lived next door. The house was in a very broken down way, no carpets, hardly any furniture, and the stairs were very rickety, and he said they had a pony which they kept in the bathroom bedded in the bath. The three top stairs were missing, so Dad said the poor little bugger, meaning the pony, had to leap the top three stairs before it could settle down in the bath. Maybe it was the truth, maybe a story; it always amused me just thinking about it!

There were a lot more characters about than today. My Dad, when a little boy, lived in Garden Street, and he told me about moonlight flits, that's to say, if families were behind with their rent, during the night they just moved house. It could just be in the same street, but they were away from the landlord they owed rent to. Dad said this was common practice amongst the poor!

THE VISITOR WHO CAME TO TEA

This was the first time I ever remember we had someone come to tea. I remember Mother telling us we were to be on our best behaviour. Well I was only about 7 or 8. Audrey and Lilian were my two youngest sisters, Lilian 3 years and Audrey 14 months younger, and they of course were not aware of the visit. I do know Mother made a big effort with the meal, her best table cloth, her best teaset, the only one she had. She did it all so nice, with cakes and fruit, and we had boiled eggs. Mother and her guest had salmon and everything was fine,

Grandad Bostock marked with an X, on a trip to the races

My Dad Albert Hadfield
and on the right, Ernie
Swan, another cobbler.
I think the other man was
Mr Mathers.

The Steam Bakery where Dad treated me to a cream scone for taking his rent on a
Saturday. It was owned by Mr and Mrs Leigh, a devoted couple, who after
closing the shop, always walked home hand in hand

but not for long. Looking back through adult eyes the visitor must have been bereaved for she was dressed in black from head to foot. She was a very large woman, she filled the doorway, her coat down to her ankles, on her head a big black hat. I was told I must kiss her, and this did not go down well with me at all and as she bent down to me I could see she had whiskers!

It was all too much for Audrey and Lilian, they both fled under the table, which was their secret play area, with a heavy table cloth down to the table legs, rather like having their own wendy house; and so they disappeared. The guest put her hat down and it must have been in reach of the children for that too went under the table and was most carefully dissected, off came the hat band followed by the adornment of fruit and flowers and of course it lost its shape. All this went unnoticed whilst the adults were talking, until the visitor came to leave and the hat was missing. My poor Mother was so upset, and the visitor so very angry; she said she would never come again and Mother had very naughty children. I remember it all very well, Mother gathering all what remained of the hat's bits and pieces, trying to put it together again. It was to be many more years before we had anyone else to tea. In fact it was my 21st birthday and I celebrated it at home with my friend Joyce and the family. And, oh yes; there was a terrible thunderstorm!

MOTHER'S ILLNESS

Really it was only recently I heard a most special story, it was told to me, quite by chance really, that our Mother had been very ill indeed. It took place in the 1930s when she was having her young family, in one of her confinements. She was in the front bedroom of this little terraced house with the cobbled Arbourhay Street directly below, and because she was so very ill she could not stand the noise from the street. In the 1930s a horse and cart was the regular form of transport, milk was delivered this way, the coal too, fish carts that creaked, they were very noisy going over cobbles. When I was told what the neighbours did to help her in her condition, it was hard to believe, for they laid sacking all over the cobbles to deaden the sound. What an act of devotion for the neighbours to do for our Mother.

The person who told me this story said *"Nancy, this kind of help was the norm in those days. Good neighbours were like your family, every one helping each other."* There was usually one elder woman in the neighbourhood who everyone called on in difficult times which included births and deaths, and because poor people had difficulty paying doctors' bills, many didn't bother unless it was vital. So these very experienced people helped in whatever, even laying out the dead. They were hard times, they couldn't have been good at

Thorp Street which ran behind Commercial Road.

The last house at the bottom of Arbourhay Street. The lamp of the pub is just seen on the right.

Grandma and Grandad Hadfield's house. Between the Butchers and Sally Wilkinson's house, they were pestered with flies in summer

Mrs Dean's Sweet Shop, Natty Whalley's Toy Shop.
The Reading Room was above the Barber's Shop.

times! Families struggled on tiny wages and yet those people had standards and morals and manners far beyond their position in life. And these were the people I belonged to!

FATHER'S PUDDING

At the time of our Mother's illness, she was in hospital for some weeks. During the week of course Dad had to go to work as a shoe repairer, so our Auntie Gladys who was Dad's sister cared for us in our home. But at night and weekends, well Dad was in charge. As there were four of us and all rather young, well you can imagine he had his hands full. One day he said he would make a pudding, something special he said, and special it turned out to be! Our Mother was not a good cook at all, puddings and cakes were not her forté, so we all watched the preparations eagerly. It was like a suet mix, with dried fruit and he formed it into a shape of a small football. I'm sure he thought it had to be put into a basin, but we didn't have one large enough. The only thing left for him was to put it into a large pan, but of course before this stage it had to be wrapped in a cloth, rather like christmas puddings are! Except we had no cloth to wrap it in, so what he did next was really unbelievable. He used some of my winter underwear, they were called combinations. They were a one piece cotton vest with small arms and legs and I always wore these in winter, very practical and warm! Off he cut what he didn't require, the arms and legs, and into the cotton body he put the pudding and to fasten it up he covered it with safety pins, so many all round the shape of the pudding.

The next thing was to get it into the pan, and the operation was not very delicate, he had to push and squeeze to get it in. Of course as it started to cook, well it swelled, and became bigger than the pan, and bulged over the sides and in between the gaps of the safety pins were more little tiny puddings. We four had never seen anything like it before. And of course I was in horror because of the loss of my precious underwear; what would Mother say? Anyhow the pudding cooked and we had it for days. Dad was very pleased with his work; he had shown great ingenuity after all, *"I told you it would be a 'good un'"*. He was not kidding, naturally I could not wait to tell Mother in hospital all about it - she just closed her eyes and shook her head. Thankfully she did recover and I have never forgotten Father's pudding. Well who would!

SALVATION ARMY

Dad was quite a character really as you can see from my previous story. He had been an army man and he was a good gardener, always keeping our larger garden neat and tidy, this being very important to him, and when we were a lot younger, he had a large allotment to care for. He was a country man, very fond of walking, and I am sure in my love of the garden and country walking I take after him.

Another thing, he loved music, rousing music, marching, drums, so of course he liked the Salvation Army band very much, and their hearty singing. On Sunday mornings in those days they would gather at the street corners, their music and their hymns would come wafting down the streets. For us, on a Sunday morning, it was always cooked breakfast, and Dad always doing the cooking. One Sunday morning he had just picked up our very large black frying pan, as heavy as lead, when the strains of 'Onward Christian Soldiers' came down the street. With the pan still in his hand he started to march round the kitchen up the hall and back again with three of us marching behind him. We all enjoyed that, but then the knock came on the door for the collection - and we had to pretend we were not in! Such innocent happy memories in the fabric of our happy family life back in those golden thirties!

SENNA PODS, COD LIVER OIL AND MALT

When I visited my grandma at Newton Hyde near Manchester, I had to go up to her bed, and give her a kiss. I hated this chore as kissing was not my forté, but with Mother watching I had to perform my duty! Then there would be polite

conversation between the two Mothers, then I always knew what was coming next, for Grandma would say *"Has she been moved"*, as if I had been transported from one place to another. With Mother's eyes moved heavenwards she was assured I had, for if not senna pods would have been on the menu. I can remember the smell to this day as boiling water was poured over them, making an infusion like tea. This drink kept Grandma regular and moved! And I also remember my Dad's fetish was 'Carter's Little Liver Pills', and he gave them to us,

© Reckitt Benckiser Healthcare

his young children. What an awful parenting thing to do; all that was required was more fresh fruit and vegetables. I have to say parents of yesteryear were not so informed and educated as the parents of today, but I suppose they were doing their best for us! I didn't realise how wise I was being when I used to run off!

The large brown jar that contained Cod Liver Oil and Malt was always given to us at the start of winter. I can see our Mother now digging into it with a spoon which came out overloaded. I loved it and would take my time licking the spoon. The vitamins and minerals help to build up your health against coughs and colds. There was also Virol, but we didn't have this. I think it was much the same, did the same thing. But if you had a sore throat then it was raspberry vinegar with olive oil, which was not quite so palatable, but I didn't mind. Our youngest sister Audrey, who was very tiny at the time, would run upstairs and hide under the bed; but we always knew where she was. Mother would say *"get her down"*, and with tears she would be fetched - but she would be the only one promised a sweet afterwards. Happy Memories!

THE CO-OP

The M.E.P.S. - Macclesfield Equitable Provident Society - or as everyone knew it the Co-op, was, well, just about where everyone shopped because they sold everything; much more than a small shop. It was a really large store and it was so popular in the early thirties because of the dividend paid out quarterly; or you could save it and have just one payment made to you at holiday time. June was our Barnaby holiday so if you could afford to leave it in, you benefited by the larger payment at a time when maybe you and the family could take a day trip to the seaside or wherever with the proceeds.

They had a delivery service; there were Friday and Saturday boys who brought your groceries to the door by bike. Once inside there were very long mahogany counters either side, a boarded floor that went right to the back of the shop, and an all male staff with a manager, who wore waistcoats and long white aprons that went almost to their shoes. All these men were smart and efficient, with a word and a smile for everyone. Indeed it wasn't getting in but getting out of the shop which was the problem, not because it was individual service and this took time, but because of the friendly banter that went on. It was a happy place to shop in.

On the right side was the hams, bacon, butters, cut meats, bread and perishable goods, and on the other, tinned fruits, vegetables, whatever. Right at the bottom was where the orders were left for the boys to collect and deliver, and to see the groceries being wrapped was pretty special, stiff brown paper and tied up with string. Small or large the parcels all looked the same, professionally done and very neat. The men had little step-ladders, up and down all day to the high shelves and lots of walking about.

Mother always went in on a Friday; more often than not I would be with her. The tinned fruit was on the top shelves. How I hated what Mother chose, apricot one week, pineapple chunks the next. She was so predictable with her choice; I would tug at her sleeve, my eyes on the tinned cherries right on the top shelf. Her reply was always the same *"not this week"*. Do you know I don't ever remember her buying cherries, perhaps she thought them not value for money, I don't know, but you would have thought just once! Anyway you will never get me buying apricots or pineapple, come to think of it I don't buy tinned cherries either. What I should have said to myself was we are jolly lucky to be having tinned fruit at all - and I also want to say we had salmon for tea on Sunday, so we did alright - bless her, she did her best for us! What a happy family we were!

SUMMER TIME IN ARBOURHAY STREET

Apart from the weather of course, you would know it was summer when front doors were opened; I mean left open, some wide open, some just a crack, so if you walked by you would get a glimpse of dark brown sideboards with ornaments like a cherry girl holding cherries to her mouth. We had a figurine of an alsatian dog, which I disliked very much. I don't know why we had it, as a family we didn't care for dogs, we had cats. Anyway chairs and stools would be brought out and old men would have their pipes. The wives would put on a clean pinny over their skirts or dresses that usually went down to their ankles! Thick Lisle stockings, black laced shoes. But they would enjoy being out, for after all it was more pleasant to be sat at the front door, and there were more people passing by, and more going on.

Few had gardens at the back, and most had communal yards which they had to share; so it was much more pleasant at the front of the house. Also they would bring out the aspidestra plants at the end of a hot day, knowing full well there would be a thunder storm. The old would say *"Ay, we'll have a drop of rain toneet",* and more often than not they were right. I would enjoy going up and down the street saying *"Hello"* to everyone; it was not everyday that so many people were out at one time. And in the evening the men would go to the pub for a few drinks - it seemed to be only at weekends that the wives joined them, for whatever reason!

 This was a time in the late thirties when shawls were really going out of fashion, but I remember three old women who still wore them. One was Mrs Parton, who, at the same time every night, with her shawl round her head and shoulders, and with her jug well concealed, went across to the Elephant and Castle for her nightly stout. Back she would come minutes later, looking neither left nor right, and straight into her house!

Many times I heard my parents say people were content, there was more happiness, less competition, you settled for what you had without complaint and if people were poor - and they were - they still had their standards. Proof is in the good families that were raised, more often than not on one wage. We never heard of muggings; and drugs, we wouldn't have known what they were. I don't think there was much burglary going on; there was the odd policeman walking up and down, or if he was mobile, on a bicycle. But it wasn't going to be too long before this way of life was to change with 1939 looming; change for everyone, everywhere.

GREEK DANCING

Whilst we were pupils at Trinity Square All Girls and in Standard 5 we were in Mrs Garside's class. Every Friday afternoon she took us for country dancing, and under her tuition it was, for me, a nightmare. First of all she was bad tempered, little or no patience - if you made a mistake and didn't join the set at the right time, you were in trouble. With Annie Garside, because of her temper, if you made a mistake she didn't believe in stopping the dance and explaining to the confused pupil, she just pushed and shoved you in your back and sent you flying back into the set. All very upsetting, for me especially, because I hated her version of country dancing. It was just not for me!

One day we were told of a change in the dance programme and Miss Cornforth was to take us. Well Nora Cornforth had always been my favourite teacher. First of all she was the youngest teacher in our school, and what's more she was glamorous, blonde, very good looking, tall, slim, and very pleasant. She told us she would take us for Greek Dancing. Well no one had a clue what this dancing was, only that we all had to be dressed alike in green dresses - the news got hotter and hotter! I said dresses but really they were tunics; they were to be short to the thigh, sleeveless, split to the waist with knickers to match. I do not remember if the material came from the school, but Claudia Pomfret made mine, she was a good dressmaker, having made me coats and hats and dresses before, so I was pretty proud of my dance tunic.

Miss Cornforth must have explained to us what the dance was about. It was rather like ballet, we were to dance gracefully, and land on our toes, not land down like a lump of lead. You had to be expressive to the music, which was *The Gold and Silver Waltz*. This was supplied by Miss Cornforth, with a hand operated gramophone, by turning the handle, and off we all went in a circle, up in the air and down again as lightly as possible, spread out your arms and look at your hands - which were not to be stuck out like sore fingers. Whatever, my new Friday afternoons were very pleasurable. Oh, and I must mention, Miss Cornforth's tunic was purple and I think it was silk; it fluttered anyhow! She too was bare-legged and her lovely long legs were tanned. So I have very happy memories of Fridays and Greek dancing, but country dancing with Mrs Garside I would much rather forget. How could she take us for dancing, she had such very big feet, and very flat; she walked like she was wearing flippers. She made us all feel like shirt buttons on a cathedral floor!

THE BRIDESMAIDS

My sister Joan had been invited to be a bridesmaid along with her best friend Mary Frost, our next door neighbour. The bride was a farmer's daughter, they farmed at Alderley Edge. It was in the 1930s. The excitement of course built up over the weeks. The best bit of all for me was when Mother told us that it would be a big black car that would come with white satin ribbons and a bow over the bonnet. Well this just fired my imagination, never having had a car at our door, let alone with ribbons; it was all too much for my eleven years. Up and down Arbourhay Street, which was a very long street, I went, informing everyone of the coming event; my news spreading quicker than a virus.

At long last the day came, which was a Saturday afternoon. I had been stood as a sentry outside our front door and for far longer than I should! The neighbours did me proud for they were out too, and those who weren't outside were twitching the curtains. This was to be my wedding as much as the bride's! The girls, who were teenagers now, were waiting in the hall, very excited and looking lovely in royal blue taffeta, ankle length, and holding their very large bouquets which were the fashion at that time; tall regal, good-looking girls, and all ready to go to the wedding; when down the street came a tiny open topped car, bobbing over the cobbles, and it stopped at our front door. Out stepped a kindly looking man whose car it was; he was a retired vicar and he had come for the girls.

There was so little room in that tiny car; Joan got in one side, Mary the other. The doors were so small they looked like oven doors with hanging brass handles. They squeezed in with their large bouquets and then they had a rug put over their knees like a couple of old grannies. With their faces hidden in the flowers away they went. Mother's face was total embarrassment, and as far as I was concerned the wedding was a total disaster. I never heard any more of that wedding at Alderley Edge. It was all Mother's fault - a big black car with white satin ribbons and a bow on the bonnet!!

THE THIRTIES

What happy years we all seemed to have in the thirties, and our family seemed no different to all our lovely neighbours. We didn't know whether our parents were having a struggle to rear us, we were healthy and happy with a good home.

Enough to eat, and kept clean with clean clothes which was of utmost importance at our home. Winter clothing, summer clothing, Sunday best for Sunday school and Church and our everyday clothes all neat and organised. We were raised with morals and standards, and these take you through life.

We didn't know what it was to have a holiday by the sea, we never knew where these places were, and were not at all bothered. But we did have treats, like Sunday School outings to Middlewood near Poynton here in Cheshire where we all enjoyed a good few hours in lovely countryside where the sun shone for us and we had fun with games to play, races to run and a picnic. Good people those Sunday School teachers to take part in this and care for us. Mr Warburton was the Superintendent, he was very bald, indeed his head always appeared to be shining. At Easter time, always on Good Friday, there was an exodus to Prestbury. Everyone walked to get there, no matter how young we were or how long it took, we got there. It seems we all had stamina and staying power in our little bodies. Then a few hours paddling in the Bollin, the stretch of water that ran alongside the village - well it was none too clean but we took little harm. It was all part of our day's enjoyment! We took our butties and bottles of lemonade, and if it didn't run to that we took water. Such happy days, no harm came to us for there was a little army of us and we all cared about each other.

I now know as we get older we reminisce more, and that's good. To look forward is good too. To be thankful for our health and all the good happenings we have had in our lives, for all the best things in life that money cannot buy and which are free for all of us. I still feel young at heart, like the child I was at 7 years, full of curiosity; still wanting to learn. Above all I'm still in love with life and its people.

COMMUNAL YARDS AND SNUFF

My Mother had a cousin, her name was Emma, and she cared for her when she was giving birth to me that July night in 1927. It was in a very bad thunderstorm and she stayed under the bed in fear through it all. But this day we were visiting her because she too had just had a baby herself and besides the new one she had several other small children. They lived in Princess Street, a long sloping street that came off of Waterloo Street, and like lots of terraced houses in that era the back of the houses opened up into a communal yard. This yard was huge, many back doors converging into the one yard, and there was always much activity going on. My clearest memory is of old ladies, who were rather bent in frame and slowly shuffled along, wearing dark wrap-around pinafores with a deep pocket. From it they would bring out a small tin box which carefully held their snuff. If we were around they discreetly took it from the backs of their hand, the powder sniffed into their nose. I was always disgusted with this, but snuff taking was a popular habit in our history and taken by the gentry. Even then you could say there were drug addicts!

We would sit round the very large kitchen table with mugs and cups of tea, a huge brown teapot in the middle of the table, no tea bags in those days, and it was always brewed and drunk strong. There was just one more item on the table, a tin of condensed milk. With a spoon in it, this sugary substance provided both milk and sugar together; it made the tea taste sickly sweet. Young and old sat together in pleasant conversation, which I loved, as I sat close to my Mother. They were happy times for me, I just loved the company of elders.

Sadly my Auntie Emma died young, but she left behind a good family who are themselves parents and even grandparents now. Kind, gentle and dignified people, she would be so proud of them all, and maybe it's a strange thing for me to say, but whenever I am in a supermarket and I see condensed milk on display, I also think of snuff, and it's always a happy thought of that memory long gone!

Much later when I was an adult I asked about these so called old people who lived in the big yard, and I was told they were not really old at all. Perhaps, I was told, they would be only in their fifties, but worn out because of the hard work, some with very large families, poor housing conditions, none of the modern aids of today, no electric, just gas; and yet the families survived. If the family did not thrive - and more often than not just one wage was earned in the house - it is not any wonder that these women aged before their time. What does it all say of these people who did not complain, but just got on with their lives and their families in these very difficult conditions. It says they were special indeed!

THE TEACHERS AT TRINITY SQUARE PRIMARY AND SENIOR

We had these teachers from 1931-1941

Primary   Miss Gibson, Mrs Ingham, Mrs Frith, Miss Mitchell (Headmistress)

Senior   Miss Caroline Moulton, Miss Nora Cornforth, Mrs Annie Garside
          Miss Miriam Swindells (Headmistress)

Good teachers make a good school, they make a lasting impression on us for the rest of our lives. They try to mould us, set us on the right path. You are taught the basics that are so important. We all thought our headmistress was rather prim and proper. I can see her now in an orange linen dress with large pearl buttons and writing on the blackboard with her thin fingers, the skin shiny and tight - I know now she was arthritic, and carried on in great pain - and she wrote 'HONESTY IS THE BEST POLICY'. But she wasn't prim, she had all the right values, in the right order. She was a special teacher! She said she wanted her girls to be known as young ladies from Trinity Square All Girls. I do hope she didn't fail! And yes! I do have a regret - I had to leave school too soon at fourteen! We were still just children about to blossom!

A SPECIAL HAPPENING

My parents didn't talk to us or impart knowledge to us very often, and really it's so sad, for you only learn by being talked to and given information. I know this is why I found such interest in watching and listening to adults. Wherever I found them - and I did, in peoples' homes, shops, in the street - their conversation was of special interest to me. But there was one winter's afternoon, in our dark kitchen in Arbourhay Street, I thought just for once my Dad was pretty special. He called me into the kitchen just as he was putting a tray of fresh fish into the oven just to show me how the fish was giving off a phosphorescent glow in the semi dark. I had never seen anything so special as what was happening in our own kitchen that dark winter's afternoon. What a lovely memory for me! Better than any school lesson!

MY FIRST JOB

If I have one regret in life it was because I had to leave school at 14 years. Dearly I would have liked to stay on until I was 15 years, but in the year 1941 myself and another girl went hand in hand to put our signatures to paper confirming we were leaving school. This took place at the Town Hall, why I don't know, possibly because it was war time. Really I did not know what kind of work I wanted to do, I just did not want to go into a mill like my sisters had, so without any help at all from my Mother I went to a little hairdressers where I had heard she wanted an apprentice. Yes she would take me on, the premium was £25.00. I had no idea you had to pay to learn! So home I went. My Mother said *"what £25.00! We cannot afford that."* Of course it was a lot of money, so I had little choice but to find something else; again no help whatsoever. I decided I would try sewing - the best thing I was to do as it turned out.

Arnold's was an old weaving mill, noisy, greasy, just very old, but upstairs they started a sewing section. This is where I started to learn to sew but not right away, you had to do other jobs like ironing first. It was a huge room we were in, at one end two long tables of sewing machines, 'Wilcox & Gibbs', and two long tables for the cutters. There were two small tables facing each other with a well in between. This was where the ironing took place, gas irons where the flame would come shooting out if you pushed too fast, which I did to get rid of the work quick so I could have a little time on the sewing machine. I was always scorching my arm from that old gas iron. It was very heavy too. But I fell in love with sewing and I couldn't wait to become a machinist.

We were all about the same age, happy girls, and we sang all day long. At 14 years the hours seemed long, 8am to 6pm till Friday, and Saturday morning 8am to 12. One day an inspector came to the mill and after his visit the young girls like myself didn't have to work on Saturdays. And of course it was war time, with everything so scarce. We were told we were to have a mid-morning chocolate drink - the chocolate was a government offering under a certain age. What luxury it was, great big blocks were broken up and water added, you can imagine our enjoyment, and no coupons to pay. I have spoken elsewhere of Margaret Dean and her lovely singing voice, well she sat facing me, she would trill out 'One Fine Day' from *Madame Butterfly*, I would stop singing and listen to her, then we would all sing the romantic songs of that time. In very hot weather we would fasten cardboard squares under the machinery which gave a beautiful draught and kept us cool.

We were blouse machinists and when buyers came to the mill, I was asked to model our latest styles. I liked that, it was a little glamour for me.

At the time one of the girls got married; she was of course one of the older girls. When she came back from honeymoon I was all agog asking her questions, *"Jean tell me what happened"*. She said *"We had a lovely wedding day"*. Well at fifteen I wanted to know more, *"and then it was time to go to bed"*, she said, and I waited with bated breath, *"we got into bed and turned out the light, it was so dark, and that's where I'm leaving you"*. What a let down for me, but what a wise sweet way to tell a nosy 15 year old who wanted to be knowing.

MRS DOORBAR

By the time I was sixteen or seventeen and growing up fast I was a customer of Mrs Doorbar's shop, and when I think about it, I was pretty pernickity too. Whilst I was choosing stockings for myself, I know now, dear Mrs Doorbar pandered to me! I was so careful with my selection, one would have thought my choice was for a very special occasion, but instead I was in the shop every Saturday, I laddered the stockings so quickly.

The shop was on the corner of Garden Street and a rather smart shop in every way. The fittings and features were of glass and light oak, and deep oak drawers held the hats. The counter was glass with a narrow oak strip, and through the glass you could see silk scarves, silk flowers, roses, etc, swiss handkerchiefs, hand-embroidered, and behind the counter, and on the wall, there were more glass and oak fitments holding silk underwear, sweaters, nightwear.

Her stockings were in deep white boxes about twenty four pairs to a box. The stockings didn't have individual packing like today, each pair was layered on top of each other, covered with tissue paper. On the top pair each box of stockings had a name like 'Moon Mist', 'Barley Beige', 'Sand Storm', so that if one week 'Barley Beige' suited you, the following week you knew what to ask for.

Whilst I was debating which pair I wanted Mrs Doorbar would very carefully slip her hand into the top of the stocking so I could see the colour on the back of her hand. Nothing was too much trouble for her whilst I was making up my mind! And by the time I was one of her customers she was really quite old, but because she was such a charming lady, she carried her years lightly. It was said to be her daughter's business, but it was Mrs Doorbar who came out to serve.

She was a large woman, her eyes were large, and she was long featured with red and purple veins on her cheeks. Her hair was titian and very wavy. In one of the deep waves she wore a slide, rather fancy, and glass beads that always matched her dress. She had manicured nails painted coral - I was so impressed with her appearance for I had never seen nail polish on my Mother's hands. And because of her age, she moved about the shop rather slowly, willing to help me in every way, and very chatty. She had just one failing: her dentures did not fit well in her mouth, she did have a very generous mouth; and then it would happen, she would be talking to you and then she would stop, in the middle of a sentence and you would hear her hiss as she sucked in her breath, and then she would have a struggle with the top and bottom dentures, and then you would hear a loud click-clack as her teeth came into the right position and she would continue with the conversation where she left off. Well you could imagine when I first encountered all this, my eyes, I'm sure, were like organ stops, but I soon got used to her loose teeth. It was alright by me, after all it was part and parcel of dear Mrs Doorbar -and don't we all have failings! She was my favourite female shopkeeper!

THE COOKERY TEACHER

When I was fifteen, I started to take cookery lessons at night school, and of course we were to have the same teacher through the course. But for whatever the reason one night there was a new person for us, who was to stay with us for just one month; but what a teacher, what a month! I felt I couldn't wait to get to the lessons, for she was so different from the norm, although how do you define a cookery teacher? This one was more like a 'Fanny Craddock'; small, no longer young, and overweight. She wore heavy tweeds, thick stockings, it must have been winter I suppose, and flat sensible shoes. Her features were large with deep set eyes, a prominent nose, a well shaped generous mouth; her thick hair she wore short and I think her natural colour was dark, but she had added colour to it and it was now quite orange. She was heavily made up, her mouth was also bright orange and painted beyond its natural shape. So her face was an exaggeration of shape and colour - she would have so very easily have fitted into a girls' school like 'St Trinians', flaunting authority and perhaps running a bookie business on the side! She had that kind of personality, but we loved her because she was kind, amusing, and very different. Why I can't remember her name saddens me, but she was with us for such a small time. She told us her religion was catholic, and she lived alone with her cat. She said to me one night, *"Nancy, even with my back turned, when the scales bang down I know it's you; you should make a good cook, but not so heavy handed, please"*. I just loved her.

One night while we were all waiting for the ovens to give up our endeavours, our lovely teacher perched herself on the table and swinging her fat little legs, and in her hand clutching sultanas which she delicately placed one by one in her mouth, she told us about the cruise for which she had saved for years. She said that she had never earned much money and therefore it had taken her so long to save. The day came when she reached Southampton and saw her boat *that would take her on her cruise. "Well" she said "was I disappointed, for the boat looked so small, and not only that it had only one funnel."* She said "You know girls it should have had three for all the money it cost me!" But now the best bit; she said *"How many women have been proposed to on board a ship at sea and in the moonlight; well this happened to me"*. We girls were all agog with this romantic story and we tried to ply her with questions but I think the look on our young faces told her she had said enough, and as quickly as she started, so she finished. She was a real character, full of life; and she was to leave a lasting impression on me.

FIRST DATE

By now I was a teenager, sixteen, seventeen and working at Arnold's Mill as a machinist, really enjoying my work, and wanting very much to learn to sew. And those good people taught me. The main one was Maude Ashton, sadly no longer with us; she went off to America, married and stayed there!

I never regretted being taught to sew, through the years it has given me much pleasure, not to mention saving me money. My daughter Sarah has gained much benefit from my reasonable skill; *"Mother will you make me this? Mother will you make me that?"* and I have, very often, at the drop of a hat, and off she went with another new outfit!

But I'm going off my story. When I was sixteen and had nothing to do with boys at all, at weekends I would meet Margaret Leyland. She was a girl I worked with and we would go to the South Park together. A little later we were to meet some very nice boys who also would get together in the park; Paul Dale, Peter Whitmore, Eric Johnstone, Peter Robinson. There was a sheltered alcove near the gardeners' tool shed, and we would all meet up, laughing and talking together. It was Peter Robinson who asked to take me to the Pictures and for me it came completely out of the blue, but it was exciting, my first date - and I agreed! It was to be Monday night at the Premier. Now I had a problem, for I only had my navy burberry coat and I went to work in that. Of course I had my best coat, but that was for Sundays only, not Monday evenings! So I had to devise a plan and lie as well! *"Mother I'm going to the pictures on Monday night"*. *"Who with,"* said Mother. *"The girls from work, and they are all wearing their best coats."* *"Well you're not going to"*, she said. *"Best coat on a Monday night, what next."* I felt quite ill, I had to plead, and eventually she said *"Make this the last time!"* And then I had to ask if I could wear my best shoes as well; what a carry on! And remember this was the first time I had ever asked to wear best clothes; the way she carried on, you would have thought it was a regular asking on my part. Not much give with my Mother! But I forgive her!

So I got my wish, but if only I hadn't been so nervous I would have enjoyed my first date so much more. Come Monday night, I could hardly swallow for nerves. How I wish so often I could remember the film we watched. Peter put his arm around me, and with his hot face next to me, I felt stuck to him! For whatever reason we had just that one date; perhaps just as well with my spartan wardrobe, and we were not to meet again for a few years, when we were both in the J.L. Riley Choir together. By now he was a fine bass singer and he went on to greater acclaim as 'Forbes Robinson', singing in Milan at the Metropolitan Opera; and so, of course I'm proud to remember he was my very first date!

THE ISLE OF MAN

It was going to be a holiday to remember, for six of us had decided to go to the Isle of Man for our Barnaby holiday. This was 1947 and I was the eldest of the girls. There was Lillian and Audrey, my sisters, and their friends Joan Mason, Marion Bloor and Beryl Shaw. We were all very excited because as far as we were concerned we were going abroad, and without parents for the first time! We were all hell bent on having a good time, wartime behind us, we were on our way.

Of course there had to be a problem before we left home and that was over the luggage; all we had was one very large heavy leather suitcase, a great heavy

The Conservative Club, Arbourhay Street.

The very bottom of Commercial Road, with Robinsons and Browns in the far background.
You can just see the cattle pens.

handle, leather caps on each corner and a dubious metal lock in the middle. *"That's all we have"* said Mother. *"All three of you will have to make do, it's big enough anyhow!"* It sure was, *"We're never going to carry that, it's a ton weight."* *"Get a porter"*, said Dad; and that was that!

What spilled over we put in carrier bags. What a sight we must have looked. Worse was to come for we had to face the sea journey; nobody had thought how they might feel, and none of us were well - we were already having second thoughts about this Isle of Man holiday.

When we got there, we were all in one room at the top of the house, a large room with three double beds, a built in wardrobe and a washbasin. It had a high ceiling so it was quite airy. The toilet and the bathroom were on the floor below, but we didn't care much about the inconvenience for we had arrived and we were here to stay for seven whole days.

We hadn't been in the room half a day when it started to look like a scene from St Trinians. Our clothes were everywhere, it looked like a 'clean well-pressed jumble sale'. None of us could wait to get dancing, and we did morning, afternoon and evening at the Villa Marina, and at Cunningham's Camp, which was all boys - and it was full of boys! I had strict instructions from home to keep a close eye on my younger sisters. Well they had other ideas, their eyes were on the dancers, and they were soon off with lads - wherever the boys were they were in the middle of it all. The Villa Marina was so large, rather like the Tower at Blackpool and the Winter Gardens.

In the early part of the week, we were having a walk around Douglas when Joan Mason saw a big fat chicken, like a little turkey really, with trussed up yellow legs. *"Oh I must buy that for Mother"*, she said; and she did, but it was far too early in the week and because none of us had fridges at home, we didn't think to hand it in to where we were staying to be kept in the fridge, so we put it in the wash basin in cold water. Of course we had to keep lifting it out so we could use the wash basin, so by the end of the week it looked rather saggy and its colour wasn't too good either. We splashed it well with water and hoped for the best. At least I waited until Friday before I bought a box of kippers and brought them home with me to save on the postage. Audrey and Lillian bought two sticks of rock, the biggest they could find - and all this extra to what we came with!

On the way back and trying to cross a very busy road at Liverpool, Joan Mason lost her rail ticket and none of us with a penny between us, so trying to smuggle her through at the station we put her in the middle and hoped we'd muddle through. But Joan was in tears at her loss. *"Oi"*, said the porter, *"what's the matter with her!"* *"She's lost her ticket"*, we said in unison. Well perhaps he

Villa Marina, Isle of Man. From left: Marian Bloor, Audrey Hadfield, Joan Mason, Lilian Hadfield, Dorothy Hunter, Beryl Shaw.

decided it was not going to be his responsibility; he just stuck his thumb in the direction of the train and said to us *"Get going"*. Joan's tears stopped immediately and we were all relieved!

Alice Mottram, a great lump of a girl who never left her Mother's side, but always had plenty to say, well she was waiting for us coming up the street. *"Your not very brown"*, said Alice. Probably we weren't, but what did that matter, we'd all been to the Isle of Man and we'd had a good time. Of course we were all knackered, fitting so much in those few short days, but we'd all remained good pals, got home safe and sound, and for us it really was 'a holiday to remember'!

COMMERCIAL ROAD

My daughter Sarah has no idea what Commercial Road, the part of Hurdsfield I knew so well, was like. I do know when she saw it in its present state, she was not at all impressed. But I will never forget it, it's still fresh in my mind, I can even remember peoples' expressions when they said certain things. I will not forget all those good people who I knew and who made their mark on me! And how strange and yet wonderful are our minds, for if you were to ask me what was I doing say a fortnight ago, I just know I'd find that difficult to tell, but when I walk down Hurdsfield, as I do quite often, I see a tiny bit of Hibel Road, all Garden Street, Steeple Street, Adelaide Street, Miss Moore's shop still there, though not sweets anymore; all the stone cottages, the pub, the Durham Ox, the few red Accrington stock town houses; they are all still there. I think, "Well, they didn't take it all, not quite!" and even if they had I would still remember it.

CHICKEN AND WINE

Now, I know for sure people in our neighbourhood only had chicken at festive times, really mainly Christmas, but they would be very large, very fresh like little turkeys, high breasted with plump legs and bright yellow horny feet; straight from the farm. And because people did not eat chicken often, it was always a treat and looked forward to as an enjoyable meal.

It will not take me long to speak of wine because we just never had any. I was a adult before I was to taste it. Now I believe red wine is good for you.

It is always amazing to me that we did not have a fridge; I don't think anyone else did either. But our house was cellared, a very large area where there was a boiler. Mother did the washing, in a huge wringer with a giant wood roller and a big iron wheel which I turned for her. There was also a large fireplace with a high mantlepiece, but it was never used. The narrow larder in the cellar had shelves where she kept her bottled fruit and eggs at a cool temperature; we were fortunate for these amenities.

Outside the back door we had a wooden cage with mesh front and sides where we kept the butter and milk and other perishables. A good idea, really practical and it worked. In the heat of summer, which always seemed long and hot, we never heard of food poisoning. I would not know about other families' hygiene, but we all survived, and when you think, our back door steps led to a long narrow yard where on Monday mornings cattle were driven up and killed in the slaughter house. We had to put up with bluebottle flies and the bad odour!

BARNABY WEEK

Around June 21st was Barnaby Week. In those days it was just that, one week; they worked hard and saved for 12 months in the mills for this week's holiday. That week the very air crackled with the excitement of people taking their holiday. Like an exodus they left town. My parents could not afford to take us on holiday, but Dad would always treat himself to a new flat cap every year, always at Barnaby. Mother would say *"Bert for goodness sake don't have the same check or colour, get something different, have a change!"* But no, home he came with just the same as usual. Dad would say *"What's the matter with it, it's*

Commercial Road

new, what more do you want?" Fashion was not his forté!

But before he bought the cap he would make his way to the Central Station, just to have a nosey really at all the people leaving. There would be so many people outside the station queuing. He would then go to Mill Street for his purchase, and would come home and say *"If you fired a gun up Mill Street you wouldn't kill anybody"* - except his language would be a little more colourful than that!

Later on he took to wearing a trilby hat and Mother would say *"Bert put your hat on straight"* - Dad liked to wear it at an angle, not pleasing her at all. He also had a crony hat, very popular for special occasions like funerals. If ever I was in town and he was too, Mother would say *"Have you seen your Father? Was he wearing his hat straight?"* I would say *"Yes Mother, dead straight!"*

SATURDAY DANCE

Saturday night was our night for dancing, me and my two sisters Lilian and Audrey. We had to have a rota for our turn in the bathroom, and one night I was waiting for Lilian to come out, and she was taking so long I banged on the door. There was no reply. We had an ancient boiler which heated the water for the bath and it was lit by gas; well there was a gas leak, and there was Lilian comatose in the bath. Audrey and I had to haul her out, and we dressed her. We could see she really was in no fit condition to go dancing, she could hardly walk, but selfish as we were I said *"I'm not staying home looking after her"*. Audrey said *'Nor me";* so we did her hair, slapped her make-up on, and said in no uncertain way, *"Our Lilian, you have got to come to the dance"*.

Poor girl, she wasn't with us at all. No matter, off we went. We both thought that she would come round bit by bit and of course we were concerned enough to take turns to look after her, but our good intentions went wrong. It only worked if one was dancing and the other was watching Lilian. During the evening we were both dancing at the same time, and Saturday night was so popular, the place was crowded, and there were no seats - so we propped her up against a pillar. But not for long - with a definitely not normal look in her eyes, Lilian was sliding down the pillar to the floor. It was a nightmare. We got in such trouble with our Mother when she learned what had happened. In later years it caused us all to smile at that Saturday night. Even with our youth we knew we couldn't leave her. But what we should have done was to put her to bed, she would have been no trouble to anyone; the trouble was all mine and Audrey's when we got home!

MORE SATURDAY NIGHTS

Our Saturday night we so looked forward to; more often than not it would be held at the Liberal Club, which is no longer there. The dance was so popular it was always wise to queue for the tickets before hand so we could all walk onto the dance together. So my two sisters, Audrey and Lilian, and the girls we worked with, had a rota system, one in turn going for all the tickets. We liked the summer time best because we could walk there and get as unruffled as possible.

By this time we were all young women, working as machinists in the mills roundabout, although not earning much on piece work - if you wasted time and put your scissors down, so was your wage! We were a happy lot, I can tell you, for I sang all day at work, romantic love songs of that era, 1943, lovely melodies. Margaret Dean sat facing me on her machine and when she sang I shut up and listened to her beautiful if untrained voice.

Anyway to get back to the dance - there are so many thoughts in my head! With working in textiles we all knew about fashion, style and design; we were very selective too, we wanted the best. The material was cut out and sewed in no time, overlocking, button-holing, the pressing completely finished. At the time I'm thinking of the fashion was full skirts, stiffened underneath, most were floral and with very pretty gypsy style draw-string blouses. We all had white high-heeled court shoes, and probably a flower in your hair, I had a white camelia, artificial but nice, and we were all ready for the dance, full of life. We were all such gracious girls. Well, so people said. So full of spirit, but innocent all of us.

And speaking of the girls of my era, do you remember the 'bra' that came on the market then; it was pretty special, tailored to give you the best possible shape, and it was called 'Kestos'. It fastened different from all the others. Bosoms were worn high at that time, it was the fashion. Wearing it was a pronounced enhancement, if you know what I mean. Mother would look at me, not a good look, and say *"One of these days you will poke someone's eyes out with those"*. I didn't care, I was proud of my shape. But one Saturday night was to end in disaster, dancing with this boy, I suddenly sneezed very hard and my bra snapped. This boy looked at me, he said "I think something gave". I was mortified, I gave him a big push, and sent him flying backwards and I fled the dance and went home. I vowed I wouldn't be going to the dance the next week. My sisters said *"Don't be daft; he will have forgotten all about your blinking bra."* And yes the following Saturday I was there!

When we look back, these were the best years of our lives. We had good parents, good homes where we were given guidelines, and we all moved around in friendly groups both at work and at leisure! Life was good!

MR ASHTON'S SHOP

Mr & Mrs Ashton's shop was on Commercial Road and it opened early and closed late. It was where it was said you could not ask for the wrong thing, it was so popular a shop. They had two daughters, Olive and Winifred, and a son Robert. Sadly he was born mentally slow, but his Father adored him and with the love of his Mother and sisters as well, Robert had a good life. It's only recently I learned Mr Ashton bred budgerigars and canaries in a back bedroom, all round the room in neat cages, and as we didn't see Robert much perhaps this was his hobby. Mr Ashton was a very tiny man with thick black curly hair and a large moustache, heavily waxed and twisted, which went past his cheeks, quite a feature of his face. As he served you all you could see was his head and a little shoulders. He had a bouncy walk so he looked as if he was bobbing up and down.

In complete contrast his wife was very tall and elegant looking. Olive was like her Mother, tall; Winifred was like her Father, very small and bonny, her feet so tiny and fat they looked like little puddings, and these squeezed into lizard skin court shoes with a flat little heel. Both girls were fashion conscious; both wore their hair long and very wavy. They were both hairdressers and Winifred dyed her hair bright yellow. At the side of the shop was a cobbled street, then there was a croft, a large scrubby piece of land, no buildings on it but at the back of it a few houses. In the end house of these, with a large window, Olive and Winifred opened their shop as a hairdressing salon. Both girls had their own customers. Mother went every Saturday for a shampoo and set, she was Winifred's customer. She would come home and say, *"Oh! Winifred's so heavy-handed, she's given me a headache, so I had to tell her!"*

I was by this time a teenager and the permanent wave was very popular. So I wanted one, and, just my luck, I became Winifred's customer and my ordeal began. The perming machine was a metal pole on runners, not that it went anywhere when you were underneath it. There was a metal circle over your head, with wires hanging down and small amounts of your hair was put into a cone shape, which was soaked in a solution, which for sure was ammonia - the smell was horrible - then plugged into the electric. Then the cooking time began, and you were given a magazine to take your mind off the heat that was coming. Soon there would be a sizzling sound and getting hotter, and if they had not put enough cotton wool on your scalp, you were in trouble.

Now I was so nervous about having this perm, being the first time. I could not believe the size of the comb she used, it was so large it looked as if it was made of bone with well spaced teeth. She dug into my hair like she was going into cement. So of course up came my shoulders, but too polite to say anything

Winnie Ashton's hairdressing shop is the first building on the left.

to her. But I did say *"Winifred you won't leave me will you, when I'm hooked up"*. Well she was most offended, *"What do you take me for"*.

Everyone who had a perm had a cup of tea from a thermos flask, and I was so looking forward to this treat. I saw the flask, but no tea for me, I'm sure because I had offended her. I considered that she added insult to injury because I ended up with tight curls close to my head, not me at all. She saw the look on my face. *"After a few washings your hair will look fine"*, said Winifred. Never did I go again; what's wrong with straight hair anyway! Today it's wonderful; you perm your hair at home and it's 'mobile', the results are so natural!

POOR CONDITIONS OF WORK

As I have said I was a blouse machinist, but I left my work for a while to make shirts. I must have just wanted a change, and for sure I got a shock as well, for really it was not a factory but a small workroom on the second floor of a very old mill. Years later it burnt down - and I was not surprised. To get to the room you went up six rickety stairs, a little turn then six more; the floor boards had to be seen to be believed, there were bits missing, very uneven, with cotton and bits of material stuck on the splinters. It looked as if it had been caught in a time warp.

There were just six machinists and they all looked the same; they were fat, old, and they had done nothing else but sew shirts all their working lives. But I will say this for them, could they sew; these six women had no conversation with each other, just the odd word, but they were experts at their work and very fast. They all had the same action and never fumbled picking up the pieces . Of course they were only paid for the work they got through, but no problem there, for they did not stop. I could sew by this time, but I was no match for them! I knew I wouldn't be staying for long in such an atmosphere.

There was another woman who pressed, she was nice, and there was Jean who was the packer. Now Jean was small, dainty, and very pretty, and both of us being young we got on so well we would sit and have our tea breaks together in a little corner, and talk about the old women, who we knew were talking about us, for we saw their glares. For one thing they did not seem to change their clothing much, they always looked the same. Jean would say, *"Nancy what do their knickers look like?"* We would go into peels of laughter with the grim thought. One of them fascinated me for at the end of her chin there was a hard round lump, not a wart, but really part of her chin. I would see this thing go up and down and what's more she had whiskers, what a sight! She said to me once *"What do you want to wear scent for?"*

Jean had a boyfriend, the son of a farmer, who was tall, broad and good looking, and Jean asked him to tea. Well for all his size he was very nervous of meeting her Mother. Jean promised to tell me how they got on with the meeting. So come Monday a very glum Jean said *'"what a disaster"*. Whilst they were having tea, on his plate was a piece of very hard cheese, and trying to cut it he went straight through the plate. *"Of course"*, said Jean, *"it was not his fault, but the plate was thought very highly of, being Grandmother's"*. And more was to follow; he plonked down on a chair and the leg fell off! Jean said she couldn't wait to get him out of the house. But, Jean said, *"Everything we have belonged to Grandmother, and so very old, and leaving the room, so nervous, he grabbed the door knob and that fell off, so within a couple of hours he had done quite a lot of damage!"* Her Mother said she was not to bring him again.

After that they went on picnics instead and later they married. Shortly after I left the shirt room I lost contact with her, and later on they went to New Zealand to farm. I bet they both still remember that tea date!

THE KISS

I had been working as a sewing machinist for five years, I was now 19 years and working at Arnold's Mill and though by this time I was going to the Saturday dances, I rarely dated anyone, apart from Peter Robinson, my very first date, and even that did not end with a kiss! Then I had a crush on a boy from our Church

choir, but that went nowhere! Then this one day, we were all talking at work as
we did very often, if we were not singing, and usually after the weekend dances
and on dull Mondays at work the girls would talk of who took them home. I
couldn't really join in this conversation for I was not dating anyone. They were
all talking about the romantic kisses they had when they were taken home; we
would scream with laughter as you can imagine, all young girls together and
some of those girls so full of life and so comical, each one telling their romantic
experiences, but by today's standards pretty innocent. This talk would take place
in our break time, and one girl said to me *"Nancy do you like kissing?"* I said
"Chance would be a fine thing". Her name was Mary Bowyer.

Now we all took it in turns to go downstairs to brew up, it took two large
enamel jugs which we took to the boiler room to an ancient copper boiler, which
took ages to boil. This was on the floor below where we worked, a dark place,
small and confined. It had not been painted for years, a terrible place really, I did
not like having to go there at all and yet something very beautiful happened for
me in that miserable place. A young electrician coming working at the place
whose name was Louis Birkett, he was tall, very good looking, about the same
age as me and Mary Bowyer. She had a word with him, and I'm sure it was me
she was having a word about. It was my turn to go to the boiler room to brew
up. When I got to the boiler room there stood the electrician waiting for the water
to boil. Side by side we stood; I know for sure I did not speak to him, but very
gently his arm went round me and he kissed me! Wow! The most beautiful kiss
I ever received, perhaps because it was the first real kiss.

That was it, the water boiled and we left each other. I bet I went upstairs in
a dream, and I don't remember speaking to Mary Bowyer about it - for sure she
was the one who organised it. Sadly he was to die very early on in life, I felt
deeply sad when I heard, yet I had never seen him again after that day in the
boiler room. But I will never forget the sweetness of his kiss, never! So come
on you girls, old girls by now you may be, do you all remember that first kiss you
had, this goes for fellows as well. Turn off the TV for a few minutes, and go
down memory lane, it really will do you good.

EVENING IN PARIS

When we were all going to the dances, after our careful choice of what we would
all be wearing, there would be the perfume. Well it was 'Evening in Paris', and
there were six of us. We all wore the same, it was so strong, so wrong for young
girls. I suppose we thought it was exotic, but it was more like incense. It cost
about 1 shilling and 6 pence for a small blue bottle in a small blue box with the

Eiffel Tower on the front of the box. If we didn't knock the boys down with our looks we sure did with our perfume, or scent as we called it! We used Max Factor cake make-up; and there was Coty face powder, still get it today, a round deep box, orange in colour and white powder puffs on the front. Snowfire face cream came in round tins, Ponds face cream too. There was Tokalon face powder and then the older women might use rouge, this too came in round boxes, and the label said 'Rouge Rossette Brune', very French. Then it also said 'Borgois, London, Paris' and in small letters 'Made in England'. You could buy this for 3 pence at Woolworths.

When I think of the trouble we went to, so important to us, our faces must have looked like little dolls. Then came a new perfume box produced by Goya. This was my favourite because it was sweet and flowery. It came in a long slim box with six tiny glass bottles, named Jasmine, Rose, Lilac, Lavender, Lily of the Valley and a last one I can't remember. Then a new lipstick came called 'Thick and Thin', two lipsticks held together with a little gold chain and this was to be my favourite, because it was the first present I ever received, along with the Goya perfume, from a boyfriend, who later was to become my husband.

JOAN MY SISTER

Joan was my eldest sister by seven years, she was tall, gentle and had a sweet and caring nature. Really we hadn't a lot to do with each other, for I was only small when she began work, and quickly we were to grow away from each other by our very years. She worked in a silk mill and it was there she met her husband to be; she was by then about 17 years old. When she and Eric were courting, on our Mother's orders they had to take me with them. One winter's night, me holding Joan's hand, we went for this country walk, not a light anywhere. It was awful for them really, me having to go along with them. They were fed up with me after a while, so they organised one of Joan's friends at work to let me stay with them whilst they did their courting, and then they picked me up later. Mother never knew, for Joan said *"don't ever tell"*, and I didn't. Eric went into the army and a couple of years later whilst he was on leave they were married. Joan was just 19 years, so a young bride. She had to save her coupons for her wedding outfit, and it was difficult to collect eggs and fruit for their wedding cake. At the reception the cake looked wonderful, but it was all cardboard and underneath was a small fruit cake, no icing. Yet a very happy time for them.

This was the time I missed her as a sister for we had shared a double bed together, and I missed her sleeping with me. I remember crying for her not being with me! Whilst her husband Eric was away in the army Joan found a little cottage and completely furnished it right through. She was so proud of her home - she let me visit with her but I was not allowed to sit down or touch anything. Much later they had a daughter Susan who became an art student in London. Now she is the Senior Art Teacher at Roedean, the famous girls' school on the Brighton Downs. Sadly my sister Joan passed away two years ago.

MONA WILLIAMS SCHOOL FRIEND

I had a lot of pals at school who I remember well and all of them became good wholesome women. But there is always one person, or girl in my case, who stands out for whatever reason, and for me Mona Williams, as she was then, is that person. She was not one of our little gang; I did meet her at school but much later on. She too lived in Arbourhay Street; her parents as her name suggests were very Welsh. Her Dad was a tall, good looking man, who worked on the railway. They had four children, Jean the eldest, Mona, John who today works in the ticket office at the railway, and Mary the youngest.

Mona's mother had a lovely Welsh speaking voice, and I would pester Mona to say for me that very long Welsh place that's famous for its many letters! No matter how many times I asked, Mona would oblige me! Her gentleness and her sweet nature left a lasting impression on me. She was inclined to be timid and she's just the same today; Mona has just not changed with the years. I met her recently and said, *"Mona, do you remember once whilst in your house we were playing with a lovely cut glass bowl, it was your mother's, and we were throwing a glass marble into it; how we didn't damage it, I don't know"*. Mona said *"I still have it today, in one piece!"* For many years she has been caring with great love and dedication for her sick husband, Dick. Not an easy time for her!

Now, I am very sad to have to write that Mona passed away suddenly. She lived only a few short months after her husband died. Her grief was too much for her. *"I'll miss you Mona!"*

SPIRELLA CORSETS PLUS

Mother thought there were no corsets like Spirella, the best you could buy, possibly because all their corsets were sold to the public by arrangement. You had to be measured for them, then made up, just for you. I remember the colours very clearly, pink or white, the material a very strong sturdy canvas, flowered pattern, with bones from top to bottom, laces at the back to draw you in, chromium clips to fasten down the front. My Mother even had an inner corset as well. In a morning I would hear a click, click sound as she was struggling into her armour, for that's what it reminded me of! She would say to me, *"You'll wear corsets like this one day". "Never, Never",* was always my reply.

Well one Saturday afternoon we both went into town shopping, we had just crossed Waters Green when Mother gave a yell. I could not believe my eyes, round her ankles was this bright blue celanese material; she had lost her knickers. Well almost! She just stood there. I pushed her against the wall, saying "Mother help me", but she was no use at all, she looked so shocked, so I had to deal with it under her coat and dress, trying to get the rest of her knickers from the tops of her legs. Because of the hard corset she hadn't felt them coming down. Though they were right under her bust, the top had fallen down like an underskirt. What a struggle I had to get them off her; I just wanted to dissolve. Into the basket they went and straight home.

We were both in a state. It wasn't that she was indecent, it was because we knew what had come down, and the fact they had let her down, if you know what I mean! I had to get the teapot out very quickly that day. She never spoke again about her loss that Saturday afternoon, neither did I, but I didn't forget. Nor did she thank me for the help I gave her, as far as Mother was concerned it might never have happened. I have often thought what if she had been on her own, she would possibly have had a heart attack!

PLUMS

It was wartime and of course, as the years went on, food that was not on ration, well it was much sought after. You only had to hear a whisper, so and so had oranges or bananas, or if it was the butcher he could have rabbit, and the queues would form. So this morning I was sent to the top market where nearly everything in those days was sold and supplied by the farmers and country people. They had stalls erected, pretty flimsy, they were wood with canvas ceiling and pretty draughty too, with the market place being a high point and the winds coming from the Pennine range. But year after year the same people came and everyone knew everyone! For the life of me I cannot remember what I was sent for, but according to my Mother I came home with something quite different.

Plums! When I saw them, I joined the queue. To my young mind a very versatile fruit, plums by themselves, plums and custard, plum tart, surely Mother would be pleased with me! So, delighted, I started off home with 10lbs in a long narrow basket with a long tin handle. I got to Brunswick Hill down the top steps and then the basket tipped and all the fruit went cascading down the hill like a little waterfall, red and purple, and me chasing after. Of course when they reached the bottom they were no longer in pristine condition, but squashed, cracked and split - they'd certainly lost their bloom. There was no one to help me get them in the basket, and by now I was not feeling too enthusiastic about my fruity purchase. What's more I had to face my Mother, and she was livid with me, and could she give you tongue sauce - worse than the time she found out about my first cigarette and glass of sherry! I did not forget either of those days. Years later when I reminded her I saw a smile. *"You were a little devil"*, she said. I thought, *"not really Mother, that was you!"*

GOOD FRIDAYS

How well I remember Good Fridays as a young girl in the thirties. Tradition was very important and played a big part in our lives, for Good Friday was always remembered as a holy day and a sad day. Easter Sunday was a popular church going day, and always you had a new spring outfit to wear.

But to go back to Good Friday people would eat fish for their meal that day and you had to get up early to queue at the fishmonger's. That was Harry Bainbridge's shop, only small really but he had a large window that was pushed up, and inside his fish was displayed on a big marble slab. Harry did a good trade being the only fish shop in Hurdsfield. We did have a man come round with a handcart, where, right at your door, he sold his fish to you. This was very convenient, and he had the apt name of Mr Fishwick!

We had our large plump chickens with their yellow legs trussed together, and our eggs we bought from the farm too; well, they still had the feathers on them; all this before the advent of the supermarkets with all their frozen products. So we had all the best. Of course I can only remember what we did in the Hurdsfield area, and we did things together it seemed, as a community, so if on the afternoon of Good Friday the weather was warm and sunny, there would be an exodus to Prestbury, walking through the fields by the River Bollin, till we got there, then a picnic of some kind, a good rest and we walked home again.

And it's not surprising that I still love to walk everyday to the countryside which we are so fortunate to have around us. Everyday I have to have some beauty in my day and so I walk, a great pleasure for me, and I would advise everyone, no matter what your problems are, take a country walk and you will feel much better and calmer for doing so! Walking is our mildest form of exercise, but surely the best if surrounded by the beauty of the countryside.

NINETEEN THIRTY-EIGHT

In 1938 I was eleven and many changes were about to take place in our home, but there were even bigger happenings in Europe. What we didn't know was that a war was looming and Hitler would become a household name causing changes for everyone, everywhere in the world

I want to talk now about my first experience of death. When anyone passed away in our street - although I don't remember many - at that time as there wasn't any chapel of rest, they were always layed in the front room, which of course was the best room and the one most little used. Perhaps it was used a bit at weekends but mainly at Christmas with get-togethers and family parties.

It was always very dignified and the neighbours were all invited in to view the deceased. The nearest neighbours would collect together for a wreath, going up and down the street for the collection. On the day of the funeral all the curtains at the houses would be closed as a mark of respect; I imagine this is still done in some parts.

So it was that in 1938 that our grandmother who lived in Newton Hyde near Manchester and who had been by this time bedfast for 15 years, became very ill. It was some form of rheumatism because her feet were contorted and misshapen and she had a great tenderness in her limbs. You had to be very careful not to knock into the bed as you passed. The time came when she had to come and stay with us, but what we children didn't know was she was by then suffering from cancer. All she saw through the long day, whilst Grandad Bostock was at work, was a good neighbour who called to put coal on the fire and take in meals. That was the only person she saw, so she had a very lonely life.

Now it was time to come to our home and have the full care of her daughter, Nancy, my mother. The hard question must have been how to get her from Newton Hyde. She should have come by ambulance I suppose, in some sort of comfort and safety. But Dad decided with a friend of his to bring her by motorbike and sidecar. Not the most luxurious form of travel, let alone for a woman who had been bed fast for 15 years!

Dad had always wanted to own a motor bike and it had never happened for him, and the chance to have a long ride was too much for him to turn down. So selfish, of course he was! How they got her in at all, I don't know, for she was a very big woman, it was like a sausage in a skin. The to be jogged over cobbled streets in that bone shaker must have been horrendous for her.

She arrived safe, if not sound. Her bedroom was our front, best room. which was a large room with a very big window - quite a plus for a terraced house really. There was a large fireplace with a coal fire and she soon looked comfortable and with plenty of company. Not that we were allowed in her room without the supervision of Mother. This took place every afternoon after school when we went in to say hello to her and take the pennies she gave us, a treat in itself. She remained with us for many months until she died. Then she lay in her coffin in the front room, and we were not allowed in the room. The mystery of death was hidden from us. Mother was in black clothing from head to toe for the mourning period, I can't remember how long, but for quite a while. Even we young children were sent to Claudia Pomfret to have special dresses made for the funeral in lilac cotton. It was here I saw Claudia's button box - never one to miss anything, not me - and I found five twinkling buttons. I had never seen anything so pretty as these buttons before. I said I wanted them put down the front of my dress. Quickly I was reminded of the sad occasion the dress was for, but it made no difference to me, I had to have them - and I did; they were my pride and joy, and I was only 11 years old.

YOUNG MEN GOING TO TOWN IN THE THIRTIES

I can just about remember how the young men dressed when going out for the evening, always somewhat formal. The fashion was hair to look shiny with Brylcream. Some wore it plastered down, dark suits, shirts and ties, pullovers with the popular diamond design, trilby hats if they chose, raincoats in wet weather, and in winter long dark overcoats. And a popular fashion feature was the wearing of a long white silk scarf with tassels, over the outside of the coat, and leather shoes which were well polished. There were not many families who did not take care of their shoes, and when the sole showed wear they were repaired. What a difference today. The young men of the thirties were smart!

The casual dress today is a nightmare; denim trousers that perhaps have really cost a lot of money - with so called designer tabs and cut, yet to my mind still looking like the working overalls of the thirties. And those awful clumsy white trainer shoes, the fashion from America. In the long street where I lived nearly all the men were employed at the Brocklehurst Mill, so when the blower went to summon them to work at 8.00 am, and blew again at 12.00 for dinner, again at 1.00 pm to return to work, and at 6 pm for home, this small army of men walked by all wearing the same blue overalls - the same denim except the style was different. They had a bib top with cross over straps from the back of the trousers and fastened at the front with metal clips.

So this is how I think of jeans today; they remind me of working overalls of the thirties. At least when their work was finished, and out they went for the evening, especially at weekends, the young men looked smart in their best clothes and individual in their taste - not everyone looking the same!

THE MACCLESFIELD ARMS

I was now sixteen, I had been working for two years as a blouse machinist. I had been on my first date, just the one date when I was fifteen. No more such excitement in my young life, and still very much under family control.

I was still in the church choir at Hurdsfield Holy Trinity. One Sunday evening there was to be a concert in St George's Church. The famous soprano Isobelle Bailey was the soloist, so after evening service we decided we would go. I think there were five of us, Eileen Robinson, Yvonne Elliott, Jean Hicks, Joan Mason and me. We were taken there in Eileen Robinson's car which was a lovely black Lanchester, such a classy car and her very own. She was a farmer's daughter, very beautiful, blonde and fashionable, and so we all went in style.

After the concert Eileen, such a generous girl, said *"I will be host"*. Just as well for me, for I went into Church with just my collection for the two churches and that was it, my money gone. She said *"We will go to the Macclesfield Arms"*. Well can you imagine this for me going into the best hotel in town, such a thing had never happened to me before, what's more she paid for us all to have a sherry and she handed round cigarettes. I tried both for the very first time, I felt I was really living it up.

The sherry was no problem for me, very pleasant if strong. The cigarette was more difficult, so it went like this - into my mouth and suck, suck, blow, blow - I thought I will never get the hang of it, I just managed half. I thought I'll take the other half home to show Mother. Oh dear; bad decision altogether! Overnight I had become wicked - in fact she called me a *'Jezabel'*. The best of it was that there were other people in the room, where we were all enjoying ourselves, who informed my Mother I was drinking *and* smoking. Can you imagine, it only made things worse for me. So I complained to Dad who said *"never mind lass, you are the sweetest Jezabel I know";* but I did not forgive her for the roasting I received with her 'tongue sauce'!

But never mind; I will never forget that hotel, with the soft music, and the male waiters in evening suits carrying silver trays with your drinks on. You paid by putting your money on the tray, then taking your change and leaving a tip for the waiter. All this was so new to me, but I knew I liked what I was doing, and I thought, one day, if I get rich, this is how it will be. Such were my fifteen year old thoughts, and never mind the outcome. Thank you Eileen for that very special evening and your generosity. Young though I was I knew then I liked people who had style and standards.

21ST BIRTHDAYS

I was still working at Arnold's when I was 21 years old, a very important year for girls at that time. Everyone collected for presents for your 21st birthday. It was a special time in our lives, changes were happening; some of the girls had regular

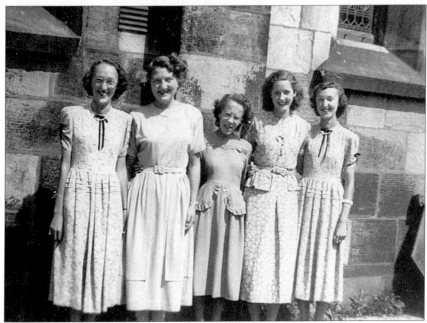

All of us here were choristers at Hurdsfield church (about 1946).
From left: May Wheeldon, Me, Joan Bailey, Joyce Mathers, Joan Wheeldon.

boyfriends, but as yet it had not happened to me. On your birthday, presents were put all round your machine and we had wine. Very happy memories, one 21st after another we celebrated that year, all good pals together.

It was still wartime and I was moved to another part of the mill, sewing flags, huge union jacks, a big change from ladies blouses, but I was quite pleased to be doing something for the War effort. This work took a few months and then I went back to my normal work.

I have to say, even at 21 years I was still giving my mother all my wage. So when this special year arrived, because I only kept a few shillings spending money, I just did not have enough money to buy presents for all the girls who were buying for me. It was a big problem, or so I thought. I went to Mother and asked her if I could 'board at home', so releasing most of my wage, such as it was.

Well she did not take kindly to what I had to say, and what's more she said to me, with tears in her eyes, *"well then, I don't want broken weeks."* I did not think that this would be a problem at the time, until that one special holiday when

About 1947. Back row: Joan Mason, Joan and May Wheeldon, Brian Cooke Front: Joan Bailey, Tom Bailey, Me

we went to the Isle of Man. I paid my board before I went, and I paid the moment I came back. How I saved it for her I just don't know!

Margaret Dean, who I worked with, said, *"Nancy, you dozy so and so, you don't pay your board when you're not there!"* All I could say was, mother had said *"No broken weeks!"* Mother must have needed the money - I was happy to be there for her.

SWOONER CROONER

As an early teenager I don't remember any pop groups. The Beatles were not yet on the scene, but in 1951-2 there was in America a young man who was quickly becoming the bobby sock idol, Frank Sinatra. And in the early fifties his first broadcast to the British public was to be from Radio Luxemburg, on a Saturday afternoon. Well Saturday afternoon was Dad's time glued to the radio for the football, the play and results dominating the scene, at least in our household. So of course a big problem for me, and I was so desperate to hear Frank Sinatra.

I told Mother I wanted to listen. All she said was, *"You'll be lucky, no one takes his football from him!"* Well I asked him; talk about 'fools rush in where angels fear to tread'. I knew his language would be colourful, and he just took one look at me - *"Not ---- likely, who is --- Frank Sinatra, anyway; never heard of him."* I could see I was losing, so in desperation up and down I started in a tantrum. Quite frankly he was amazed at my temper, he was just not used to any opposition. He said to my Mother, *"That --- girl's gone daft."* But I carried on and he stormed out of the room, and I heard Frank Sinatra for the first time!

Before the programme had finished back came Father, I suppose he just *couldn't believe he had given way to me.* *"Well,"* he said, *"he can't ---- sing; he will never earn his living with that ---- voice. If you want to hear a singer",* he went on, *"Richard Tauber's....."* But I was happy.

Now when I think back, not so long ago when our daughter was playing her kind of music, I would shout upstairs *"turn that jungle music down",* so each generation has its music. But she never had the struggle I had!

THE FESTIVAL OF BRITAIN 1951

I was 19 years when I joined the J.L. Riley choir. Just prior to that I was taking singing lessons with Elsie Southwell of Hurdsfield Road. Her husband took pupils for piano. They were really an odd couple, they would shout at each other over the silliest things, like who had the most cake from the cake box. Mrs Southwell would bang on the piano, then Mr Southwell would come in, and he would bang on the piano, then calm would take over and my lesson would begin. I would get used to them both in time and I came to like them. One day Mrs

Southwell said *"Would I like to be a member of J.L. Riley Choir"*, and I was introduced to the conductor. All he said was *"Are you keen?"* *"Yes very"*, said Mrs Southwell. I don't think I was!

Mr Riley was a most unusual looking man, he had great persona and I felt very nervous of him, but he had this effect on all the young ones. The older members who had been with the choir from 1929 gave as good as they got. But what a great choir, 70 voices strong, who were to go from strength to strength. It was with this choir that I grew up, for I had only been with the church choir, never travelled really and was young and naive. I was made a great fuss of, and was popular with all these good people from all walks of life. It was to be the best teaching I could have hoped to receive. For sure I know now that my character was being moulded in the right way. And I was happy.

During one of my lessons with Mrs Southwell she told me she had entered me into the Co-op Music Festival. Well a few days before the festival took place she was due to help the adjudicator with the morning pianoforte class. *"But I'm so busy, I want you to go in my place"*. Well I didn't have it in me to say no to her! *"You will be given plenty of instruction, he's a charming man, he will take you to lunch"* - and he did.

Mrs Southwell could have done the job with her eyes closed, but not me. There were a lot of competitors to take care of, to see onto the platform, take their papers and then sit with the adjudicator. It was, and did seem, a simple enough task, but just one paper, which was a vital exam paper to that one competitor, got mixed up. Well after we had been for lunch at the Co-op Restaurant, this woman came charging up the room at me. *"My son did not play wrong notes as you have stated"*. She was so upset; but so was I. The adjudicator covered for me very well, but the mistake had been made.

All this did not help my confidence, and in the afternoon I was to sing solo, my test piece in the soprano class and my first music festival. I couldn't wait for Mrs Southwell to turn up to boost my tiny confidence. Well of course I did not do very well for in the audience were many people I knew, like several mates from Riley choir who had come to listen to me. My written results were *"Pretty voice, reasonable interpretation; Breath; Breath!"* Afterwards the men of the choir said to me, *"Never mind Nancy, you had the best legs!"* I was not to sing solo again, well not at music festivals, just in church where you did not have to be so special. Although when we were on invitation to Mr Riley's home, to learn new pieces of music, we knew we had to sing solo and that was an ordeal in itself.

My first boyfriend when I was fifteen was Peter Robinson, who became famous at the Metropolitan Opera House, Milan, as Forbes Robinson, and

The J.L Riley choir, Berners Hotel, Festival of Britain 1951. The cross is Me.

travelled the world. But by this time we neither acknowledged each other, even though we were both members of the 'JL'. Both of us had a lot to learn, and a long way to go in life.

In 1951 came the Festival of Britain, with cities, towns and villages recovering all over our land. Men and women were returning from the forces to take up their normal lives again and to rebuild them. It was an exciting time for everyone with the building of the Festival Hall on the South Bank in London. There was as much hype as for the Millennium Dome. And in that great hall was to be a music festival, the national finals.

Before that much work had to be done in competitions at Blackpool, Wallasey and Morecambe. The winners would compete at the Festival Hall in London. We performed with all the other choirs, and most of them were the crème de la crème, they really were. Sale and District, Huddersfield, Vocal Union and many others who were so good. So the competition was fierce to reach those finals in London - and it was at Morecambe we knew we were on our way to London, having won!

There was so much work to be done to find accommodation for 70 people to stay from the 21st-24th June. Two hotels had to be booked, the Berners and the Victoria, some distance apart really, but that did not matter for London was swinging and of course becoming overloaded with tourists from all over the world, all coming to celebrate the Festival of Britain.

And then of course what would we wear for this memorable occasion? Enquiries were made at Brocklehursts W.A. Ltd, who responded readily and a small deputation was sent to inspect the materials. It was hyacinth blue Macclesfield Silk, fifty lengths for the ladies, and the Directors of the Company said they were to be a gift, very generous really for so many of us. And silk stockings were kindly given by another Macclesfield firm, Mr W.R. Wadsworth.

Soon we were on our way to London, and I was to share a room with a lovely older girl, Elsie Jones. The night was free to us until 2.30 pm the next day, so we decided to go to the theatre to see the famous French show 'Follies Bergere'. What a show, all naked, we enjoyed it very much, and the place was packed. There was a tap on my shoulder and an American soldier gave me a box of chocolates. Would you believe it? Elsie and I were really living it up!

We had tension days ahead of us, for we had been told that on the last night, Princess Elizabeth would be in the Royal Box to present the huge silver cup to the winners. From 6 pm that night, choir after choir competed; we were placed to go on number 10. Then it was our turn to mount the stage, to be told that the Princess had just left the Palace a short time ago. Then such a loud whisper went up, *"she's here!"* and we led the singing of 'God Save The King'.

So with the Princess listening to us from the Royal Box we sang our pieces, and we won! She came down the stage and presented Mr Riley with the huge silver trophy. She looked so beautiful, small, dainty, with a wonderful smile; we were all so close to her, we could have touched her. It was a night to remember all our lives.

The Mayor of Macclesfield was Mrs Amy White, a most gracious lady, and we were given a civic reception at Wesley's Chapel, Sunderland Street, where we met every week for rehearsals. That night the chapel overflowed, chairs, seats and stools were put in the aisles to accommodate everyone. The huge silver trophy was on display on the rostrum, just behind Mr Riley. So many tributes were paid to us in that year 1951!

SMILING

Smiling is infectious,
You catch it like the flu,
When someone smiled at me today,
I started smiling too.
I passed around the corner,
And someone saw me grin,
When he smiled I realised,
I'd passed it on to him.
I thought about the smile,
And realised its worth,
A single smile like mine,
Could travel round the earth.
If you feel a smile begin,
Don't leave it undetected,
Let's start an epidemic quick,
And get the world infected.

GERMANY 1952

When our gang of girls went to the Isle of Man for our first holiday away from our parents watchful eyes, we really felt we were abroad. But in 1952 I was 25 years old, eager to taste life, and by this time I had been employed 11 years in a sewing factory. So when the opportunity came for me to go on holiday to Germany I was excited to go. The girl I went with was German, she had married a British soldier in Germany, so every year she would visit her Mother.

I should say right away we didn't get along, we just did not hit it off! But because I have been blessed with a lively personality I got along just fine, people liked me. I liked her mother very much, she was a good woman, and everything was new for me, I was interested in everything I saw.

Our journey started from Manchester Railway Station to Harwich, where we arrived in the evening and boarded the boat for the Hook of Holland. We had sleeping berths, arriving next morning. Through customs I felt a little nervous, for my friend went one way, and I the other, because she was German, and I British - and there were a lot of soldiers around with guns.

After a long train journey through Holland into Germany we arrived at Hamburg, then through to Lubeck and finally the village of Krummesca. It seemed to me to be very small and old fashioned, not a lot of progress, for the main street was just a dirt street, no proper road or pavement. That first week we had heavy rain so the street was just filled with mud. I was rather shocked - our village streets were far superior. The house we went to was large, with staff, mostly young lovely German girls, long blond hair, plaited, and long skirts, covered with white aprons down to their ankles. They worked hard, always ironing, cooking, laying tables, always busy!

I stayed at a small inn in the village with the owners, a very old couple who were very kind to me. At weekends I joined the family at the house and ate with them. The family were loyal Nazi supporters and I felt uncomfortable eating off the silver cutlery stamped with the swastica, but they were good people and made me welcome. I had been going to the house for sometime when the question was asked, did I think Hitler was a bad man? *"Yes"*, was my reply, *"and mad too!"* Well they asked, and they did not seem to mind my answer!

They lived very well, food wise they had plenty of choice, and they were big eaters, the men were big and they put a lot of food away at mealtimes. One Sunday I went to lunch, and after we had eaten a big meal, the young girls, who were staff, cleared away all the dishes. Then off came the huge table cloth, the men retired for a Sunday nap, and the young girls started again at one end of the table. Another cloth was laid for tea, sandwiches, huge cakes, for when the men woke up from their nap!

As they slept the ritual for the women of the village was to go to the cemetery, taking baskets full to care for their graves, and I went along too. This was the routine; every Sunday afternoon, whilst the men slept, the women did all the work!

After the first week of bad weather, it became hot and sunny, and swimming was popular in the canal. It looked strange to me. There was a lot of TB in the village and it was said that perhaps the canal was the problem!

They were all proud of the fact that they were recovering well from the War. I remember we still had shortages at home. Several times we took the trip to Lubeck which was a large town, and I liked it for there were many fine buildings, with lots of smart restaurants staffed by men, with smart black uniforms and white napkins over their arms. In the afternoons people flocked in to eat gargantuous cakes filled with cream, and other cakes and pastries the like I had never seen. They drank strong black coffee, served with tiny jugs of cream. They were very kind and gave me their cream but all this richness was too much for me and I came out feeling rather sick. I thought to myself, the German people have very sweet tooths and eat far too much!

A German doctor who heard there was an English girl in the village called and invited me to go with him on his rounds. It was very interesting; I was shown the Russian outposts, the Baltic seaside resorts and the countryside. He spoke English quite well, and we got on together. As we had recently started the NHS he was most interested in this. He said, *"I wonder if it will be a good thing for the British people to obtain free medical help? Will you all become reliant and then abuse the system? I wonder will it work?"* And of course, I could understand his thinking!

I remember clearly the day I cycled into Lubeck; when I think about it I must have been mad because it has never been my mode of travel. I've always been a walker, and what's more to put the brake on you had to back-pedal. I don't think I thought about it, I was young and off I went. For sure I was not safe, yet I got there and then I got a bit lost. I came to this huge square with a policeman on duty, tried to put the brake on and fell off at his feet. He looked very surprised, helped me to my feet and said *"mad English girl"* but he smiled.

My holiday was nearly over. It had gone so quickly. One day I sat in the garden and one of the young staff girls came out and said could she put my hair up for me, for I wore it quite long. When she had done this she said *"You know you look more German than we do."* She had plaited it - so I came home with a different hairstyle.

MY WEDDING DAY 1963

Me and my lovely sisters.
From left: Audrey, Joan, Lilian.

From the left:
Rosemary Baker-Brian, Lily Brown (who made all the dresses), Susan, Carl, Denise and Jane

PARIS 1983

Our daughter Sarah was about to leave school, and as she was coming of age, eighteen - in my day it was 21 years - I thought what can I do to give her a lasting memory. So I thought I will have her portrait taken and of course she would have to have a lovely dress also. So I took her to Nina, a dress designer in our town and she produced a beautiful soft pink gown. She looked so lovely, and Brian Ollier took the portrait, and with his skill it was an outstanding success. We decided to put the portrait in *Cheshire Life*. Her Dad Carl, and Nina and Brian, all generously contributed to the expense of the insertion which was a full page!

Then I thought I wanted her to have something from me alone, so I decided to take her to Paris. So off we went, it was July, and Paris in July was hot. Sarah could speak schoolgirl French well, so we did very well, and for five days we had a little holiday to remember.

I remember on the first day sitting at a pavement café, such a lot of people all sat drinking outside in the sunshine, and we ordered a sandwich. It was all so swish, male waiters, black suits, trays and napkins, very professional. When the sandwich arrived it was not what we thought of as a sandwich, but two long bread rolls, very crusty. One would have been enough for us, and the bread so hard - so we decided to take them back to the hotel and struggle with them there.

We had a lovely hotel near the Arc de Triomph, with our own suite of rooms and balcony. Paris does live up to its name, it is so romantic, the lovely River Seine and the bridges, the tree lined avenues, wonderful fountains where the water starts small and then changes higher and higher, and at nightfall, floodlit wide boulevards where people just sit outside the cafés in the warm night air.

One day we took a boat trip on the River Seine going under all the beautiful bridges. The boat was open topped and it was so hot that as I bent down to take photographs I burned my knee on the deck! All along the river there are wide pavements right up to the river's edge and people were sunbathing, nearly all topless, quite a sight! And I really must say walking in Paris, you can walk for ever, it's so vast, so flat shoes are a must.

Of course we had to see the Mona Lisa at the Louvre, which was quite a distance, and when we finally reached the grounds we came across a party of people who were being photographed. They were models, they were so tall and so thin and dressed in heavy winter clothing, fur coats, hats, boots - and in that heat! Several of the models were coloured and very striking. Of course their work was for the fashion magazines, so we watched for a little while, enthralled.

The Mona Lisa was for me a disappointment, really so small and behind a very heavy glass. There was a female attendant who kept saying *"no flash"* as cameras were going - no one took a bit of notice of her, me included. I thought I've got this far, I'll just have to take a picture, but it did not come out! At least we can say we have seen the famous portrait.

Then came 26th July which was *my* birthday. We happened to pass a most beautiful florist's shop and I saw these roses of such fine quality, and because it was my birthday I bought a dozen pink roses, long stemmed and dressed in cellophane with ribbons and bows. Proudly I walked back to the hotel, such a nice memory.

Before the holiday I had been reading the autobiography of Pierre Cardin, the famous Paris fashion designer, a most down to earth man and a most interesting person. Heaven knows why I did it, maybe because of the excitement of the holiday to come, but I decided to write to him and to tell him I was bringing my 18 year old daughter to Paris as a very special present, and that I was just an ordinary British mother giving my daughter a very special memory. Off went the letter, I don't know what I expected from it, but shortly afterwards a lovely thick envelope arrived from Pierre Cardin's secretary to say if we brought the letter to the address of Rue de Faubourg, we would be given a little tour of the salon. Can you imagine how I felt, I couldn't believe such kindness, and this is what happened.

The person we met was a very tall Japanese model who looked so perfect she looked unreal. Her skin was cream porcelain, her hair was black, long and with a fringe, her lipstick was bright red, and dressed all in black, she was very arresting. She spoke quaint English. We were treated so kindly we couldn't believe it was really happening. That experience must have made a big impression on our daughter for shortly afterwards Sarah left for Italy, to stay for seven years.

I must tell you of the evening of my birthday. It was July 26th and we sought out a lovely restaurant for a little celebration birthday dinner, just the two of us. Again the presentation was ideal, tables well dressed, candles and flowers, smart waiter service. It was early evening, there were not too many people in the restaurant but at the next table to us there were eight men who were already well into their meal. We chose fresh salmon, or rather Sarah did for me, I was not too keen but it was very fresh and beautifully served and so we felt very happy.

Suddenly I felt something soft brush against my leg, so I lifted up a corner of the tablecloth and there at our feet was this huge alsatian dog. Well of all the dogs I am afraid of it's alsatians! I screamed out. The dog belonged to the people on the next table to us, the men diners, and they were not pleased with me. They shrugged their shoulders and waved their hands about, but I was so upset the dog was removed. I told them this would never be allowed in England. They looked even more angry. So my birthday meal out in Paris, my only one, was memorable, but spoiled. You never know though, perhaps I will go to Paris again. But should I go for a meal you can be sure I will look under the table.

We will never forget Paris, so romantic, so exciting! If it can happen to us, it can happen to anyone. I recommend it!

It was the last night of our holiday and our money had almost run out and it was a very difficult last day with all the heat and our money so anorexic. But I had just enough to buy Sarah a sorbet ice in the evening, not far from our hotel at a newly opened fish restaurant. Very expensive it looked. The tables were so beautifully dressed in long damask cloths, candles and crystal, and what looked like huge tiered cake stands on which their fish dishes were displayed. The large glass windows opened out onto the pavement where there were great tubs of greenery and a balustrade, all beautifully lit. So we sat outside.

I will always remember how Sarah looked that night, a not very tall, slender 18 year old with her beautiful long brown wavy hair, a wonderful feature of hers. She was wearing a long white broderie Anglais dress with a broad pink sash. She looked her best; such a lasting memory for me. Well it wasn't long before she was attracting the attention of a group of noisy young French males, and of course I could not understand what they were saying to her. So being a Mother I kept trying to draw her chair ever closer to mine. Just inside the restaurant were an elderly couple and seeing my concern, would you believe it, they invited us inside. The man was German, his wife French. They bought us a long cold iced drink, and they spoke English so we felt very comfortable with them, and very grateful for their hospitality.

By this time it was midnight when suddenly, through the restaurant, came a small party of men, dressed in black evening suits. My eyes went to the man in the middle, I knew who he was immediately. He was wearing a cape, his full hair looked as if it had been brushed out, his olive complexion, his lovely brown eyes, so very soft; it was Omar Sharif; and they were walking toward where we were sat. He stopped, inclined his head to Sarah and said *"Good evening"*, then took her hand and said *"You are very beautiful"*.

Sarah had no idea who he was, she was just embarrassed, but for me it was like a dream. The couple told us they would have had a meal in the restaurant before going on to a casino. They said Omar Sharif lived quite close in an exclusive area of Paris with his housekeeper; they had seen him before. To think he had spoken to Sarah, and this would not have happened but for the kindness of the couple. For a few years after we exchanged Christmas cards.

NEW YORK 1987

It was an ordinary evening some 4 years later. Carl and I were watching TV, when I said I'm going to take Sarah to America. I remember there was no interest from him, but the seed was set in my mind at least. I was going to go with Sarah, but first there was the visit to the bank for the finance, so off to Manchester I went, on my own, with only the explanation of what my dream consisted of. It soon turned to reality for I was given the loan and plans were able to start!

I knew we wanted to go solo as it were, not with an organised tour, we wanted to be more free. I knew we wanted to be in Manhattan, and I had advice on the hotel from the travel people. The choice was the Roosevelt, a lovely establishment, well known, pretty expensive for us but we had to feel safe for our five week holiday.

That morning in August, we said goodbye to Carl and our little dog Beauty, and we left Manchester with Carl waving us off from a flat topped area, Sarah and I passengers in a Tristar plane. The plane journey was very pleasant, exciting to be sure, and would you believe it, we got speaking to one of the senior male stewards from Prestbury in Cheshire. I don't know how long into the journey we were when from the sound system came something like, the Captain requests the pleasure of Miss Sarah Brocklehurst to visit the front of the plane. Well, I said immediately *"May Mother come too?"* I was not letting Sarah go anywhere without me.

Through first class we went, what comfort we saw, the seating like chaise longues, people looking very comfortable and relaxed. I remember thinking, this is the way to travel! And then through to the cockpit, I think you call it. The Captain was Dutch, a large man with huge strong looking arms bulging from a white short sleeved crisp looking shirt. They were very kind to us, they offered chocolates from a saucer, and for a little while we talked and laughed together, and told them a little about our intended holiday. Before we said goodbye they gave Sarah and I four little bottles of champagne "to drink in our hotel" to start our stay in America. We thought what a good omen for the start of our holiday.

On our arrival at J.F.K. - Kennedy Airport - we were truly in America but really quite a long way from New York. There were loads of taxis waiting to take you but the taxi drivers were so aggressive, mostly big coloured men, really pressing the people to use their service. Fortunately for us we were close to an elderly couple who had done the journey before. They said to us "Don't use the taxis, there's no need, they will overcharge you. *Wait with us and take the bus.".* And so we did. They were so kind and helpful to us, a retired doctor and his wife from Dorset.

So we arrived safe and sound, though tired, at the Roosevelt Hotel, Manhattan, New York. Oh, and the address was Madison Avenue! I remember the weather was warm and pleasant, and I think like most people who visit New York for the first time, well you can feel the vitality that's there; the atmosphere is special somehow. I suppose it's the masses of people who move about constantly with few gaps between the noisy traffic, and of course the buildings make your eyes pop out with wonder. You will get full sun on one side of the street, deep shade on the other, and people have gardens up there and you can see the trees on these skyscraper buildings. They don't always go straight up but are built at another angle and out they come again; truly remarkable to see. In fact they vanish into the clouds sometimes, with more buildings in the sky than below. So we kept getting good eyefuls of all that was around us, and I remember thinking, well here we are just the two of us, and for a little while feeling nervous, and a little lost, but excited and ready to enjoy it. And we did, you can be sure!

The first thing we noticed was the ordinary people in the restaurant underneath the hotel on their way to work every morning whilst we had our breakfast. They would call for coffee and buns to buy and take away with them to work; it was such a busy place. We were quite mesmerised with it all - mountains of food everywhere and coffee in large cartons. Perhaps they shared with other people?

How can you imagine me going to America and I cannot use a lift, and never will, so it was a big problem for me. We were given a large bedroom and bathroom on the 3rd floor, because, of course, I explained my problem. Sarah can use lifts, thank goodness, but there were many times I got to reception before she did whilst she was waiting for the lift to arrive!

The hotel was a very lively place always with great mounds of luggage, all linked together and closely watched by the enormous staff. There were several airlines that used the hotel, they had their own area in reception with their own coffee machines and huge blackboards, and always the tourists were being talked to rather like being in a classroom. Then they would vanish for wherever, and the next lot of people come in. So it's go, go, all the time and with all the other guests you can imagine what a busy place it was; but I have to say people were ever watchful at the hotel for your well being.

After a couple of days we felt ready to explore a little. I said to Sarah *"We must move about as if we belong here, and not with our mouths open all the time!"* Being in the heart of Manhattan we were so near to all the famous stores. For a few days we visited them but walking is very tiring in those huge stores they have. What impressed me was the immaculate floors - they are like walking on glass even though they were wood.

Several days later I was to wish my daughter Sarah *"Happy 21st Birthday"*. We were in Times Square and I gave her a present of a watch she wears it to this day.

Then there were the parades we saw. For Labour Day they close off the streets and the parade begins, hundreds of people taking part. They also have street markets where no traffic is allowed and on a very warm day I bought two red cashmere woollen scarves they said were from Scotland. I thought very odd!

St Patrick's Cathedral, what a joy to visit for us both, hundreds of people from all nations worshiping together, in fact you have to queue to get in. Whilst we were there we paid several visits to St Patrick's, and one day I took communion. I said to Sarah *"You must stay in your pew, for you have not been confirmed"*. But Sarah thought otherwise - like the acorn falls close to the tree! She was kneeling at my side at the alter rail, what could I do, so she took communion with me.

We did all the usual tourist things. Taking a boat trip around the Statue of Liberty, round Ellis Island to Staten Island. I thought what if this boat sinks, there were so many aboard. A great treat was going to Greenwich Village, I really loved that. And being in Washington Square.

We took photographs all the time. I had started to photograph a door to a house or an apartment, the number was 74 which is our house number, when a passing man said *"Do you know who once lived here, it was Cary Grant"*. I couldn't believe it. *"And a little bit further down the street was where Clarke Gable lived, when they were both struggling to become stars."* When I looked more closely at the man I noticed he was wearing make-up, including his eyes, his mouth and coral nail polish. I thought "this a very odd place, yet interesting for sure!" There we had our first American icecream, wonderful Hagen Daaz, so many flavours you wouldn't believe how they thought them up.

One night after a rather humid day we decided to visit the famous Plaza Hotel my husband Carl had visited during the war. We took a taxi, but the traffic was so heavy he could not take us right to the entrance of the hotel, so we had just a few yards to walk. Well it began to rain, and in that very short distance, the rain coming down like stair rods, we were both soaked to the skin. We had to take another taxi back to our hotel to change. When it rains in New York it rains as you wouldn't believe!

The Trump Building, all marble and glass and indoor waterfalls, leaves you with your mouth open! Sarah went to the top of the Empire State Building whilst I waited. We visited the famous Radio City and during the day they have

organised tours, it's such a huge place. There again I was unable to use the lifts
with everyone else, but what happened was I was given a personal escort to
another area and taken to Gregory Peck's office when he worked there. He had
come, I was told, from Coney Island, and he reached the senior position at Radio
City, hence his office. I was told staff were not allowed to speak, they wore white
gloves at all times to give hand movements; what a strange operation. Then I
joined everyone on the vast stage of Radio City where the famous dancers called
the 'Rockettes' performed. All very interesting, and for sure a day to remember!

   That first day of autumn, or the Fall as the Americans say, it was still a very
warm and very sunny day, but because summer had gone at least on their
calendar, they all changed clothing. They were now dressed in dark colours,
winter clothing, boots and furs. We were still wearing summer dresses, but in
that part of New York, which is Manhattan, they are so fashionable and such very
exclusive people; it really shows in the way they dress. Sarah does not miss
much and for my benefit she said, for anyone who looked very special indeed
coming towards us, *"at eight-o-clock, four-o-clock, 12-o-clock, etc"*. But by the
time I got my mind round the clock talk they were gone! We laughed a lot, we
had fun playing at this silly way of looking at people passing by. There were
masses of people at any one time passing on the pavements together. And those
people enjoyed the best for the Park Avenue hotels all have awnings coming right
over the pavements and carpeted too, so whatever the weather people just stepped
into their cars or taxis under cover. The very air crackled with vitality. What the
other boroughs of New York were like we were not to know, I suppose they could
be very different really, but we were on holiday, we only wanted to see the best.

   We decided we would like to take a trip to the seaside but where to go? Out
came the map and it seemed Long Island was the nearest, but of course you have
to leave New York under the Hudson River, and because I am a claustrophobic
being confined is unbearable. Well off we went to Penn Station, a huge place, a
great long slope with shops either side, like a mall really. You start to feel cool
air and then you have reached the trains. I said to Sarah, *"I'm not sure about this
journey really"*. *"Mom, you will be fine"*, she said, *"You will be in the train"*.
And she was right, the journey was quick and I was not too uncomfortable - but
I was happy to get there.

   To get to Jones Beach you have to walk through a leafy suburb. The houses
were large and lovely, it seemed that very prosperous people lived there, but there
were no signs of life and all the windows were shuttered. We think they were
holiday homes; we did not see one person. I began to wonder where we were
heading, then suddenly the ocean was there. What a rewarding sight, a great

golden sandy beach, so very clean, and it went on and on in a very straight line. It would have held thousands of people, but that day it was isolated, very few people about, and every now and then, on great mounds of the firm sand, were tall wooden chairs, with guards on top to give them a good vista.

The day was warm and sunny and Sarah settled down to sunbathe. I looked about me and thought this is not going to be very peaceful - the sky was peppered with light aircraft which carried long banners of birthday messages and advertisements; no sooner one went by than there was another. It was so noisy because they were flying low! Then as if this was not enough, along came beach patrols with their buggy carts, and if you were on their patrol path like we were, you were told in no uncertain way to move back.

Then a 'little pest' appeared, a little boy of about 12 years, who did not look too well cared for, I thought, but very alert. He came close and sat down, not speaking but staring at Sarah. After a while I was getting uncomfortable with him, and I asked him to move away, then he spoke for the first time. He said to me, *"Are you her grandmother?"* I couldn't believe this. Of course Sarah got the giggles and thought it very funny, but he did move back a little, still staring at Sarah as if he had never seen a girl before.

Friendly New York police

I took this from the boat coming back from Staten Island - notice the Twin Towers

My lovely daughter, Sarah.

So with this and the aircraft we decided to go back to the station! The journey back was a nightmare, for we were caught up with the rush of workers going home, the train was so packed. There were many other trains converging into the tunnel and after we had been going for a short while, the lights dimmed and the train slowed down and stopped. It was so scary. Sarah knew how I felt and held my hand. Maybe it was a normal for the regular passengers, but I felt trapped and half an hour before the train started to move again I said to Sarah *"never again!"*

Then there was that awful night when Sarah had been given free tickets at the hotel to see the Chippendales, very beautiful young men, very fit, and would you believe I went along too. I never should have gone. They came in on motor bikes, the noise awful, huge lights swung round the audience, then obese middle-aged women started putting dollar bills on the bodies of the gyrating young men. It was not my scene at all, and I asked Sarah in no uncertain way to get me out of there. She didn't want to but she went off to speak to someone. They stamped her wrist, and outside she got me a taxi. So across New York I went, back to the hotel alone.

But the night did not end there. I sat in reception, a very pleasant place, and just watched people come and go, and in came eight Japanese men who sat at the large table with me. Their English was not too bad and they told me they were going to England - they were having a struggle with the place, so I said *"you are going to Stratford-upon-Avon"*. They were delighted with my naming the place. They also had trouble saying William Shakespeare, so I said to them *"you are going to visit 'Old Willy'"*. I might have said the funniest joke in the world, for they threw back their heads in laughter. *"Then we have question, you are lost in jungle, you are in deep pit, many snakes at bottom, at top leopard waiting, what do you do"*. *"Heavens gentlemen, what a lot of choice I have; I pray very hard, or I die of shock."* I thought what a funny question, but they clapped hands and said *"Very Good"*. Most peculiar, but then they were Japanese! In their quaint English they said, *"You speak Mrs Tacher English, every willing to oblige."* I smiled at them and said *"but of course"*.

It was about the third week of our holiday when I informed Sarah it was time to move on to visit New England. But Sarah by this time had other ideas. The Hotel was filling with stars and fans for the Forest Hills Tennis Tournament, and of course Sarah was being noticed and made a fuss of. She was loving all the attention - and only newly 21 years old.

But I insisted, so with our luggage off we went to Penn Station for the rail journey of 4¹/₂ hours to Boston. Well Sarah cried, she sulked, would not co-operate in anyway, and for the whole of the train journey she threw her hair over her face, so all I saw was long brown wavy hair. We reached Boston, and took a taxi to Cambridge.

I had already planned our hotel, but it was hopeless, she was so upset. We were there for about an hour, and then it was another taxi to Logan Airport and back in New York in half an hour. I did not see Newport Rhode Island, Martha's Vineyard, Nantucket, Edgar Town or Kennybunkport. Very sad, but my fault as I gave in. But to visit New York is very special - we enjoyed our holiday with few regrets. Travel opens your eyes and broadens the mind; you feel so privileged!

We were well into our holiday, with about a fortnight to go when I realised our finances were running low. I told Sarah that perhaps we might have to return home soon. *"Mom, I don't want to go home yet!"* Well, of course, nor did I, but I could see we had little choice, so Igave it much thought as to what I was to do! I told Sarah I suppose I could ring home - meaning the bank in Manchester - but as I had already had a hefty loan from them to come to America, I daren't. I told Sarah I really don't like asking for more money. She amazed me; *"Mom; let me ask the bank; let me try."* Talk about out of the mouths of babes and sucklings. *"You write down what you want and I will pretend to be you."* What confidence. So shortly afterwards in the early hours, it was 4.15am New York time, we set off to find an outside phone. Of course we had a phone in our room, but that would only take us to reception, and they would have helped us, but I did not want them to know of our financial plight.

It was 9.30am in Manchester, they had just opened when we rang. Sarah, just like an actress, did all I asked of her so well. I really believe she grew up in those early hours in New York. The loan was agreed; I was so proud of her, they said of course it would take a couple of days to come through. They were most concerned for us that we had enough money to last us before it came.

We had to find the bank, Chase Manhattan in the Wall Street area, so next day we set off to find it. It was a beautiful building, very elegant, lots of people, but the smell of smoking was so apparent, not only the public, but the bank staff also. They were doing their work with cigarettes hanging from their mouths. I thought this is not very professional. Anyhow the following day after our visit, we were solvent again, and all because of my young daughter who had the confidence to ask where I feared! So I gave her a surprise gift, I took her into Bonwit-Teller, another famous New York store and bought her a pair of large hooped tortoiseshell ear-rings. We were both relieved and happy to be able to stay our full time.

So we went to Central Park, what a vast place really, the only green legacy the New Yorkers have and in its cherished area so much goes on! As you can imagine there are so many ways to enter the Park, it's so huge an area, but we made for the entrance where you took a horse and cab to go through the Park. The owner of the horse and cab wore tails and a tall green top hat and he spoke with an Irish accent, I suppose with a bit of American mixed in also. When he spoke we could not make out his conversation, and he did not stop talking throughout the journey in the park. It was beautiful, but it's not really safe especially at night. It was the only time we ventured there, for whatever the time, day or night, it's not really safe for strangers.

I also wanted to visit the famous Waldorf Astoria, the hotel, because I knew Cole Porter's piano was there, roped off, but you are allowed to get very close, and we took pictures! We went to a store, I cannot remember if it was Sak's or Bloomingdales, and so many floors you needed to take a rest from time to time from all the walking. The cafeterias are beautiful, so immaculate, such variety of food, and at all times very popular. We chose to sit at the bar area, beautiful padded stools, so comfortable. Sarah had a milk shake, which they are very good at, with countless flavours. I sat to her left and a young man was to her right. I hardly noticed him but suddenly Sarah gave a yell and almost fell of her seat - this young man was sliding his hand up her thigh under her skirt. Well of course he was off like a shot through the café, but with me in chase shouting obscenities at him - and I can run; but I could not catch him. I caused an uproar, but when I got back to Sarah, no one was prepared to talk about it, it might not have happened. I was so angry, but perhaps as tourists in a place like New York we were pretty lucky nothing else happened to us! I became more watchful of Sarah!

One day we went into a shoe shop for Sarah to buy shoes. When this woman came to serve us it was hard to believe, she was so old, very heavily made-up and her legs covered in varicose veins and so very swollen. I thought, could she be the owner? She moved so slow, she could hardly walk; we felt so sorry for her working at such an age. And when we walked through the men's department, there too were men serving who were of an advanced age; we were quite shocked!

Eventually our holiday came to an end, but neither of us will ever forget New York and our time together there

MY TRUE GHOST STORY

I suppose when people think of ghosts or spirits the scene is set with a dark winter's night, perhaps an old house, a wild wind that rattles window panes, with creaking doors and floors and maybe a place where bad or mysterious happenings have taken place.

My story, my ghost story is not like that at all, and here is how it happened. The year would be I think around 1994-5 and a late summer's afternoon around 4.30pm, for this is the time I take my walk and have time for myself. I had walked along Byrons Lane here in Macclesfield. I had got to the point where the few houses end and a long hawthorn hedge begins, then comes a five bar gate overlooking a large flat field that rises to the Hollins Golf Course. It's a lovely open view with a walking area for the public, sadly not as popular now as it was. I always stop at this gate to take in the view. The long hawthorn hedge on my left had another small scrubby one behind forming a natural passage.

Then it happened, I saw this female rise up from the ground, her face was pale, a sweet face that looked tired and worn. On her head, I can only describe it as a helmet hat, close fitting around her face, then the hat went back at an angle, the colour a strong blue. For a moment I thought what on earth is she doing and went quickly to open the gate for her, but she had already passed through and was going away from me down Byrons Lane. Then I could see she was wearing some kind of uniform, a long coat the colour blue. Then I saw she had no arms or legs. I was of course stunned but not afraid for then I realised I had seen my first ghost.

A few years later, in one of our local newspapers, there was a small insert asking if anyone had an experience of a strange encounter, and there was a telephone number to contact. So I got in touch; two men came to my home with a camera and sound and said *"would I tell them my story"* and they would put it on film, for this was their work. But I declined taking it to this level.

Of course they were interested and said they would investigate, but I heard no more from them. They did say she could have been a nurse of some kind, perhaps serving in a war, or nursing in the area where I saw her, even home on leave. Well perhaps we will never know, but always when I pass that spot I stop and look just in case I should see her again. That day I carried on with my walk, but I don't suppose I saw very much scenery, my head was too full of thoughts of a ghostly nature!

RAINBOWS

I wonder just how much our school teachers realise what influence they have on their pupils, and by this I don't mean just through their skill of teaching, but for me through their personalities. I have to say I liked all my teachers, having one favourite, who was Miss Nora Cornforth, a tall, beautiful blond woman.

A close second to her was Miss Caroline Moulton. She was just the opposite for she was small and rotund with a lovely sweet nature, a Girl Guide teacher who had lived as a child in Manchester, and was so very proud of her parents who were bakers in the First World War and kept their business going in such difficult times. I believe at some time she had lived at Knutsford here in Cheshire, for one day she said to us *"Girls, girls, I want to tell you about Knutsford and rainbows"*. They apparently went together, and little was she to know she has left this connection with me for life, for every time I visit the town you can be sure I will look for a rainbow over the stretch of water that lies at the bottom of the two main streets. We are really like blotting paper, we soak up and store the knowledge that has the greatest appeal to us. And to this day I'm quite lost with their beauty.

Now I can tell you my rainbow story. When my daughter Sarah started dating, she was upstairs getting ready, and I was washing up in the kitchen. I looked up; there was such a lovely rainbow; was I thrilled, and just at that special moment Sarah yelled downstairs *"Mother go to the front door"*. I just didn't want to leave my rainbow, but I dashed off and grabbed the young man at the door. *"Hello"*, I said, *"quick follow me"*, pulling on his arm and rushing him into the kitchen; and over the kitchen sink we watched the rainbow disappear.

Afterwards this lovely young man said with a smile on his face, *"Yes, I too like rainbows"*. He only came to the house that once, not surprising really after the treatment he received at my hands! He was a young pilot, and he came in his Father's car, which was a low red vintage sports car with a leather strap around the bonnet, which Sarah thought was only holding the car together! Little did she know! The fact that he had to crank it with a starting handle as well was all too much for Sarah, *"I'm not going out with him again."* Silly girl, just too young to know!

NANNY CARER

After our holiday in New York, I knew Sarah wanted to travel more if she could. For three more years she was at home with us, and by now a confident and really lovely young woman. She was very interested in fashion and eager to get on with her life. Travelling alone was no problem for her - not the same as me; how could I think that way with my life! The day came when her Dad and I said goodbye to her, and I will always remember the way she looked. I knew we were letting her go to find for herself the life she really wanted. Our children are only lent to us; sooner or later they have to leave. The two decades we enjoy with them are their formative years, and the best.

So off to Italy she went, I thought quite brave really; and with no knowledge of their language, but she soon settled to the Italian way of life. She loved the people, the climate, the food, so very natural and healthy, and the language she soon learned living there. She was very happy! She became a photographic model and her love of travel became a way of life from then on. Of course she came home from time to time and her Dad and I visited her in her lovely home. And she treated us to many holidays; Sri Lanka, Spain, France, Germany, Holland.

In the eight years she lived in Italy, I missed her very much, and I needed to do something for me, for as one part of life closes, hopefully another will open, and it did! I began work as a nanny for I have always had a love for babies and young children and so for another decade this was my work. I was very happy and very fortunate, my work took me into the homes of celebrities, caring for their children. I have some very special memories of all the families I knew; all such good, kind people who came to regard me as family, and I them. And it was all adding more colour to my life, the enrichment that only children can bring!

THE BURGLARY

It's a few years ago now that one night I was caring for three small children in a very large house in the country. The children were sleeping, but suddenly the smallest boy woke up and was sick. So I took him downstairs and I was nursing him, when from the ceiling there was a slight movement. It had been a hot day and my husband Carl always told me that during the day ceiling joists can expand and at night contract so I thought no more about it. With the little boy back to sleep I took him back to bed, and the time was not late, it was about 9.30 pm.

What I didn't know was there were intruders in the house, at least two, maybe three. They must have been small and probably young. They had a ladder, got over a high wall, knocked out security lights, then crossed the lawn and chose a small window. They didn't break the glass, but took the whole frame out and entered the master bedroom! They completely ransacked the room.

I don't know what they stole or if they got caught; I don't want to know. They left the house the same way as they had entered replacing the window in its frame, but leaving the ladder behind. It was a dreadful shock for the young couple who were the parents, to see the state the bedroom was in. I had been taken home and had just got into bed when the phone rang. *"Nancy, we have been burgled."* I said *"What since I've just left you."* Then I was told it happened while I was there. You can imagine I was shocked at the audacity of these people.

The following day I had to relate my story to a police inspector and in no uncertain terms I told him about hearing the ceiling movement. There was a slight smile on his face; he said it was just as well I didn't know they were in the house. But I tell you this, if ever I was to hear my ceiling just creaking, I would not now be thinking of expansion and contraction. I would be upstairs like a shot to investigate just in case we had unexpected and unwelcome visitors. I suppose we have to experience these happenings to learn!

WHAT IS A SENIOR CITIZEN

A Senior Citizen is one who was here before television, the pill, penicillin, polio shots, and antibiotics. We were here before frozen food, nylon, radar, fluorescent lights, credit cards and ballpoint pens. For us time sharing meant togetherness; a chip was a piece of wood or potato; hardware meant hardware and software wasn't even a word.

Girls never wore trousers; we were before tights, drip dry clothes, dishwashers, tumble driers, freezers and electric blankets, before men wore long hair and earrings, and women wore dinner suits. We were here before yoghurt, the 40 hour week and the National Health Service. We got married first and then lived together - how quaint can you get? We were even here before Frank Sinatra and cup sizing for bras.

Girls wore Peter Pan collars and thought cleavage was something the butchers did. We were here before Batman, D.D.T and vitamin pills, disposable nappies, Jeeps, pizzas, instant coffee and decaffeinated anything. Wimpy, McDonalds and Burger King were unheard of, as were metrication and decimalisation.

We were here before word processing, electronic music and disco dancing - and that's not all bad! In our day smoking was fashionable, grass was for mowing, coke was something you burnt in a stove and pot was something you cooked in. A 'gay' person was the life and soul of the party, and nothing more, while AIDS meant beauty lotions or help for people in trouble. We are today's Senior Citizens, a hardy bunch when you think how our world has changed and the adjustments we have had to make!

I was given this script by a very old lady I met on holiday in Southport 1999. She was such a lively person and held her years lightly, she had been a singer with ENSA during the War and knew many famous people. She wrote poetry; she was a real gay old girl. One day she took me to an Italian ice cream parlour and bought me the biggest ice I had ever had. We laughed throughout the afternoon, she was such fun, in fact she was outrageous.

She gave me the script and of course I asked was it her own work. *"Some old biddy",* she said which I took to be herself but I don't really know! I sent it to Buckingham Palace for the Queen to read because it was so funny, and yet so true! And I received a reply thanking me for the script and saying how much it was appreciated.

My letter from the Queen

THE LITTLE BOOKSHOP BY PATIENCE STRONG

This is a real bookshop selling second-hand books with shelves outside the shop overlooking a cobbled street in Lewes, Sussex. I found this little poem in the magazine 'This England' whilst I was in the library July 14th 1996, Wednesday.

I know a little bookshop in a quiet alleyway with books in rows on shelves outside in artful array - of volumes faded, tattered - and they look me in the face - and seem to say: "Once we were wanted, once we had a place." 'Poor waifs and strays'! My heart goes out - I'd like to buy them all, I'd like to give each one a home, pressed close against my wall - to shelter them beneath my roof in warm and firelight nooks - who would not take compassion on these lonely orphaned books? How can folks let them come to this? A book can be a friend - and after years of faithful service - what a dismal end! All jumbled up together - good - and - bad they have to mix, and imagine being two pence, when you are really three and six!

Patience Strong

MY GARDEN ROOM

I should write about my little garden room where I have written my stories. I have only been the proud owner of it for about four years now, but it's my pride and joy, overlooking my small garden, but very well stocked so I have colour and some beauty all year round. My garden room is attached to the end of the house so I have to go outside down the narrow passage to get in! But once inside there is nothing but joy for I am able to see so much more sky and on a lovely day the clouds go floating by. I love clouds, I am always looking for images which you can see with a little imagination of which I have plenty! Inside my garden room I have my radio, but I don't use it that much, some plays, the news always - and Michael Parkinson with his programme on Sundays, a special man, down to earth, and so professional, my favourite radio person!

I have adorned the inside of my room with artificial flowers and plants of all kinds, made of silk, so very hard to detect they are not real! So I have a garland just over the top of the windows, my deep window sill is full of this and that, photographs, and on the floor more plants and pots, white cane seats I brought from home, a blue rocking chair that belonged to my husband's people, a long small white wooden table holding my radio and some photographs of the children that have been in my care. And a small pair of red binoculars with which I watch the birds, amazing little creatures really, and I am growing to know them more. Just outside and close to the window is my rose arch, with the most lovely climbing rose called 'school girl', salmon pink, so beautiful and not too tall, about 8 foot. The rose opens to large blooms, the old fashioned look which I like so much, and here the birds alight. So with the windows open I whistle to them, they have such wonderful hearing and when they hear my whistle they go crazy, looking every where they think the sound is coming from. Such bright intelligent little creatures and right now this month of April they are so busy collecting the fur from our Persian cat, 'Mia'. She has to be groomed everyday with comb and brush otherwise she would lose fur everywhere, so the surplus we put on the chicken wire around the washing pole and the sparrows, blue tits and starlings are taking mouthfuls to line their nests for their coming young.

So isn't nature wonderful, and I have large fat balls hanging from my birdhouse so they will have more sustenance also. I have a long brick wall on one side of the garden, a beech hedge on the other, a small brick garden wall at the bottom and a little summer house. On top sits my black witch weather vane, on windy days I love to watch her go whizzing round. And what I find so fortunate is considering we live in terraced property, we are not overlooked. So as I sit in my garden room all I can see is the sky and roofs of the houses in Peel Street. Small can be beautiful! But then I have one more special luxury in my garden room, it's a relaxer chair called the '365', quite an expensive item for me but so wonderful to use. You have an operated lever at the side of the chair, which then lifts your legs high so your body is contoured in a very relaxing position, it's like taking a holiday every day, takes away stress. I heartily recommend the relaxer chair '365'!

My garden house

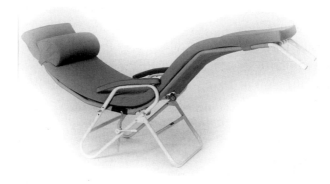

GOOD-BYE

I have come to the end of my stories. If it was for one part a bread and butter life, I loved it, when we were all young together, and our parents too, giving their families the best they had to offer. It's been so enjoyable writing them down and it all started on a day I was on holiday in Sri Lanka, way back in 1994. Not writing all the time, just when a memory came to me of my golden childhood in the thirties and of the very good people who made it so.

My little garden in Spring